THE
MIRACLE
OF THE
HUMAN BODY

BY HARRY ROBERTS

ODHAMS PRESS LIMITED

LONG ACRE, LONDON, W.C.2

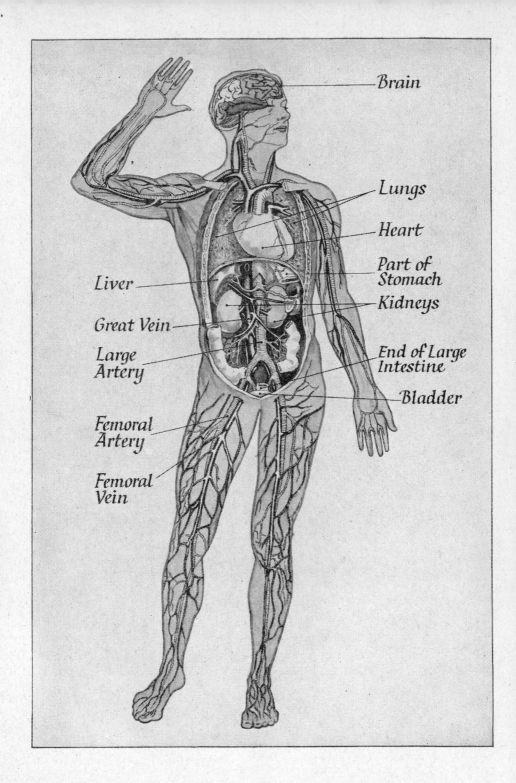

Brain

Lungs

Heart

Part of Stomach

Liver

Kidneys

Great Vein

Large Artery

End of Large Intestine

Bladder

Femoral Artery

Femoral Vein

CONTENTS

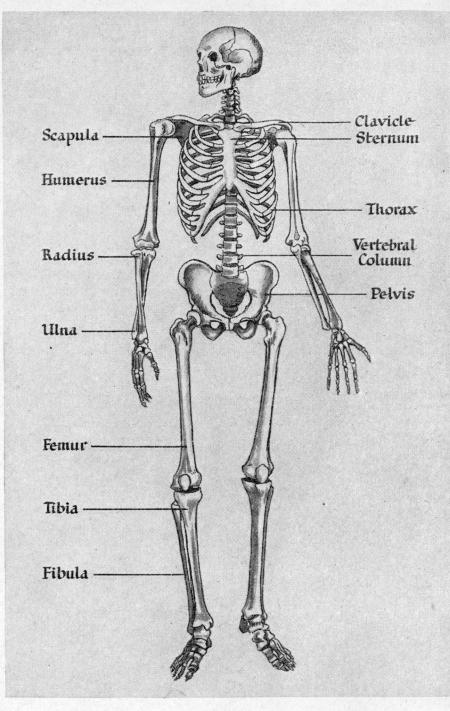

Scapula

Humerus

Radius

Ulna

Femur

Tibia

Fibula

Clavicle
Sternum

Thorax

Vertebral
Column

Pelvis

Fig. 1. *Skeleton of man, showing the names of principal bones.*

4

CHAPTER I

THE FRAMEWORK OF THE HUMAN BODY

STRUCTURE OF VERTEBRATES: BONES OF THE SPINAL COLUMN: THE SPINE
AND ITS CONNEXIONS: BREAST BONE AND RIBS: BONES OF THE ARM
AND HAND: PELVIS AND SACRUM: BONES OF THE LEG AND FOOT: STRUCTURE
OF THE SKULL: SKELETONS OF MAN'S ANCESTORS: COMPOSITION OF BONE

THE SKELETON (Fig. 1) is an internal system of bones, bound together at joints by ligaments and tendons, which determines and maintains the shape of the body, and helps to protect the delicate tissues and vital organs. It is made up of over two hundred bones of various sizes.

These bones, as well as the other parts of the body, have Latin names which, in many cases, will be new to the reader. Science has a habit of giving difficult and unfamiliar names to simple and familiar things. An explanation of the scientific terms used will be found in the glossary at the end of the book.

For some animals such a framework is unnecessary; the amœba oozes through life without a skeleton, yet even it is held together by the structureless capsule at its surface which we call the cell membrane. The higher we move in the animal scale the more essential does some kind of skeleton become in order to support the body.

Vertebrate Animals

Man belongs to the highest group of animals, the vertebrates, or animals distinguished by having a spinal column. Skeletons are not unknown in invertebrate groups, but they usually take the form of an outside armour or husk, such as the shell of the snail or the horny wings of beetles, rather than in internal framework. External armour of this kind occurs even

among many of the lower vertebrates.

The reason for this is not far to seek. The vertebrates as a whole are an agile company given habitually to rapid movement. If the body is encumbered by armour plating, movement is hampered and speed reduced, as the knights of the Middle Ages found to their cost. An internal skeleton, with a backbone to which limbs are attached, makes for activity.

A Primitive Vertebrate

The vertebrate pattern may be seen in its simplest form in a strange fish-like creature, the amphioxus, a small, translucent organism which swims in tropical marine waters but spends most of its life half buried in the sand—a habit which suggests that complete freedom of movement is still a little foreign to it. It has no real skeleton; but along its back, and running the entire length of its body, is a structure called a notochord, a long tube filled with a jelly-like substance enclosed in a tough sheath, which provides it with firm but flexible support. Above the notochord lies a definite nerve cord, comparable with the spinal cord in man, and the body muscles are arranged in segments along the length of the notochord.

Similar segmentation can be traced in the human embryo during the early stages of its development, and is echoed in the arrangement of the vertebræ of the spine.

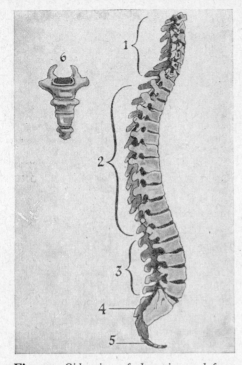

Fig. 2. *Side view of the spine and front view of its last bone, the coccyx. 1, Seven neck (cervical) bones; 2, twelve chest (dorsal or thoracic) bones; 3, five loin (lumbar) bones; 4, five bones of base of spine (sacral) forming the sacrum; 5, four tail (coccygeal) bones; 6, coccyx, which is all that modern man possesses by way of a tail.*

In higher animals the notochord is replaced by the backbone, of which it is the predecessor in evolutionary development.

Prodigal though Nature may appear in some ways, she is fundamentally economical, not to say parsimonious. Far from being specifically designed to carry out his various functions, man is structurally a complicated patchwork of gadgets taken over from remote ancestors. When the first amphibians tried to quit the primeval slime, they had hardly a lung to breathe with, their circulatory systems were shocking and incompetent makeshifts, they were deaf and very stupid. The determination shown by their descendants, the reptiles, to become full-blown land animals might,

one would have thought, have induced Nature to provide them with a bodily structure on an entirely new model. Instead, she contented herself with a few ingenious improvements; she moved a bone here, added a partition there, and generally made do with the material to hand. And so the process has gone on throughout the ages; every sort of temporary stopgap arrangement has been adopted—and oddly enough most of them have worked. Man is the final product to date of this system.

The human skeleton is not only designed to make movement easy and brisk, but is also partly protective. The brain, man's most valuable possession, is enclosed in a bony box; the heart and lungs are protected by a cage formed by the ribs and breast bone; the bones of the hip girdle have broad, flat wings which help to protect the important organs in the lower part of the abdomen.

The Spine

The line of the spine (Fig. 2) in a four-footed vertebrate usually shows a slight upward curve in the region of the neck towards the head, while the back forms a rounded arch supported in front and behind by the limbs, which act as pillars to the arch. The fact that man stands upright has changed the line of his backbone; to get his centre of gravity over his hip joints he has developed a forward curve of the spine just above the pelvis.

The average length of the entire spine (Fig. 3) in man is only twenty-six inches, but it is made up of more than thirty bones, as follows:—

Seven cervical or neck vertebræ.

Twelve dorsal or thoracic vertebræ.

Five lumbar vertebræ.

Five sacral vertebræ, fused together to form the sacrum.

Four or five coccygeal or tail vertebræ.

The first two bones of the spinal column differ from all the rest. The top one is called the atlas, after the giant of classical mythology who was supposed to bear the

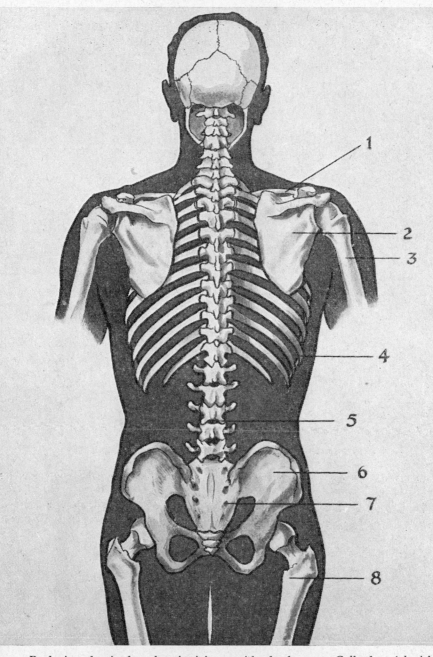

Fig. 3. *Back view, showing how the spine joins up with other bones. 1, Collar bone (clavicle); 2, shoulder blade (scapula); 3, main bone of the arm (humerus); 4, ribs; 5, backbone (vertebral column); 6, pelvis; 7, base of spine (sacrum); 8, thigh bone (femur). The backbone, or vertebral column, in man is about twenty-six inches long. It is the possession of a backbone which distinguishes the vertebrates, the highest class of animal, from other groups.*

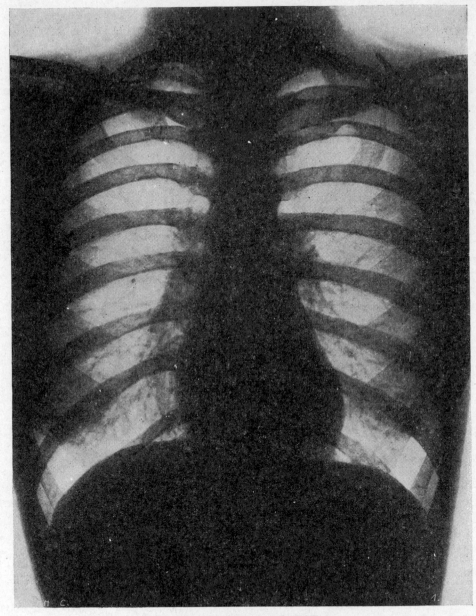

RADIOGRAPH OF CHEST

Notice the small flat handle of the breast bone to which the collar bone and the first rib are attached. The next six ribs are attached to the middle part of the breast bone in front, and to the backbone behind. As we breathe in, the ribs rise upwards and outwards, increasing the space inside the cavity of the chest; as we breathe out, the ribs sink downwards and inwards, reducing the volume of the cavity and so driving air out of the lungs. These actions, similar to those of bellows, are carried out by muscles. The spaces between the ribs are also filled in by muscles, which prevent the ribs being sucked in or blown out during breathing.

world on his back. It carries the skull, and is a simple ring of bone with two slightly concave surfaces on its upper aspect, upon which rests the base of the skull. These surfaces are covered with a thin glistening layer of cartilage or gristle, and the bony surfaces of the skull with which they are in contact are covered in the same way, an arrangement which enables the two adjacent surfaces to slide easily upon one another so as to allow the head to nod backwards and forwards.

One curious feature is found in the atlas which is absent from the other vertebræ; the hole through the centre of the bone is divided vertically into two by a strong ligament. In the larger of the two cavities thus formed lies a prolongation of the brain, the medulla oblongata, which is continuous with the spinal cord below; into the smaller cavity, which lies in front, a spike of bone called the odontoid process projects upwards from the second vertebra and makes a pivot on which the head can turn from side to side.

Cervical Vertebræ

The second vertebra, of which the odontoid process is a part, is called the axis. Below it are five more cervical or neck vertebræ (Fig. 2) which have a distinctive shape unlike that of the atlas and axis. Each forms a bony ring, but the ring is thickened in front into a solid lump of bone called the body, and prolonged behind into a process called the spine of the vertebra. At each side of the ring are lateral processes of bone, which have cartilage-covered surfaces jointing them to the vertebræ below and above. These joints between the vertebræ allow us to bend and twist our necks. The possession of seven cervical vertebræ is a distinguishing characteristic of mammals, all of which, whatever their length of neck, have the same number.

Below the seven cervical vertebræ are twelve dorsal vertebræ (Fig. 2) which are similar in shape, but with rather longer spinous processes behind and more solid

bodies in front. If you run your finger down your back you can feel the tips of the dorsal spinous processes standing out like a row of beads. Twelve pairs of ribs spring from the twelve dorsal vertebræ; they are joined to the lateral processes of the vertebræ behind and curve round towards the breast bone in front.

Joints of the Vertebræ

The joints between the dorsal vertebræ are exactly the same as those between the cervical vertebræ; they allow us to move our backs forwards, backwards and sideways. Movements of the back and neck are not unlimited; only contortionists can bend far enough backwards, for example, to look up at their friends from between their legs. This limitation is due to the fact that the bodies of the vertebræ—the solid pieces of bone at the front of the vertebral rings—are also jointed together, but in a much firmer way than are the lateral processes. Between the body of one vertebra and that of the next there is a thick solid pad of cartilage interlaced with fibrous and elastic tissue—fibrocartilage it is termed —and this ties the vertebræ together firmly, though not immovably. Thus we have a spine which is a support and which allows a certain amount of play.

Below the dorsal vertebræ are five lumbar vertebræ (Fig. 2), of which the bodies are large and solid and the spinous processes short and thick. They lie in the small of the back, and are stout and strong because they transmit the weight of the body to the pelvic girdle and the legs. Below them, the next five vertebræ take an unusual form, their bodies and their lateral processes being fused together to form a stout triangular bony mass, called the sacrum (Fig. 3). To each side of the sacrum the bones of the hip girdle are strongly fixed by fibrocartilaginous joints. Below the sacrum lies all that is left to us of a tail —four, sometimes five, little nodules of bone, so much modified that they hardly bear the characteristics of vertebræ at all.

The spinal column then is a series of bony rings lying one above the other and jointed together. The spinal cord runs through the canal formed by the cavities of the rings, just as a string runs through a set of beads. It is thus effectively protected, being enclosed by the strong yet supple column formed by the vertebræ. Only rarely is this bony defence damaged sufficiently for the spinal cord, which is essential to life, to come to harm.

We have seen that each of the dorsal vertebræ bears a rib and that these ribs are jointed to the lateral bony processes of the vertebræ. They bend round like the hoops of a barrel (Fig. 4), and each is completed in front by a strong piece of cartilage, about two inches long, which attaches the rib to the breast bone. In the case of the upper seven ribs the cartilages are attached directly to the breast bone itself; the next three cartilages join the cartilage of the seventh rib on each side, and the last two ribs, tipped with cartilage, are not attached in front at all, but only to the spine. They are called free, or floating, ribs.

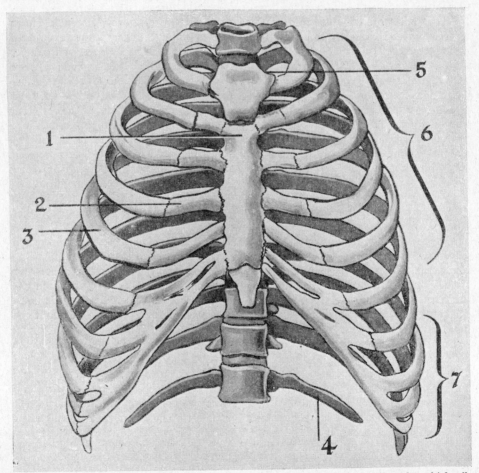

Fig. 4. *Bones of the chest (thorax). 1, Breast bone (sternum); 2, cartilage by which ribs are attached to breast bone (costal cartilage); 3, bone of the ribs; 4, floating ribs; 5, surface where collar bone is attached; 6, seven true ribs; 7, five false ribs, not directly attached to the breast bone, but joining the cartilage of the seventh rib.*

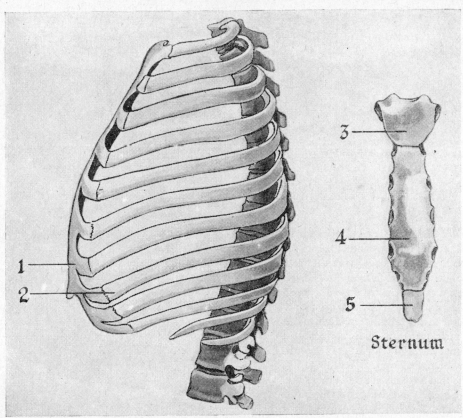

Sternum

Fig. 5. *Side view of chest and front view of breast bone. 1, Cartilage of rib; 2, bone of rib; 3, top part of breast bone to which collar bone and first rib are attached (manubrium, or handle); 4, blade of breast bone, to which next six ribs are attached; 5, cartilage tip at lower end of breast bone (ensiform cartilage).*

The breast bone or sternum (Fig. 5) is a short, flat structure, shaped like the sword of a Roman soldier. It consists of three parts. The top part, called the handle, or manubrium, is a flat piece of bone about the size of a penny; to this the collar bone and the first rib are attached. The middle part has attached to it the cartilages of the next six ribs. The tip of the breast bone is itself a piece of cartilage, and can be felt in the notch between the lower ribs in front. The cartilage of the seventh rib on each side is attached partly to the tip and partly to the middle portion of the breast bone.

It will be seen from the arrangement of

the ribs that they are not intended to be fixed or immovable. If they were, we could not breathe. As we breathe in, the ribs rise upwards and outwards, thus increasing the space inside the cavity of the thorax, or chest; as we breathe out, the ribs sink downwards and inwards, reducing the volume of the thoracic cavity and driving air out of the lungs. The process is exactly similar to the action of a pair of bellows, and is carried out by means of a series of muscles.

In primitive vertebrate animals and many reptiles ribs are numerous and are found jointed to every vertebra above the tail. Since we have found it convenient

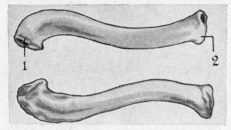

Fig. 6. *(Above) Upper, (below) lower, surfaces of collar bone. 1, Shoulder blade end; 2, breast bone end.*

to develop a freely movable head with a thin flexible neck, ribs have become unnecessary to us in the cervical region. We have also got rid of them in the abdominal region, though it is not clear why unless it is because trunk movements are thus made much freer. In fish, where they first originated, ribs were used to support the powerful body muscles; Nature, with her talent for making old structures serve new purposes, has converted them in mammals into part of the mechanism which they use in breathing.

Each rib has a head, a neck and a shaft. The head is the part attached to the vertebræ behind (Fig. 3). The shaft is the flat curved band running round the chest wall, and the neck is the short, narrowed part intervening between shaft and head (Fig. 4). The first rib is short and broad; below it, each successive rib becomes longer and wider in its curve until we come to the seventh, after which the ribs become progressively shorter. The floating ribs are usually quite short, the twelfth being often shorter even than the first rib.

The arms are attached to the thorax by an arrangement of two bones, the collar bone, or clavicle (Fig. 6), and the scapula, or shoulder blade (Figs. 7 and 8). The collar bone is a tough curved bone with a double bend in it, like an old-fashioned letter S. It is attached in front to the upper part of the breast bone, and can be felt running under the skin to the tip of the shoulder. Here it is jointed to a strong hook of bone, the acromion process (Fig.

8), belonging to the scapula. This bony junction forms a protective prominence above the shoulder joint, and no doubt saves us from many injuries to what is otherwise rather an exposed structure.

In animals which employ their shoulder joints chiefly for running straight ahead, such as the cat, dog and horse, the clavicle is poorly developed or absent. In man it serves as a prop to keep the arm at the side of the body, where it is most useful.

The scapula is a flat, triangular plate of bone lying at the back of the upper part of the thorax, and kept in position by various bands of muscle which allow it a great deal of play. Crossing the scapula near its upper angle is a strong ridge of bone, called the spine of the scapula (Fig. 7), which terminates in the acromion. At the upper and outer angle of the scapula is another

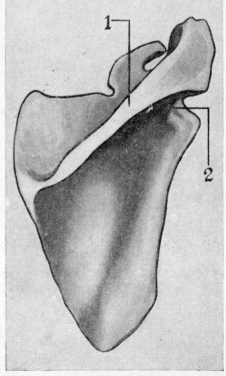

Fig. 7. *Inner surface of shoulder blade (scapula). 1, Spine of shoulder blade; 2, socket for shoulder joint.*

process of bone, forming a hook, which is called the coracoid process (Fig. 8); and just below this is the socket for the shoulder joint, a shallow saucer-shaped area, lined with cartilage. In this socket lies the rounded head of the humerus, the first long bone of the arm (Fig. 9).

The Humerus

The head of the humerus is so freely movable in this cavity that we are able to perform a very wide range of movements indeed at the shoulder joint; if we could do as much with our hips as we can with our shoulders we should all be candidates for the Russian ballet. This freedom of movement has great advantages in gymnastics, ball games, swimming and many manual activities. It has, however, one serious disadvantage; movement is free only because the socket into which the head of the bone fits is shallow, and though the humerus is tied into position by strong ligaments, these are not proof against severe mechanical strain. Dislocation of the shoulder joint is not an uncommon accident. The hip joint, as we shall see, is a much more solid and stronger affair.

The humerus (Fig. 9) has a long, strong shaft broadening out below to form a joint with the bones of the forearm. Two surfaces on the humerus take part in this joint and they are perfectly suited to their purposes. One is a rounded knob; the other is shaped like an empty cotton reel with, above it on the back aspect of the bone, a deep notch or cavity. The two bones of the forearm (Figs. 10 and 11), the radius and ulna, are designed to fit on to these two surfaces. The radius, which is on the outer side of the forearm, has a round, button-shaped head with a shallow fossa or cavity on its upper surface. This fossa fits on to the rounded nodule of bone at the lower end of the humerus. The other bone of the forearm, the ulna, has a beak or hook, the olecranon process, at its upper end, which fits over the surface shaped like a cotton reel. When the arm is straight the tip of the

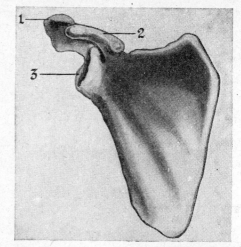

Fig. 8. *Outer surface of shoulder blade. 1, Hook of bone at joint of collar bone and shoulder blade (acromion process); 2, beak-shaped bone extending from shoulder blade towards breast bone (coracoid process); 3, socket for shoulder joint.*

olecranon fits neatly into the cavity on the back of the humerus, and when the arm bends it slides round the joint surface, acting like a hinge.

But the elbow joint does not merely act as a hinge; we can perform another set of movements at this joint, by means of which we can turn the palm of our hand so that it faces either downwards or upwards. These gestures are called, respectively, pronation and supination; pronation occurs when we turn the palm face downwards, and supination when we turn the palm upwards. These two movements are performed at the elbow joint by the movement of the head of the radius on the rounded ball at the lower end of the humerus. The arrangement allows great liberty to the forearm.

The radius and ulna lie side by side in the forearm when the hand is in the pronated position. In supination the radius pivots on the lower end of the humerus and its lower end crosses to the front of the ulna near the wrist. It is this twisting movement which actually turns the hand.

In the region of the elbow joint the radius is the smaller of the two bones; the olecranon process of the ulna is a much more solid affair. Near the wrist the relative sizes of the two bones are reversed: the radius has a broad, strong lower end which

of the ulna as far as the styloid process, the bony knob at the inner border of the wrist. At the outer side of the wrist you can feel a corresponding knob on the radius, but you cannot follow the radius up to the elbow joint because it is thickly covered by muscles.

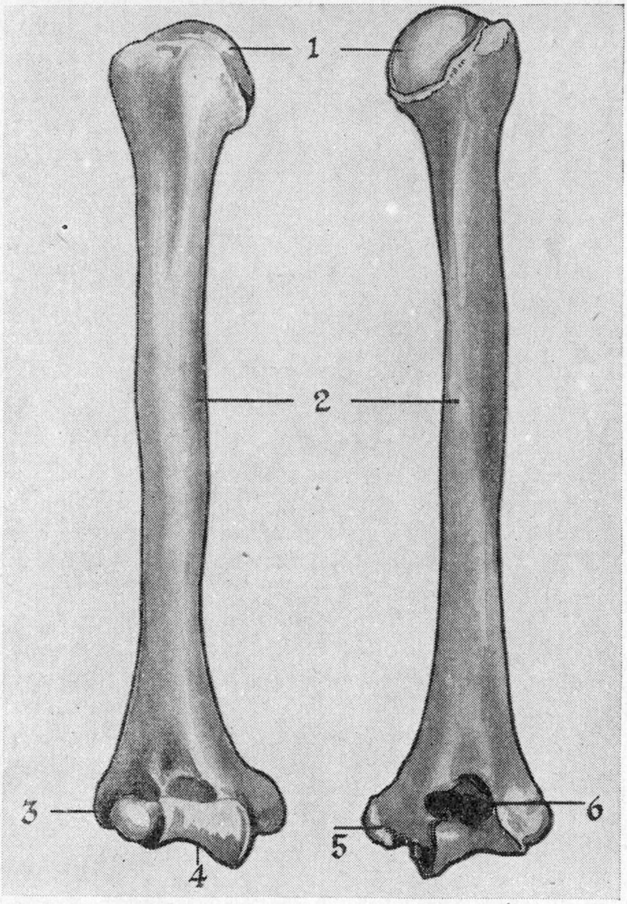

At the wrist, the radius forms one joint with the ulna and another with the bones of the carpus (Fig. 12). These are eight tough stocky little bones packed in between the forearm and the hand; they are irregular in shape and range from the size of a pea to that of a filbert. Where the first row is jointed to the radius there is free hinge-like movement; and the bones of the carpus themselves are jointed together in such a way as to provide a pliable area between the hand and the wrist in which a good deal of movement can take place (Figs. 12, 13 and 14).

On the hand side (Fig. 12) the carpal bones are jointed to the five metacarpal bones, one of which corresponds to each finger. The metacarpals (Figs. 13 and 14) are miniature long bones each ending in a rounded head which is jointed to the first phalanx of its appropriate finger; upon them the palm of the

Fig. 9. (Left) Front view and (right) back view of main bone of the upper arm (humerus). 1, Head which lies in the socket of the shoulder blade; 2, shaft; 3 and 4, rounded knob (external condyle) and notched surface (trochlea) forming parts of joint with forearm; 5 and 6, outer part of condyle (radial epicondyle) and notch of trochlea (olecranon fossa).

forms the greater part of the joint at the wrist, and the ulna ends in a comparatively thin spike which takes no actual part in the wrist joint. If you run your finger from the elbow down to the wrist on the inner side of your arm you can feel the whole length

hand is constructed. Small muscles lie between them, and the long tendons of the fingers cross them to reach the three small bones, the phalanges, of which each finger is made up. In the thumb only two such bones are present. The terminal phalanges of all the digits are rounded and roughened and carry in life the pulpy tip of the finger and the nail bed.

Our limbs are made on a very old pattern; they tally, almost bone for bone, with those of the primitive amphibians, except that with amphibians the number of digits varied. Primitive vertebrates had bony scales on their skins to protect them, reptiles replaced these with horny scales, and we have retained just enough of that protective layer to guard the tips of our fingers as nails.

The hip girdle (Fig. 15) is formed by the sacrum and two large irregular bones firmly jointed to it on either side. The old anatomists despairingly called these two the "innominate" bones (Fig. 16), their imagination failing to conjure up any object to which they could be said to have even a remote resemblance.

The two innominate bones bend round to form, with the sacrum, a ring or basin called the pelvic cavity (Fig. 15). At the back and sides they fan out into those wings which we can feel easily beneath our own skin, and which we call our hips. Below and behind they are prolonged into two tough prominences, the ischial tuberosities (Fig. 15), which are covered below by a thick pad of fat and which take the weight of the body when we are sitting. Towards the front each innominate bone divides into two bars which unite again near the mid-line. The two innominates meet in front and are fixed together by a

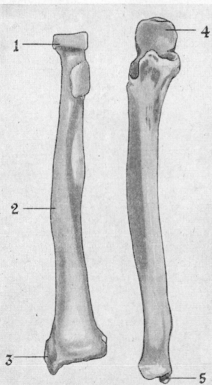

Fig. 10. *Front view of bones of forearm.
1, Head; 2, shaft; 3 and 5, knob at border
of wrist (styloid process); 4, bony prominence
projecting at the elbow (olecranon).*

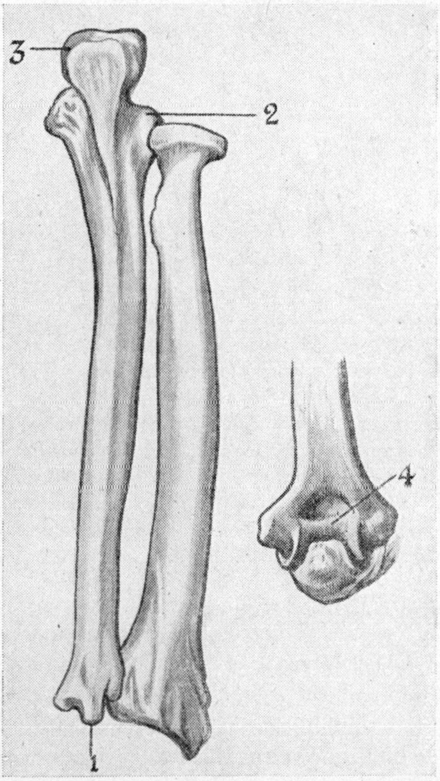

Fig. 11. *Back view of bones of forearm.
1, Knob at wrist (styloid process); 2, part
of elbow joint (coronoid process); 3, bone of
elbow (olecranon); 4, bones of elbow joint.*

pad of fibrocartilage. In the outer side of each innominate there is a deep round cup, the acetabulum (Fig. 16), which is the socket for the hip joint. Actually each innominate is not a single bone at all; in early life it is composed of three bones which become welded together at puberty.

The pelvic cavity is smaller in man than in woman, because in childbirth the head

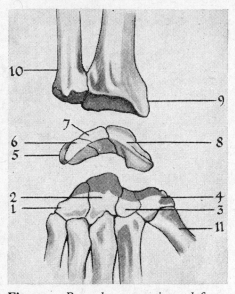

Fig. 12. *Bones between wrist and fingers (carpals). The bones of the hand are named in accordance with their shapes. 1, Unciform or hook-shaped; 2, os magnum or large bone; 3, trapezoid; 4, trapezium or diamond-shaped; 5, pisiform or pea-shaped; 6, cuneiform or wedge-shaped; 7, semilunar (shaped like a half-moon); 8, scaphoid or boat shaped; 9 and 10, bones of forearm (radius and ulna); 11, upper bone of thumb (metacarpal).*

and body of the child must pass through this bony canal. If the pelvic cavity is too narrow, or if the head of the child is exceptionally large, it may not be possible for natural birth to take place, and in such cases it is nowadays customary to perform cæsarean section, that is to remove the child through an opening made in the mother's abdominal wall. The pelvic cavity has a muscular floor, and provides

a stout protection for the organs which lie in it; these are the bladder and rectum, and, in the female, the uterus and ovaries.

Fitting into the acetabulum, the socket on the innominate bone, is the head of the femur (Fig. 17), the first bone of the leg. This is the stoutest long bone in the body, and well it may be, for it has to carry a great deal of weight. The head of the femur, like the head of the humerus, is rounded, but whereas in the humerus the rounded area is comparatively small, in the femur the head forms nearly a whole sphere and fits deeply and tightly into its socket, where it is held by powerful ligaments. The head sticks out on a well-marked, sturdy neck, set at an angle to the main shaft of the bone; at the shaft end this neck is overhung by a thick ridge of bone, the great trochanter, to which several muscles are attached. The strong, powerful shaft of the femur terminates below in two rounded joint surfaces, the condyles of the femur, which form a joint with the head of the tibia or shin bone (Fig. 18).

The Tibia

The tibia corresponds to the ulna in the forearm, but is a much more solid bone. The top is broad and flat with two shallow saucer-like areas upon it which come into contact with the condyles of the femur above to form the knee joint. The tibia has a strong straight shaft with a sharp-edged anterior border, which can be felt running down under the skin of the leg. The shin, as we call this border, has all too many nerve endings sensitive to pain.

At its lower end the tibia broadens and forms the bony prominence, the internal malleolus, which can be felt at the inner side of the ankle; it also plays a large part in forming the ankle joint. In this it differs from the ulna, which has no part in the wrist joint. On the outer side of the tibia lies the fibula (Fig. 18), which corresponds to the radius in the forearm; it is a light strip of bone taking no part in the knee joint, though it is jointed to the tibia at its upper end. At its lower end it helps to form the ankle joint; the bony process at this lower end, the external malleolus, can be felt beneath the skin, but the rest of the fibula is embedded in the thick layers of muscle which surround it.

One more bone contributes to the knee joint, the patella or knee-cap (*see* CHAPTER II), a flat disc of bone in the front of the knee; it lies in the substance of a tendon, that of the thick band of muscles on the front of the thigh.

Tarsal Bones

Corresponding with the carpal bones of the hand there are seven tarsal bones in the foot (Figs. 19 and 20). They are much more solid and distinctive than the bones of the carpus, for they have to transmit the entire weight of the body to the feet. Only one of them, the astragalus (Fig. 19), is jointed to the tibia and fibula. It is a stout, rather square block of bone with a curved convex joint-surface above. The two malleoli (Fig. 18) clip down over the astragalus like a pair of tongs, forming a close, strong joint, well designed for weight bearing. Below, the astragalus rests upon the heel bone, the os calcis, and in front is jointed to another of the tarsal bones, the scaphoid.

The os calcis is the largest bone of the tarsus and is situated at the very back of the foot; to this bone the stout tendon of the calf muscles, the tendon of Achilles (*see* CHAPTER II), is attached. This tendon can be felt

as a thick tough cord under the skin just above the heel. The heel bone slopes downwards and backwards from the astragalus and so forms the posterior pillar of one of the arches of the foot. The anterior pillar is formed by the swelling at the base of the big toe, and the top of the arch consists of the scaphoid and the other bones of the tarsal group.

In addition to the scaphoid, the astragalus and the os calcis, there are four other bones in the tarsus (Fig. 19), the cuboid and the three cuneiform bones, which fit in between the rest of the tarsus and the five metatarsal bones. The metatarsals correspond to the metacarpal bones in the hand. They are miniature long bones, of which the first and fifth deserve special mention;

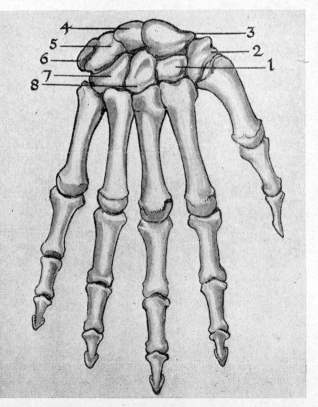

Fig. 13. *Bones of the right hand, back surface. 1, Trapezoid; 2, trapezium; 3, scaphoid; 4, semilunar; 5, cuneiform; 6, pisiform; 7, unciform; 8, os magnum.*

the first is the strong bone, the head of which forms the anterior pillar of the arch of the foot; the fifth metatarsal has an unexpectedly thick strong base, which helps to carry weight at the outer border of the foot. The phalanges of the toes correspond with those of the fingers, except that they are much shorter and comparatively poorly developed. There are two phalanges in the great toe, three in each of the remaining toes of the foot.

Our great toe, unlike that of the apes, has lost the power of "opposing" itself to the little toe: we can no longer grasp with our feet. But we retain a memory of a tree-dwelling ancestor in the way we walk. Tree dwellers find their feet too much like hands for comfortable perambulation on the ground; they would rather be swinging from branch to branch, but if they must walk, they walk with the weight thrown outwards—and so do we.

The skull (Fig. 21) is made up partly by a rounded vault above, which forms the cavity holding the brain, and partly by irregular bones in front which make up the bony structure of the face and lower jaw. The vault of the skull is simply and cleverly contrived out of four smooth curved plates of bone. One of these lies at each side of the vault and the other two, the frontal and the occipital, lie fore and aft.

The occipital bone is shell shaped and has a large hole running through it. At either side of this hole is an oval area covered with cartilage; these areas, as we have already seen, form joints with the first cervical vertebra, the atlas, upon which the skull rests. The hole in the occipital bone, the foramen magnum (Fig. 22), lies directly over the actual spinal canal formed by the vertebræ; part of the brain, the medulla oblongata (*see* CHAPTER VIII), passes through it and is prolonged downwards to form the spinal cord. The occipital bone is jointed in front to two other bones, the parietals (Fig. 21), which meet each other in the mid-line to form the top of the vault of the skull. They are curved bones, oblong

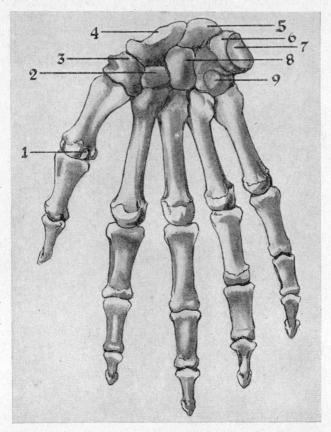

Fig. 14. *Bones of the right hand, palm surface. 1, Sesamoid bone (this gets its name from the fact that it is shaped like the seed of the sesame, an Eastern plant); 2, trapezoid; 3, trapezium; 4, scaphoid; 5, semilunar; 6, cuneiform; 7, pisiform; 8, os magnum; 9, unciform. The finger bones are called phalanges.*

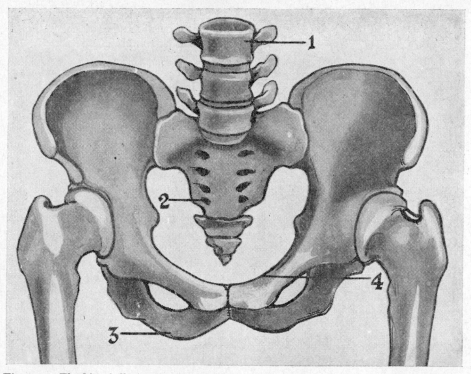

Fig. 15. *The hip girdle: section through upper part of the base of the spine (sacrum) and hip bones (ilium) showing how the pelvic arch is constructed. 1, Backbone; 2, base of spine; 3, bones and protuberances which bear the weight of the seated body (ischium and ischial tuberosity); 4, basin formed by hip bones, base of spine and ischium (pelvic cavity).*

in shape, and they stretch forward to meet the frontal bone of the forehead.

The frontal bone (Fig. 21) has two well marked ridges on its front aspect, the supraorbital, or eyebrow, ridges which are prolonged sideways to form a process of bone which joins the cheek bone. Between the supraorbital ridges above and the cheek bone below is a deep rounded hollow, the eye socket. Across the forehead the frontal bone is a smoothly curving plate and forms the front part of the skull.

Floor of Skull

If the vault of the skull is removed as a circular cap, we find ourselves looking into an interesting cavity (Fig. 22). The brain does not lie in a smooth round basin but in an irregular area of hills and valleys some-

thing like a relief map. There are what may be described as three terraces making up the floor of the skull.

At the front, over the eye socket, is a flat shallow terrace on each side of the midline, separated from its fellow by a sharp little ridge of bone like a cock's comb. One of the strong bands of ligament which help to keep the brain in position is tied down to this little crest. At either side of the crest there is a narrow strip of bone, about three-quarters of an inch long and a quarter of an inch wide, which is so pierced with tiny holes that it looks like a miniature sieve; this is the cribriform plate of the ethmoid bone (Figs. 21 and 22), and through it pass the fine hair-like nerves of smell which run down from the brain to the mucous membrane of the nose. Apart from this small

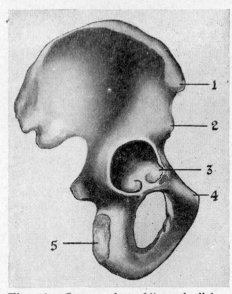

Fig. 16. *Outer surface of "nameless" bone
(os innominatum), so called because its shape
seems to have no resemblance to anything
else. 1, Upper front spine of hip bone; 2,
lower front spine of hip bone; 3, socket into
which the thigh bone fits (acetabulum); 4,
spine of the front wall of the pelvis (pubis);
5, protuberance at base of body which bears
its weight when seated (ischial tuberosity).*

piece of ethmoid bone, the anterior terrace,
or fossa, is floored by a thin plate of bone
stretching from the back of the frontal
bone and roofing over the eye socket.

Behind the anterior fossa on each side
lies the middle fossa of the skull, the second
of our three terraces. This is deeper than
the anterior fossa and is pierced by various
holes through which blood vessels and
nerves enter, or leave, the skull. It is divided from the middle fossa of the opposite
side by an interesting bony structure called
the Turkish saddle (Fig. 22). The posterior fossa of the skull, the last of our three
terraces, is continuous across the middle
line with its fellow of the opposite side. It
is deeper than the middle fossa.

Two bones make up the floor of the
middle fossa of the skull: the sphenoid
in front, the temporal behind. The temporal bone (Fig. 23), in addition to a strong

ridge, the petrous portion of the temporal,
which forms half the floor of the fossa, contributes a flat round plate of bone to the
outer surface of the skull at either temple.

The temporal bone is pierced by a canal
with an outside opening which we know as
the earhole; this canal runs inwards through
the petrous portion of the bone to meet the
nerve of hearing. The auditory mechanism
consists of a minute three-chambered apparatus embedded in the petrous portion
of the temporal bone.

On the outside of the skull just behind
the earhole there is a prominence of bone,
the mastoid process (Fig. 23), which feels
and looks solid; actually it is not solid but
contains air cells which communicate with
the middle chamber of the ear. Sometimes
these air cells become infected with micro-
organisms and an abscess forms in them; a
mastoid abscess of this kind may be dangerous, because the pus cannot escape, and

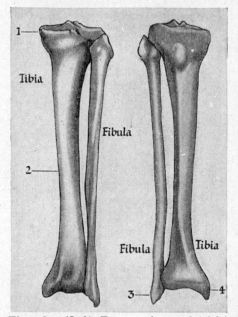

Fig. 18. *(Left) Front surface and (right)
back surface of bones of the right leg. 1,
Protuberance forming part of knee joint
(internal tuberosity); 2, shaft of shin (tibia);
3 and 4, bony protuberances at ankle joint
(external and internal malleolus).*

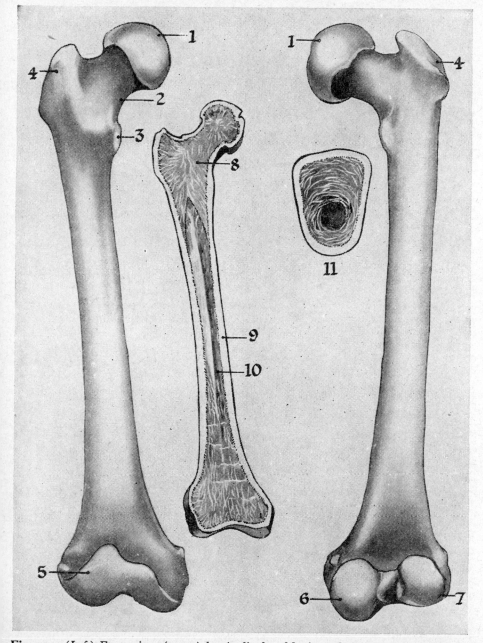

Fig. 17. (Left) Front view; (centre) longitudinal and horizontal sections; and (right) back surface of the thigh bone (femur). 1, Head of thigh, fitting deeply into the joint socket; 2, neck; 3 and 4, ridges of bone to which muscles are attached (lesser and great trochanter); 5, surface for joint with knee cap; 6 and 7, parts of joint with shin bone (internal and external condyles); 8, spongy tissue (cancellous); 9, compact tissue; 10, inner core of the bone (medullary canal); 11, horizontal section of bone.

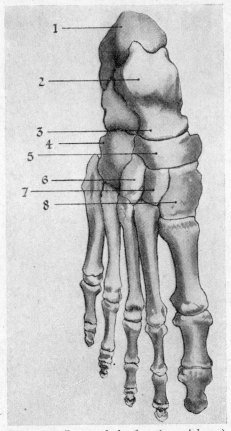

Fig. 19. *Bones of the foot (tarsal bones). 1, Heel bone (os calcis); 2, ball of ankle joint (astragalus); 3, head of astragalus; 4, scaphoid or boat-shaped bone; 5, cuboid or cube-shaped bone; 6, 7 and 8, cuneiform or wedge-shaped bones. Note similarity of construction of bones in the foot and the hand.*

an operation has to be performed in order to get rid of it.

If you look at the shape of the sphenoid bone (Fig. 24) you will see that it is rather like a bat with its wings spread. The body of the bat is in the mid-line and carries on its back that curious structure, the Turkish saddle; the wings spread out in a great curve to contribute their share to the floor of the middle fossa on either side.

The Turkish saddle is important. In the middle of the body of the sphenoid there is a rounded indentation; crests of bone like the pommels of the saddle rise behind and in front of it. This small saddle-shaped cavity, which has a tough, strong, membranous roof and fibrous walls, is in fact a little box, and so secret and close does it appear that one cannot help supposing— quite rightly—that it holds something precious. We have already noted how carefully the body guards valuable property; and this box is no exception to the general rule. It contains the pituitary gland.

Pituitary Gland

The pituitary is attached to the base of the brain by a thin stalk which pierces the roof of the little cavity in which it lies. The old anatomists were puzzled when they opened the Turkish saddle and found nothing within it but this apparently insignificant organ; but Nature had not made a mistake. The pituitary gland is one of our most precious organs and deserves the protection granted to it.

There is reason to believe that when signs of a brain began to appear in the most primitive of vertebrates, the fish, the first attempt at a brain-case took the form of two cartilaginous bars lying one on either side of the pituitary; if this be so, the pituitary has from the first been given distinguished consideration by the body.

The three fossæ which occupy the base of the skull contain three great lobes of the brain, the frontal lobe, the temporal lobe and the cerebellum (*see* CHAPTER VIII); the vault of the skull arches over the cerebral hemispheres. The inner surface of the vault is smooth, except for a few grooves in which blood vessels run. It is made up of "membrane bones," that is, bones laid down in membranes. Their origin can be traced back to the bony plates formed in the skin of primitive fishes who wore their skulls outside their heads. Vastly different though the human skull has become, it still retains the essential elements laid down by those prehistoric fish.

Most of the bones which make up the face we have seen already in the vault and floor of the skull. Forming the forehead we have the broad smooth frontal bone with its two supraorbital ridges; below these are the eye sockets, roofed by a thin plate passing backwards from the frontal bone. Below the eye sockets, and to the outer side of the face, are two strong bridges of bone, the malar or cheek bones, which join, at their inner ends, the stout bone forming most of the face and upper jaw, the upper maxilla (Figs. 27 and 28). The lower maxilla (Figs. 25 and 26), bearing the bottom row of teeth, is the jaw bone; its horizontal part, shaped like a horseshoe, juts out as the chin in front; at the back, two vertical pieces, the rami, pass up at right angles to the horizontal part, and are hinged to the skull above.

Movement of the Jaw

Each upright part, or ramus, ends above in two stout prongs of bone. The hinder prong is rounded, and fits into a groove in the temporal bone, just in front of the ear; it acts partly as a hinge and partly as a gliding joint, and enables us to move the jaw in speech and in chewing. The other prong of bone, at the front of the upper end of the ramus, is attached to the great temporal muscle which covers the temporal bone at either side of the skull. These paired muscles help to move the jaw, in association with the other muscles of mastication.

We owe our jaw, like the vault of the skull, to our primitive fish ancestors; it is derived from one of the bars that supported the gills. The human embryo, at one stage of its development, makes a good attempt at gill formation, but no longer stops to make gill bars—it skips that stage and makes the jaw bone of modern man.

Looking at the upper maxilla (Fig. 27) from the front we see that its lower part consists of a curved mass of bone forming the upper jaw, but that it is prolonged above into two processes of bone which have a triangular gap between them. The

nose fits into this gap. Two small nasal bones bridge the space in its upper part, and the front lower part of the bridge is formed by a plate of cartilage jutting forwards from the middle of the nasal cavity; this cartilage forms the partition, or septum, which divides the nostrils from each other, and is continuous behind with a bony septum which divides the whole inner nasal cavity from end to end. The construction of this septum is interesting. Near the front of the base of the skull are

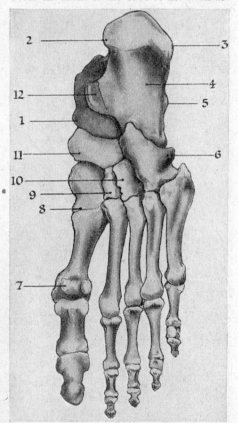

Fig. 20. *Bones of the foot and toes. 1, Head of ball of ankle joint; 2 and 3, rounded projections of bone (internal and external tubercles); 4, heel bone (os calcis); 5, projection of bone connected with the splint bone or fibula (peroneal tubercle); 6, cuboid bone; 7, sesamoid or sesame-shaped bone; 8, 9 and 10, cuneiform bones; 11, scaphoid bone; 12, supporting bone (sustentaculum).*

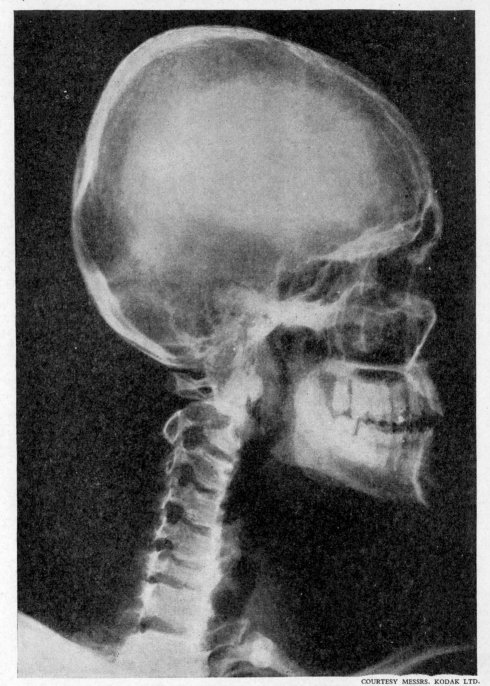

RADIOGRAPH OF HUMAN SKULL

This side view of the skull shows the position of the bony masses and the way in which the brain is connected with the spine through the cavity in its base.

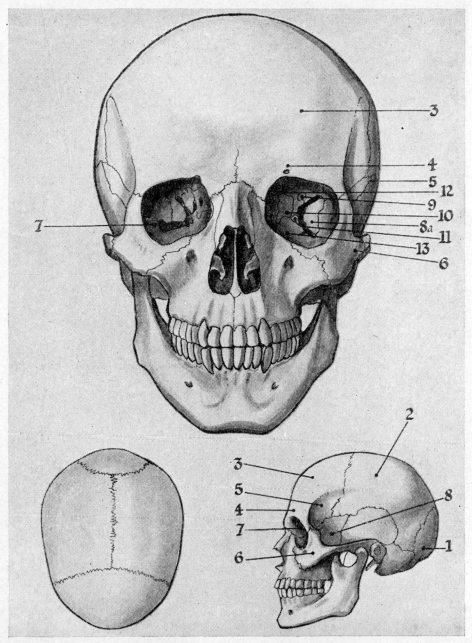

Fig. 21. *The skull and its bones. 1, Bone of the back of the head (occipital), which is jointed to (2) bones forming top of the vault of the skull (parietal); 3, bone of the forehead (frontal); 4, eyebrow (supraorbital) ridge; 5, temple (temporal bone); 6, cheek bone (malar); 7, eye socket; 8 and 8a, wedge-shaped bone (sphenoid); 9, cavity; 10, sieve-shaped perforated bone, through which the nerves of smell pass to the nose (ethmoid bone); 11, palate bone; 12, bone containing the tear duct (lachrymal); 13, upper jaw bone (super maxillary).*

two little perforated plates of bone lying on either side of the mid-line, the cribriform plates of the ethmoid bone. From between these two plates a thin piece of bone projects down into the nasal cavity to form the middle part of the nasal septum, and the ethmoid also sends down two lateral plates of bone which help to form the outer walls of the nasal cavity.

The ethmoid bone (Fig. 21) looked at from before or behind, has the shape of the letter *m*; the middle leg forms the nasal septum and the two outer ones the outer walls of the nose. One more bone takes part in making up the nasal septum, the vomer, a flat triangular little bone, shaped,

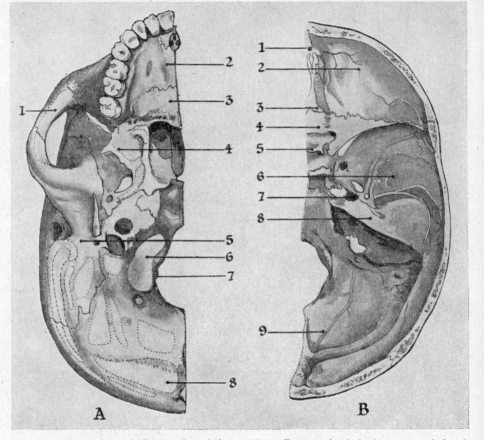

Fig. 22. *Base of the skull, seen from below.* (A), *1, Bony arch of cheek (zygomatic bone); 2, outgrowth from jaw bone, forming the palate (palatine process of maxilla); 3, horizontal plate of palate bone; 4, sphenoid bone; 5, breast-shaped, or mastoid, bone containing air cells communicating with the ear; 6, part of joint between bones at back and side of the skull (occipital condyle); 7, cavity at back of skull through which passes part of brain to connect with the spinal cord (foramen magnum); 8, bone of back of skull (occipital).* (B), *1, Shallow cavity (foramen cæcum); 2, first layer, or terrace, in the floor of the skull (anterior fossa); 3, part of bone through which nerves of smell pass (ethmoidal spine); 4, sphenoid bone; 5, bone structure containing pituitary gland (Turkish saddle); 6, middle terrace of floor of skull (middle fossa); 7, opening of tube leading through the bone of the temple to the great artery of the head (orifice of carotid canal); 8, hard (petrous) portion of temporal bone; 9, occipital bone. The lobes of the brain lie in the terraces of the floor of the skull.*

it is said, like a ploughshare, which fits in at the back. The nasal septum, then, from before backwards, is made up of cartilage, the middle leg of the ethmoid bone, and the vomer.

The side walls of the nasal cavity are made up by the ethmoid above and the upper maxilla in the lower part. These side walls are not smooth. Projecting from them into the nasal cavity itself are curled, scroll-like pieces of thin bone which are covered with delicate mucous membrane; their purpose is to increase the area lining the nose, so that the air entering the lungs has a good opportunity of being warmed and moistened before it passes into the windpipe. Air cavities, or sinuses, very much like those already described in the mastoid process (Fig. 22), but larger, are present in the ethmoid bone and the upper maxilla. They open into the nose by small canals and, like the mastoid air cells, may sometimes be infected by micro-organisms.

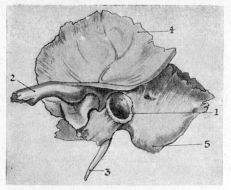

Fig. 23. *Outer surface of bone of the temple. 1, Earhole; 2, arch of cheek (zygomatic bone); 3, projection from base of temporal bone (styloid process); 4, surface to which temporal muscle is attached; 5, mastoid.*

The Palates

Between the nasal cavity and the mouth are the hard and soft palates. The hard palate is an outgrowth from the upper maxilla, and is completed by a pair of small bones at the back, the palatine bones (Fig. 28), from which the soft palate hangs down like a curtain. In persons with cleft palate, the hard palate is incomplete and the nasal cavity is in direct communication with the mouth. Each palatine is L-shaped, but contributes only the short arm of the L to the back of the hard palate. On each side the long arm of the L runs up at the back of the nose and forms the final prop between the hard palate below, the body of the sphenoid above, and the ethmoid and upper maxilla in front.

Now that the bones of the face have been described, it should be possible to understand the arrangement of the bones lining the eye socket (Fig. 21). We have said already that the frontal bone forms the roof of this deep cavity. The outer wall is formed chiefly by the malar, or cheek bone, which sends a plate inwards for this purpose. The floor is contributed chiefly by the upper maxilla, which sends a plate backwards from its upper border. The inner wall is composed near the front by the upper maxilla and a small separate bone, the lachrymal, which carries the tear duct; behind that, small portions of the outer surfaces of the ethmoid and palatine bones are visible; in the deepest part of the socket the wing of the sphenoid can be seen crossing the back of the cavity and forming its posterior wall. The eye socket is pierced by openings through which the optic nerve and other nerves and vessels reach the eye.

Primitive Skulls

Primitive skulls allied to those of modern men have been found in geological deposits dating from a million years ago. The earliest skull so far discovered is that of the ape man (pithecanthropus) of Java. He had a skull with a low vault and a small cubic capacity but, even so, his brain was larger than that of the apes of his own day. Other early skulls, strongly resembling that of the ape man of Java, were found in a cave near Pekin. A skull found at Piltdown, in

Sussex, has given rise to much discussion, partly because most of it is missing, and partly because it does not fit neatly into the series of skulls so far discovered. The deposit in which the skull was found suggests that the latter dates from about 150,000 years ago. The skull was intact when some workmen threw it up, but unfortunately they smashed what they termed "his coconut" and distributed most of it on the neighbouring roads.

From the pieces recovered, a skull has been reconstructed which appears to be that of an advanced type of man with a comparatively high forehead and a good skull capacity. The Piltdown man is, in fact, almost modern in type, except that the lower jaw is much more ape-like, with a retreating chin and long pointed eye teeth to distinguish him from modern man.

Later skulls, dating from 50,000 to 60,000 years ago, have been found in the Neander Valley of western Germany; they

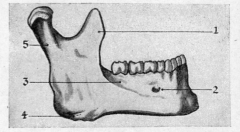

Fig. 25. *Front view of lower jaw bone (lower maxillary). 1, Beak-shaped (coronoid) bone; 2, cavity (foramen mentale); 3, outer line of jaw (external oblique); 4, angle of jaw; 5, neck of jawbone.*

belonged to a low-browed race with a jutting, ape-like lower part to the face, from which the chin receded. Though his face may have been of a somewhat inferior type, Neanderthal man had a skull capacity little different from that of men of living races.

Thirty or forty thousand years ago a new race of men came up from the south

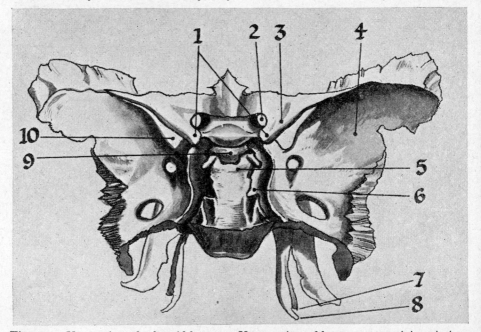

Fig. 24. *Upper view of sphenoid bone. 1, Upper points of bony case containing pituitary (Turkish saddle); 2, eye socket; 3 and 4, lesser and greater wings; 5, lower point of Turkish saddle; 6, groove for great artery of the head; 7, wing-shaped (pterygoid) artery; 8, hook-shaped bone (hamular process); 9, Turkish saddle; 10, split in the bone (sphenoidal fissure).*

RECONSTRUCTION OF NEANDERTHAL MAN

and invaded the territory of Neanderthal man. These newcomers were the true ancestors of *homo sapiens*, the man of to-day. Their bones, found at Cro-Magnon, in France, and Grimaldi, in Monaco, leave no room for doubt that man as we know him had at last appeared on the earth. Cro-Magnon man had a forehead as high as our own, a good chin, a thumb capable of grasping, and teeth, like ours, designed for a mixed diet. To judge from their skeletons, men of this race were as highly developed physically as any living race today. Moreover, they were artists and drew spirited and fluent pictures of animals on the walls of their caves.

In the foregoing description of the skeleton, bones of various types, including many large ones, have been described. It will be clear that if all these bones were solid the skeleton would be so heavy that we should scarcely be able to move. But most of the bones are either hollow, or filled in with a light network of fine bony strands which helps to maintain strength without adding to weight. In some bones, for instance those of the skull, air spaces have developed which make for lightness.

Bone may be formed either from a membrane designed for that purpose or by the ossification of cartilage. Cartilage is the shining bluish-white gristle which covers all joint surfaces. Seen under the microscope it appears as a smooth structureless material, in which lie scattered cavities each containing a cell. The chemical constitution of cartilage is similar to that of gelatine.

In the embryo cartilage is a precursor of bone. Models of all the long bones are first laid down in cartilage and are later replaced by bone as follows: first, bone cells begin to grow in from the membrane which covers the shaft of the cartilaginous

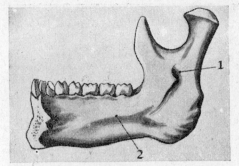

Fig. 26. *Inner surface of lower jawbone. 1, Lower cavity of teeth (inferior dental foramen); 2, ridge of bone (mylo hyoid ridge).*

model; soon afterwards, secondary bone-forming centres appear at each end of the bone and also begin to replace cartilage by bony tissue. Complete ossification may not occur for a long time: the centres at the ends of the bone remain separated from the shaft by a pad of cartilage so long as the bone is growing, and growth may not be complete until adulthood.

Some bones, such as those of the vault of the skull, develop not from cartilage

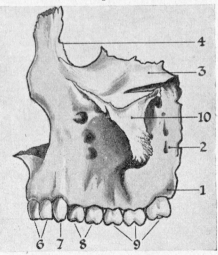

Fig. 27. *Outer surface of upper jawbone. 1, Protuberance of jaw (maxillary tuberosity); 2, grooves for teeth (posterior dental canals); 3, orbital surface; 4, bone carrying tear duct; 5, tendon of the eye; 6, incisors; 7, canine teeth; 8, bicuspids; 9, molars; 10, joint surface with cheek bone.*

but from membranes which have the power of producing bone. At birth ossification of the skull is not complete; the new baby, as we all know, has a "soft spot," or fontanelle, towards the front of his skull, through which the brain can be felt pulsating. This gap is only completely closed by bone in the second year of life.

Under the microscope the solider parts

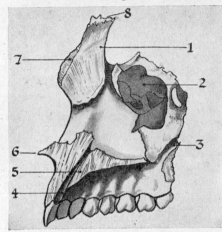

Fig. 28. *Inner surface of upper jawbone. 1, Ridge of bone; 2, cavity; 3 and 4, canals of the palate; 5, plate of palate; 6, front spine of the nose; 7, joint surface for bone of nose; 8, joint surface for bone of forehead.*

of bone appear as a series of systems, each of which has a central canal containing blood vessels and nerves surrounded by concentric rings of calcified material in which bone cells are embedded. The hardness of the bone is due entirely to the deposits of calcium and other mineral salts which are laid down by the bone cells. The hollow inside of the bone is traversed by fine strands of bone so arranged that they help to bear the stresses and strains to which the bone is subjected, like girders in a bridge. The marrow which lies between these strands consists of cells in the process of developing into blood cells. Our bones are, in fact, our chief blood-forming organs—an example of the economy of space and purpose so often seen in the bodies of living creatures.

CHAPTER II

MUSCLES AND JOINTS

MOST PEOPLE realize in a general way that all our movements take place as a result of the contraction of muscles. When a muscle contracts, it does so in response to impulses conveyed to it through nerves. Some of these messages are originated by our conscious will; and we speak of the muscular movements resulting therefrom as voluntary movements. We wish, for example, to walk across a room; a succession of appropriate and orderly movements follows, and we are at the other side of the room. This is very wonderful; but, we may think, not very different from the mechanism of a complicated piece of industrial machinery.

Muscle Fibre

Actually, the processes of muscular movement are a thousand times more complex than this generalized picture suggests. In the first place, a muscle is not just a cord, or a bundle of cords, which can be considered as a single entity. Every muscle is composed of hundreds of thousands of separate fibres, each one of which has its own nerve connexion, and functions in obedience to the impulse conveyed to it. Many of our largest muscles do not contract all of a piece; some of their fibres come into play only on occasion, or when a certain stage of a complex movement has been reached. Moreover, there are few bodily movements in which only one muscle or small group of muscles comes into operation.

Think of the complexity of so routine a proceeding as the raising of a cup to the mouth. The advance of the arm; the leaning forward of the body; the extension of the hand; the complex movement of the fingers first opening, then closing with just that degree of force needed to grasp the vessel; the raising of the cup to exactly the right height; the accurate aim at the mouth; the tilting of the cup; the sequence of movements of the lips and of the throat. Even this is but a précis of the muscular and nerve activities involved whenever we take a sip of tea. We call this a voluntary activity; but few of these actions have been consciously determined; few, indeed, are ever recognized by our consciousness. The central orders, for which alone we have any real responsibility, are merely these: take a cup, raise it to the mouth and drink. All the technical parts, the thousand acts of fine adjustment, the dissimilar but harmonized contractions and relaxations of numerous muscle fibres, are done unconsciously.

Muscular Tone

It is not only a graduated contraction of muscle fibres that takes place when we perform a movement of any sort. There is coincidently, in every case, a graduated relaxation of other muscle fibres. Normally, every muscle in the body is all the time in a condition of slight tension or contraction. We call this muscular tone. When we bend our forearm the muscles on the front of the arm contract; at the same time other muscles on the back of the arm relax so as

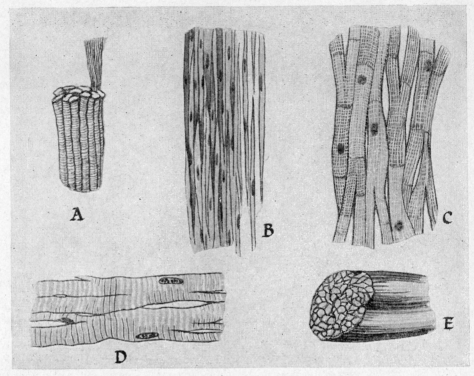

Fig. 1. *Types of muscle fibre.* (A) *Bundle of muscle fibre; one fibre has been detached to show its composition;* (B) *muscle (from intestine) whose action is independent of the will (involuntary unstriated muscle);* (C) *muscular tissue of the heart;* (D) *muscular tissue under control of the will (note the ringed (striated) surface);* (E) *section of muscle.*

to help straighten the arm. Were these latter muscles to retain their ordinary tone of slight contraction, the work involved in bending our arm would be very much greater than it actually is. The balancing muscles do not completely relax; if they did so and went out of action, we should, when attempting to drink from a cup, dash it against our face with painful violence. Small children whose co-ordination has not fully developed often do this. Adults are similarly "clumsy" when first engaging in some form of work or sport not hitherto attempted.

Muscles consist of numbers of contractile fibres bound together in bundles; these bundles are in turn bound together into a thick band, usually spindle-shaped, and always contained in a fibrous sheath (Fig. 1). The sheath is prolonged at the ends to form strong fibrous bands or cords, the tendons, by means of which the muscles are fastened to the bones. Sometimes when muscle is used to roof over a cavity, as occurs in the case of the abdominal wall, the tendon, instead of forming a cord, forms a thin broad sheet of strong fibrous material to which the name fascia is given. As the function of muscles is to move joints, the tendons are normally attached to two bones which are joined together; when a muscle contracts it pulls one bone towards the other, thus causing flexion, or bending, of the joint; an opposing muscle is used to straighten the joint again. As a general rule, each joint is connected with two sets of muscles which are antagonistic to each other in action.

Under the microscope the fibres of voluntary muscles (Fig. 1), that is, of muscles under the control of the will, have a ringed appearance and so are known as striated muscle fibres. Much of the muscular tissue in the body, for example, that in the walls of the stomach and intestines, is beyond the control of the will. Under the microscope this has a smooth appearance and is consequently known as plain or unstriated muscle tissue (Fig. 1). The heart muscle has a characteristic appearance of its own: its fibres have circular markings like those of voluntary muscles (though the heart is

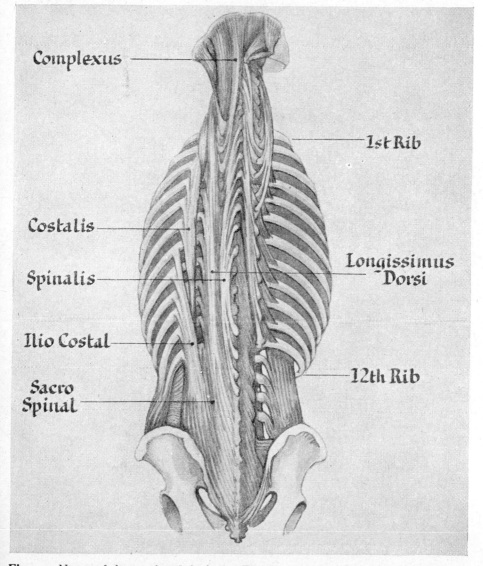

Complexus

1st Rib

Costalis

Spinalis

Longissimus Dorsi

Ilio Costal

12th Rib

Sacro Spinal

Fig. 2. *Names of the muscles of the back. These muscles, whose action is exerted on the spinal column, are designed to help it maintain its position as an upright support for the body, bend backwards in order to maintain balance and tilt the head.*

not, of course, under the control of the will) but instead of running separately side by side, these fibres are connected with each other by numerous cross branches.

The joints between the vertebræ are designed to allow only slight movement, sufficient to enable us to bend or twist our backs. These movements are made possible, not only by the shape of the bones which take part in the joints, but by strong fibrous bands, called ligaments, which bind the joints together, and by the muscles which supply the power of movement. Between each two vertebræ is a stout pad of fibrocartilage, which is in itself slightly elastic and allows some movement; each vertebra is fixed to its neighbours above and below by a small joint on each of its lateral processes, and each of these joints has a little circular fibrous collar, the capsular ligament, surrounding it. Capsular ligaments are lined with smooth shining membrane (synovial membrane) which pours out just enough fluid to keep the joint lubricated. Finally, strong bands of ligament pass up the front of the spinal column along its whole length, binding the bodies of the vertebræ together, and similar ligaments pass down the back. As a result the spinal column is

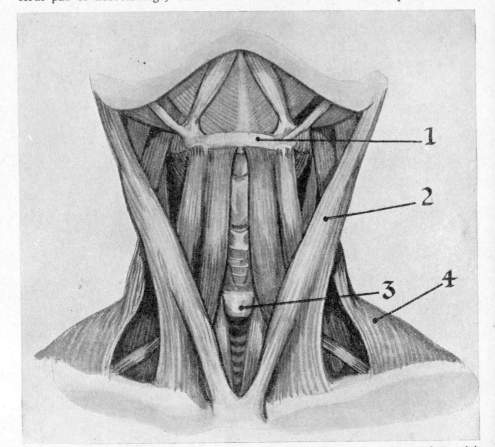

Fig. 3. *Muscles of the front of the neck. 1, Bone to which most of the muscles used in swallowing are attached (hyoid bone); 2, muscle running from mastoid bone to the top of the breast bone (sternomastoid), used in turning and bending the head; 3, part of thyroid gland; 4, muscle which moves the shoulder blade (trapezius).*

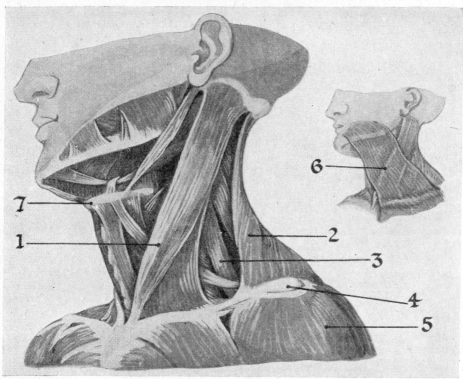

Fig. 4. *Muscles of the neck. 1, Sternomastoid muscle, used in bending the head forwards, or turning it from side to side; 2 and 3, muscles acting on shoulder blade (trapezius and scalene); 4, collar bone (clavicle); 5, muscle covering shoulder (deltoid); 6, muscle running from collar bone to face, used in moving mouth (platysma); 7, horseshoe-shaped (hyoid) bone.*

a strong resilient rod and the muscles acting upon it are largely designed to help it to maintain its position as an upright support for the rest of the body (Fig. 2).

Most of these muscles form a number of vertical bands up the back; some of them spring from the crests of the innominate bones and from the sacrum (*see* CHAPTER I), and are attached above to the ribs or to the spines of the vertebræ. The most important of these, the sacro-spinal muscle and its upper continuations, the spinalis and longissimus dorsi, not only help to maintain the erect position but bend the trunk backwards to counterbalance any heavy weight carried in front of the body. Their action can be seen well in a young child who picks up a baby

slightly too heavy for her to carry; she plants her feet firmly, clutches the baby to her stomach and leans back from the hips. Towards the upper part of the spine muscle bands arise on each side from the lateral processes of the upper dorsal vertebræ and are attached to the back of the skull. These are the complexus muscles, and it is these muscles which tilt the head backwards when they contract.

The complexus muscles at the back of the neck act by tilting the skull upon the joint formed by the atlas and the occiput, this movement being counterbalanced and corrected by two small opposing groups of muscles attached to the front of the atlas and to the occiput in front of the foramen magnum (Fig. 3). These muscles are much smaller and weaker than the complexus muscles behind, but are able to hold their own because they are helped in their task by the sternomastoid muscles. These are situated one at each side of the neck and run from the mastoid process to the top of the breast bone. When the sternomastoids act together they bend the neck and bring the head forwards. When either acts separately it turns the face to the opposite side, and the muscle can then be seen standing out under the skin as a strong band running from behind the ear to the notch at the top of the breast bone.

Many other small muscles help to make up the strong column of the neck; some of them play a part in helping to rotate the head, others act upon the base of the tongue and the larynx and are called into play during mastication and swallowing. Most of these swallowing muscles are attached to a small horseshoe-shaped bone at the front of the neck—the hyoid. The neck muscles of another group are attached to the shoulder blade (Fig. 4).

Abdominal Muscles

So far, we have considered only muscles which act on the back of the spine and are concerned with bending it backwards. Nearly all forward bending of the spine is carried out through the action of the abdominal muscles (Fig. 5), the chief ones involved being the recti abdominis, those two straight bands of muscle, marked by transverse grooves, which pass down the front of the abdomen and are so often seen to advantage in Greek sculpture. They are attached above to the cartilages of the fifth, sixth and seventh ribs, and below to the front of the pelvis, and are enclosed in a tough sheath of fascia crossed by three tendinous intersections.

When these recti muscles contract they draw the thorax down to meet the pelvis, thus forcing the back to bend. If either acts singly it helps to bend the body towards its own side. If the spine and pelvis are held steady and rigid, the two recti cannot pull the thorax down towards the pelvis; they can only compress the organs in the abdominal cavity. This movement is used during normal defecation, and by women in labour.

Roof of the Abdomen

Three layers of muscle roof over the abdomen between the recti muscles in front and the spine at the back (Fig. 5). Two of them run obliquely: the external oblique and the internal oblique. The muscle fibres of the external oblique spring on each side from the lower ribs and form a broad band which passes downwards and forwards, sweeping round the abdominal contents, to be attached to the fascia covering the rectus muscle of its own side. The muscle fibres of the internal oblique run diagonally across those of the external oblique; the muscle arises from the hip bone and runs upwards and inwards to be attached to the sheath of the rectus. The transverse abdominal muscle, the innermost of the three layers, runs horizontally, its fibres wrapping round the abdominal contents from each side like a broad straight bandage. It arises from a band of fascia lying at the side of the lumbar vertebræ and from the lower six ribs and the crest of the hip bone; like the other two muscles in this group it ends by becoming merged in the fascia which covers the rectus muscle of its own side.

The abdominal muscles enable us to bend forwards and sideways or to twist so that we can look over either shoulder. The abdominal organs which they shelter lie in a cavity bounded above by the diaphragm, behind by the spinal column and its muscles, and below by the pelvic basin and the muscles which form its floor. The pelvic floor is an important structure. It is made up of muscles attached to the inside of the pelvis and meeting in the middle to form a strong resilient diaphragm upon which the pelvic organs rest; these organs are the bladder and the rectum and, in the female, the uterus and vagina.

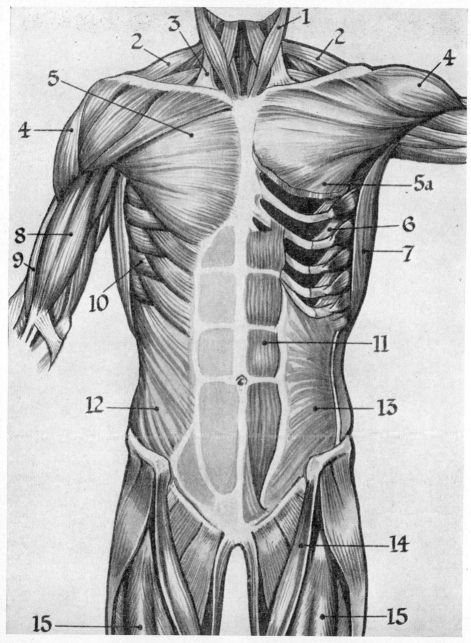

Fig. 5.   *Muscles on the surface of the body.   1, Sternomastoid; 2, trapezius; 3, scalene; 4, shoulder muscle (deltoid); 5 and 5a, muscle covering upper chest (pectoralis major); 6, muscle between ribs (intercostal); 7, muscle of back and arm (latissimus dorsi); 8, biceps; 9, arm muscle (brachialis); 10, muscle connecting upper ribs and shoulder blade (serratus); 11, 12 and 13, muscles of abdomen (rectus abdominis, external and internal oblique); 14, tailor's or sartorius muscle; 15, muscle of thigh (rectus femoris).*

Two flat muscles, the levator ani and the coccygeus, compose the floor on either side. The coccygeus is a triangular sheet stretching from the ischial tuberosity to the side of the coccyx; its function is to draw the coccygeal vertebræ forwards and upwards after they have been pressed back during defecation. The levator ani is by far the more important muscle of the two; it is a broad thin muscle arising from the inner surface of the pelvic cavity and sweeping towards the mid-line to unite with its fellow of the opposite side, thus forming

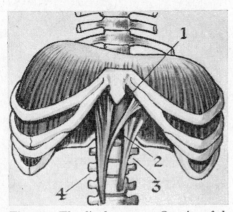

Fig. 6. *The diaphragm. 1, Opening of the gullet (œsophageal opening); 2, opening of the main blood vessel of the body (aortic opening); 3 and 4, tendons connecting with vertebræ (right and left crus).*

the greater part of the pelvic diaphragm. Besides offering support to the pelvic contents it helps to constrict the lower end of the rectum and vagina, and acts as an important auxiliary to the anal sphincter—the valve closing the lower end of the digestive tract.

The levator ani and the coccygeal muscles act together to oppose the downward thrust produced by any rise of pressure in the abdominal cavity. During muscular exertion we may contract our abdominal muscles so much that pressure inside the abdomen is greatly increased; at such times the pelvic muscles also contract and supply a counter pressure to resist the strain, so that the abdominal contents are not forced down into the pelvis. During labour the pelvic muscles relax and allow the abdominal muscles and the powerfully contracting uterus to press the child through the birth canal.

The Diaphragm

The chief muscle of respiration is the diaphragm (Fig. 6), which forms a dome between the abdomen and the thoracic cavity. It arises partly by two strong bands which spring from the lumbar vertebræ behind, and partly from the inner surfaces of the lower six ribs and the cartilage at the tip of the breast bone. All these fibres unite in the middle to form a central tendon which is the vault of the dome.

The diaphragm is not a complete sheet; it has openings in it which allow the gullet and great vessels to pass through. Its action is simple; when the fibres contract, they pull on the central tendon, flattening it and pushing down the abdominal organs. As a result the volume of the cavity inside the thorax is increased, because the dome of the diaphragm has descended; the lungs are subjected to a negative pressure, and, being elastic, expand to fill the partial vacuum which has been created. When the diaphragm relaxes, the muscle fibres slacken and the abdominal organs push the dome upwards; the capacity of the thorax is diminished and, as a result, air is squeezed out of the lungs.

In every interspace between the ribs run two muscles, the intercostal (Fig. 7). They are arranged rather like the external oblique and the internal oblique muscles of the abdomen in that the fibres of the external intercostal muscles run forwards and downwards, while those of the internal intercostals run downwards and backwards. They arise from the lower border of the rib above and are attached to the upper border of the rib below, and fill completely the intervals betwen the ribs all the way up the thorax. Oddly enough they are not exactly muscles of respiration. They contract together and form strong elastic supports which prevent the spaces between the ribs from being sucked in or blown out during respiration.

The ribs are moved upwards during inspiration by two sets of muscles. The scalene muscles in the neck are attached to the sides of the cervical vertebræ and to the first and second ribs; when they contract they pull these two ribs upwards. They are assisted by the posterior superior serrati, which lie on either side of the upper part of the thorax at the back. Each serratus arises from the lower cervical and the upper dorsal vertebræ, and is attached by muscular bands to the upper ribs. Other muscles, low down in the back, assist respiration by anchoring the lower ribs in such a way that the diaphragm can pull upon them.

The muscles mentioned so far have been concerned with breathing in. Breathing out is managed partly by the elastic recoil of the walls of the thorax and partly by the abdominal muscles, which push the abdominal contents upwards as the diaphragm relaxes. One small muscle, the triangularis sterni, attached to the back of the breast bone and to the inner surface of the rib cartilages, helps to pull the ribs downwards and inwards, and so assists in the process of expiration.

The spinal column and the ribs give us examples of joints in which movement is slight and supple rather than free. When we come to the limb joints free movement is of primary importance because, like all

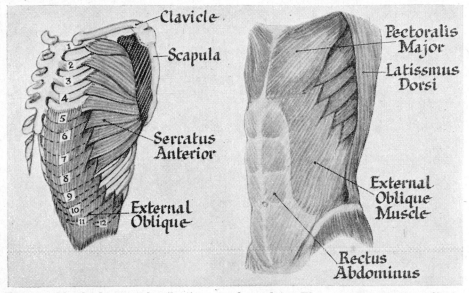

Fig. 7. *Muscles between the ribs (intercostal muscles). These muscles completely fill the spaces between the ribs. They are attached to the lower border of the rib above and the upper border of the rib below, and form strong elastic supports for the ribs.*

vertebrates, we are naturally active; and we are fortunate in possessing mobile joints which are at the same time strong enough to resist easy dislocation. As usual ligaments are used to maintain the joint surfaces in apposition, but they are nearly always reinforced in the limbs by muscles and their tendons.

The shoulder joint (Fig. 8), a typical ball-and-socket joint, has one peculiarity not found in any other joint in the body: it has the tendon of a muscle running through the cavity of the joint. This

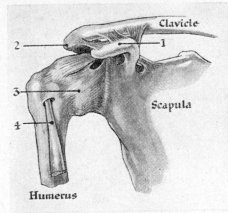

Fig. 8. *The shoulder joint. 1, Hook of bone (coracoid process); 2, shoulder blade; 3, ligament of the joint (capsular ligament); 4, tendon of biceps, running through the joint.*

tendon, one of two belonging to the biceps, arises inside the joint just above the glenoid cavity, curves over the head of the humerus and comes out of the capsule beneath a small transverse ligament which makes a bridge to let it through. This tendon helps to steady the head of the humerus in all movements of the arm and also helps to keep the head firmly in contact with the glenoid cavity; so that though the biceps muscle takes no part in moving the shoulder, it is none the less a very valuable adjunct to the joint. Both the head of the humerus and the glenoid cavity are covered with cartilage, and a synovial membrane lines the joint, as it must always where movement is required.

Shoulder Muscles

A large number of muscles combine to produce movement at the shoulder. The freedom of the joint is due partly to the arrangement of the head of the humerus in the glenoid cavity and partly to the mobility of the scapula which, except for its jointed attachment to the clavicle, is quite free and only held in position by various muscles. Three of these, the two rhomboid muscles and the levator scapulæ are attached to the inner border of the

scapula. When they contract, they can either tilt the inner border of the scapula upwards and the glenoid cavity downwards, or fix the inner border of the scapula in such a way that antagonistic muscles can pull against them. Bearing this arrangement in mind, we can consider the various movements at the shoulder.

Movement of the Arm

The arm, as we know, can move forwards or, to a lesser extent, backwards; it can be lifted away from the side and up to the vertical, or brought down to the side and across the mid-line. It can also be rotated outwards or inwards.

The forward movement (Fig. 9), which we call flexion or bending, is carried out chiefly by two muscles; the pectoralis major and the coracobrachialis. The pectoralis major is the thick muscle covering the upper part of the chest in front. It arises from the clavicle, the breast bone,

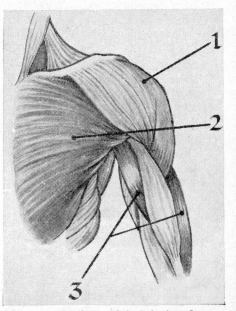

Fig. 9. *Muscles used in bringing the arm forwards. 1, Shoulder muscle (deltoid); 2, muscle of upper part of chest (pectoralis major); 3, muscle running from shoulder blade to upper arm (coracobrachialis).*

and the sixth and seventh ribs, and its fibres converge to form a stout tendon which is attached to the humerus in a groove just below the head. It can draw the arm forwards, when the arm is hanging freely, but it has several other purposes as well. The coracobrachialis arises from the coracoid process of the scapula and is attached to the middle of the shaft of the humerus; when it contracts it shortens the distance between the two points and so brings the arm forwards. We use these muscles every time we toss an underarm ball for someone else to catch.

Stretching the Shoulder

The humerus is extended, or drawn backwards, by two other big muscles, the latissimus dorsi and the teres major (Fig. 10). The latissimus dorsi is a wide band of muscle springing from the lower six dorsal vertebræ, the fascia covering the lumbar vertebræ and sacrum, and the crest of the hip bone. This great fan of muscle converges to form a single tendon which is attached to the humerus close beside the tendon of the pectoralis major. When it contracts, it pulls the arm backwards and downwards. If the arms are fixed, for example, if their owner is hanging by both hands from a horizontal bar, the latissimus dorsi combines with the pectoralis major to pull the weight of the body upwards; so that it is also a climbing muscle.

The teres major, which assists the latissimus dorsi in drawing the arm backwards, rises from the lower angle of the scapula and is attached to the humerus close to the pectoralis major and the latissimus dorsi. These three muscles, then, all pull upon the same point; the direction in which the humerus is drawn depends upon which of them is pulling most strongly at the time.

Abduction, or the process of raising the arm sideways, takes place in two stages. One muscle brings the arm up to a right angle and another brings it thence to the vertical. The muscle which raises it to a

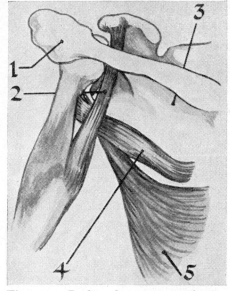

Fig. 10. *Backward movement of arm. 1 and 3, Shoulder blade; 2, head of triceps; 4 and 5, muscles acting on upper arm (latissimus dorsi and teres major).*

right angle is called the deltoid (Fig. 11); this is the large thick muscle which wraps over the point of the shoulder and gives the familiar rounded curve to the top of the arm. It arises from the clavicle and from the spine of the scapula, and its thick fleshy fibres converge to form a strong tendon which is attached to the outer side of the humerus half-way down.

It is easy to see that when this muscle contracts it must pull the humerus up to a right angle. But how is the arm raised beyond this point? Further contraction of the deltoid can serve only to ram the head of the humerus more tightly into the glenoid fossa. Here is a case in which the mobility of the scapula shows its great value. First, its inner border is pulled forwards by the action of a large flat muscle called the serratus anterior, which arises from eight or nine of the ribs, near the front of the chest wall; the fibres of this muscle stretch backwards and form a flat tendon, which is attached all along the inner border of the scapula on its under side. When this muscle contracts it pulls the inner border of the scapula forwards and downwards and so tilts the glenoid cavity upwards; this naturally tends to raise the arm, which is being held in line with the glenoid fossa by the deltoid muscle, above shoulder level. Another muscle, the trapezius (Fig. 12), now comes into play, and tilts the scapula still farther.

Each of the two trapesii is triangular in shape, and arises from all the dorsal and cervical vertebræ; its fibres gather into a broad flat tendon which is attached to the spine of the scapula. Together, they form a great diamond across the back with the upper point on the occiput, the lower point in the small of the back, and a point on each shoulder (Fig. 13). When the fibres of one trapezius contract they draw the scapula towards the middle line of the body and at the same time twist it so much that the glenoid cavity points almost directly upwards; in this way the arm is raised to the vertical. We perform this complicated feat every time we lift our arms to put on a hat or comb our hair, and it says much for the co-ordination of our muscles that we do it without a hitch.

Lowering the Arm

The method of adducting the arm, or drawing it down to the side again, is by comparison simple. It is carried out by the pectoralis major and teres major which contract and pull directly on the humerus, drawing it downwards just as you pull down a blind. The movement of rotation inwards is also performed by these two muscles; by contracting just a little farther they twist the outer border of the humerus round towards the front, and so rotate the arm. Two small muscles attached to the scapula, the infraspinatus and the teres minor, are their antagonists and can twist the arm back again.

The elbow joint is partly a hinge and partly a pivot joint. The hook-like end of the ulna (the olecranon process) fits over a joint surface at the lower end of the humerus; the head of the radius is jointed both to the lower end of the humerus and to the ulna at its outer side. All three joints are enclosed in the capsule of the elbow joint which is, as usual, lined with synovial membrane. The ligaments forming the capsule fit rather loosely, especially at the back, where allowance has to be made for the stretching of the capsule when the elbow is strongly bent.

This portion of the capsule occasionally gets nipped between the olecranon process of the ulna and the lower end of the humerus, a painful

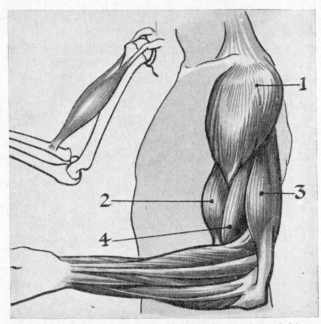

Fig. 11. *Muscles of the arm, showing action of biceps. 1, muscle covering shoulder (deltoid); 2, biceps (i.e., double-headed muscle); 3, triceps; 4, brachialis, or arm muscle.*

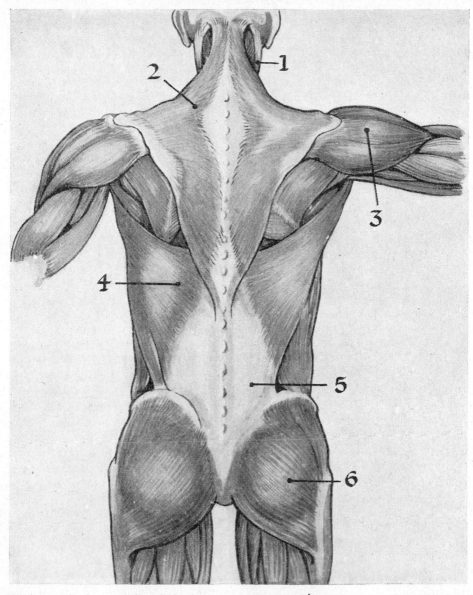

Fig. 12. *Surface muscles of the back. 1, Muscle running from mastoid to breast bone (sternomastoid); 2, trapezius muscle, which tilts the shoulder blade; 3, shoulder muscle (deltoid); 4, wide band of muscle attached to upper arm (latissimus dorsi); 5, sheet of membrane (aponeurosis); 6, muscle of the buttock (gluteus maximus).*

accident which usually causes an excess of fluid to be poured out into the joint by the injured synovial membrane, thus producing one form of the con-dition known as tennis elbow. In addition to the capsule surrounding the whole joint, a strong circular band, the annular ligament (Fig. 14), encircles the head of

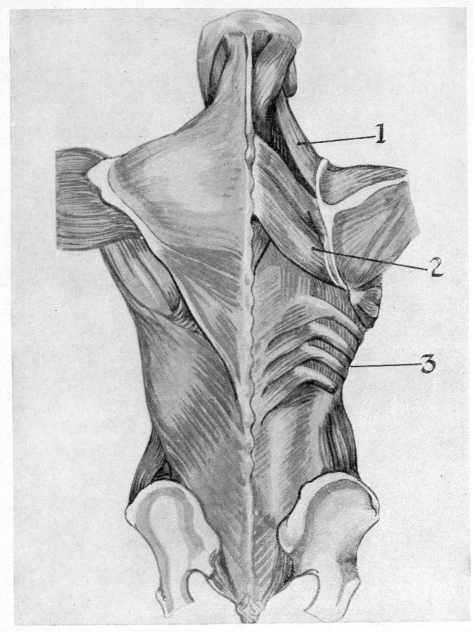

Fig. 13. *Second layer of muscles of the back. These lie below those shown in the previous illustration, which have been cut away in order to reveal the lower layer. 1, Muscle used in raising the shoulder (levator scapulæ); 2, rhomboid muscles, so called on account of their shape, connecting the backbone with the shoulder blade; 3, ninth, tenth, eleventh and twelfth rib and the muscles between them (intercostal muscles). These fill up all the space between the ribs and prevent the ribs being sucked in or blown out during respiration.*

the radius and keeps it from being pulled out of place by the force of the muscles acting upon it. This ligament is also of value in the pivot action of the radius, providing a sort of collar in which the head of the bone is able to turn to and fro.

The movement of the ulna on the humerus is purely that of a hinge, and is brought about by the two great muscles which flex the arm, the anterior brachial and the biceps. The former arises from the front of the lower half of the humerus; its fibres unite to make a thick tendon which is attached to the ulna just below the joint. When contracted it brings the forearm up towards the humerus, a very powerful gesture. The biceps arises above the anterior brachial and is formed by two tendons. One springs from the top of the glenoid fossa to run through the shoulder joint, piercing the capsule at its lower border; the other arises from the coracoid process of the scapula. The muscle fibres from the two heads unite to produce the fat bulge of muscle on the upper

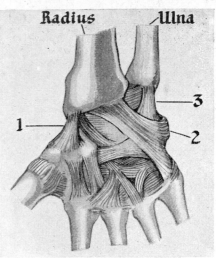

Fig. 15. *Ligaments of the wrist. These ligaments make it possible to turn and twist the wrist. 1, Lateral ligament; 2, radio-carpal ligament; 3, medial ligament.*

arm of which schoolboys are so proud. Below, the muscle narrows to a single tendon which is attached to the radius just below its head. Like the anterior brachial, the biceps flexes the elbow joint, but it does so by shortening the distance between the forearm and the shoulder girdle.

A third muscle, lying not in the upper arm but in the forearm, assists the action of these two great flexors of the elbow— the brachioradialis, which arises from the outer side of the lower end of the humerus and is attached to the lower end of the radius just above the wrist.

The triceps muscle, lying on the back of the upper arm, opposes the action of the three muscles flexing the elbow joint. It arises from the lower border of the glenoid fossa and from the back of the humerus and is attached to the tip of the olecranon process of the ulna. When it contracts it pulls on the olecranon and straightens the elbow. This is an action which shows how cleverly leverage is employed in the body to help muscle action. When the forearm is flexed on the upper arm the olecranon tilts backwards, and the

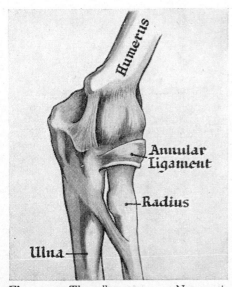

Fig. 14. *The elbow joint. Notice the strong band round the joint (annular ligament) which prevents the radius bone from being pulled out of place by violent action.*

tendon of the triceps pulls upon it just at the tip; the lower end of the humerus acts as a fulcrum and the olecranon as the arm of the lever. The triceps, by pulling on the olecranon, causes it to rotate round the lower end of the humerus (the fulcrum), and by this means swings the forearm into line with the upper arm.

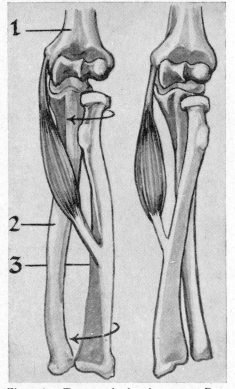

Fig. 16. *Turning the hand over. 1, Bone of upper arm (humerus); 2 and 3, bones of forearm (ulna and radius). The main muscle concerned is the pronator radii teres.*

The second movement at the elbow joint, that of the radius on the lower end of the humerus, has nothing to do with bending the arm, but only with supination and pronation of the hand. The pivot action of the radius can turn the hand over so that it lies with the palm facing downwards or backwards, or turn it so that the palm faces upwards or forwards. In order to do this the radius must twist on the surface which joints it to the ulna, and as this joint allows considerable movement, the head of the radius can pivot on the lower end of the humerus without causing the ulna to move at all.

To understand the processes of supination and pronation properly we must consider the arrangement of the forearm bones at the wrist (Fig. 15). The radius and ulna are jointed together at their lower ends just as they are at their upper ends, and again the joint is a pivot joint. The lower end of the ulna fits into a notch on the radius and both surfaces are covered with cartilage and enclosed in a capsule lined with synovial membrane, so that this forms a complete and distinct joint in itself. It allows the lower end of the radius and ulna to rotate on each other in opposite directions so that when the hand is pronated the radius revolves round the ulna and crosses first to the front and then to the inner side of it, carrying the wrist joint with it.

Joints of the Hand

The carpal bones are jointed only to the radius so that when the radius moves, the wrist and hand move with it. Between the first row of carpal bones and the lower end of the ulna there is a pad of fibrocartilage separating the wrist joint itself from the radio-ulnar joint. The actual cavity of the wrist joint lies between the lower end of the radius and this pad of fibrocartilage above, and the first row of carpal bones below. The lower end of the radius and the pad of cartilage form together a concave surface into which the bones of the carpus fit; they are held there by a capsule formed of four distinct ligaments, one in front, one behind and one at each side. This is reinforced by strong bands of ligament which bind together the lower ends of the radius and ulna and all the carpal bones and attach them all to the bases of the metacarpal bones.

In addition to the joint between the radius and the carpal bones, there are

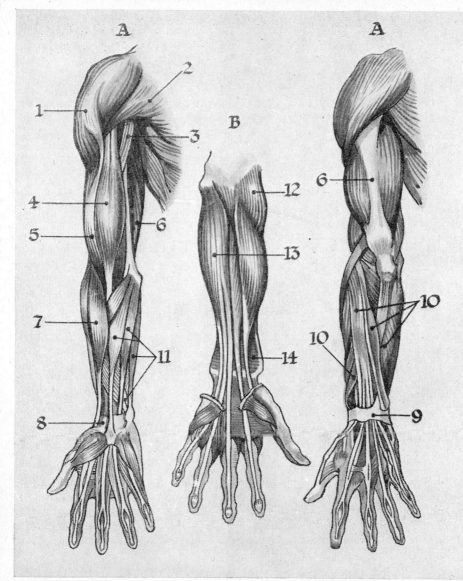

Fig. 17.   (A) *Surface muscles of the arm and* (B) *deep muscles of the forearm.*   (A) *1, Thick muscle covering the shoulder (deltoid); 2, muscle running from arm to upper part of chest (pectoralis major); 3, muscle running from arm to shoulder blade (coracobrachialis); 4, biceps; 5, brachialis; 6, triceps; 7, muscle used in turning the palm upwards (supinator longus); 8 and 9, ligaments holding bones of hand together (palmar carpal ligament and dorsal carpal ligament); 10, muscles used in stretching (extensor muscles); 11, muscles used in bending (flexor muscles).* (B) *12, Muscle used in turning palm upwards (supinator brevis); 13, muscle used in bending fingers (flexor digitorum profundus); 14, muscle used in turning palm downwards (pronator quadratus). These muscles act on the various bones of upper arm and forearm, and enable us to raise, lower and bend the arm, and turn the hand.*

joints between all the carpal bones themselves. These joints are lined with synovial
membrane and faced with cartilage, so that
gliding movement is possible everywhere
in the wrist, adding greatly to its flexibility. Wrist movements include, as might
be expected in a hinge joint, flexion and
extension, and also considerable lateral
movement, especially towards the mid-
line of the body. It is also possible to twist
the hand round in a circular manner; this
movement is called circumduction.

Muscles of the Hand

The manner in which the carpus, and
through it the whole hand, is jointed to the
radius makes it clear how pronation and supination are performed; but we have not
yet considered the muscles responsible for
these movements. The main pronator of
the forearm is the pronator radii teres
muscle (Fig. 16). It arises from the inner
side of the lower end of the humerus and
from the top of the ulna, and is attached to
the outer side of the shaft of the radius. In
this way it wraps round the upper part of
the front aspect of the forearm, and when
it contracts twists the radius round so that
the latter rotates and carries the hand over
until the palm lies face downwards (Fig. 17).
It is helped by another stout square little
muscle, the pronator quadratus, which lies
between the lower parts of the radius and
ulna and is attached to both of them. This
muscle helps the lower end of the radius to
rotate round the lower end of the ulna.

Supination is performed chiefly by the
supinator brevis muscle, which arises from
the outer side of the lower end of the humerus and from the back of the olecranon
process of the ulna, and wraps round the
outer side of the arm, its fibres running
from behind to be attached in front to the
upper part of the shaft of the radius. By
pulling on the radius from behind it twists
it back from the pronated position until it
lies parallel to the ulna. Various other
muscles help a little in these movements.

Hinge movement at the wrist (Fig. 19) is
also performed through various extensor
and flexor muscles, the flexors bending the
wrist forwards and the extensors first
straightening it and then bending it backwards. The extensor muscles arise in a
thick group from the outer side of the
lower end of the humerus, and the flexors
in a similar way from the inner side. The
flexors form a firm band of muscles which
can be felt on the front of the forearm.

In addition to moving like a hinge, the
wrist can bend a little sideways. The muscles which bend the wrist towards the
little finger side are the two ulnar carpal
muscles, flexor and extensor. Acting alone,
the flexor muscle, as we have seen, simply
bends the wrist forwards, whereas the extensor, acting alone, extends it; but when
both act together each counteracts the
effect of the other upon the hinge joint of
the wrist, and they simply pull the hand
inwards towards the mid-line of the body.

In the same way, at the outer side of the
hand the radial carpal muscles act together
to bring the hand away from the mid-line of
the body; but this movement is a comparatively weak one, in spite of the fact that
three of the thumb muscles help in it, the
long and short extensors and the abductor
of the thumb.

Moving the Fingers

Not all the muscles of the forearm (Fig.
17) are concerned with movements at the
wrist; many of them have long tendons
which run over the palm and back of the
hand to move the fingers (Fig. 18). Before
discussing them, the joints between the
metacarpal bones and the phalanges must
be examined. They are very simple. The
four metacarpal bones belonging to the
fingers lie in a straight line attached to the
carpus, but the metacarpal bone belonging
to the thumb is set at an angle to allow for
grasping movements; this characteristic is
confined to the human thumb and the
thumbs of apes and monkeys.

The phalanges of all the digits are joined
to the metacarpal bone in the usual way;

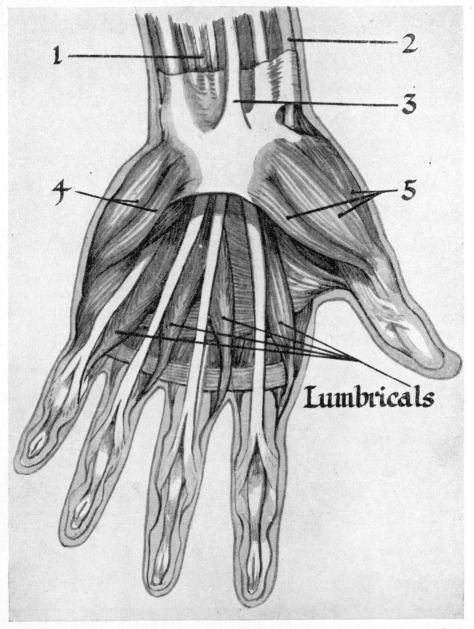

Fig. 18. *Muscles and tendons of the hand. 1, Muscle used in bending the fingers (flexor sublimis digitorum) running from lower end of upper arm and dividing into four tendons, one for each finger; 2, muscle used in bending the thumb; 3, muscle covering base of palm (palmaris longus); 4, muscles used in moving little finger; 5, muscles used in moving thumb. The lumbricals help both to bend and stretch the fingers. They arise from the tendons of the deep muscles used in bending the fingers, blend with the finger-stretching muscles, and are attached to the joints between the bones of the hand and those of the fingers.*

the slightly rounded base of the phalanx fits on to the slightly concave head of the metacarpal and the two are held in contact with each other by a capsular ligament. Similar joints exist between the different phalanges themselves. All the joint surfaces are covered with cartilage and lubricated with synovial fluid, so that movement at the joint is free.

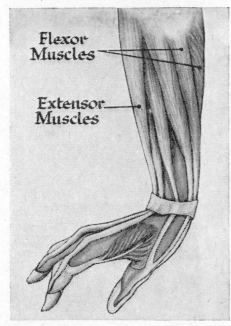

Fig. 19. *Muscles used in turning the wrist. The bending muscles (flexors) bend the wrist forwards and the stretching muscles (extensors) straighten it and bend it backwards.*

So many activities depend on the movements of the fingers that it is not surprising to find them ingeniously supplied with tendons which allow for movement at every one of the joints just described. The muscles which bend the fingers lie in the forearm (Fig. 17); one of them, the flexor sublimus digitorum, arises partly from the inner side of the lower end of the humerus, with the other flexor muscles, and partly from the upper ends of the radius and ulna. The muscle divides into four tendons, one of which goes to each of the four fingers:

opposite the bottom joint of the fingers each tendon splits and the two tendinous slips are attached to the second phalanx at either side. When the muscle contracts it bends the fingers at the joint between the first and second phalanges.

The second flexor muscle of the fingers, flexor digitorum profundus, lies in the forearm under the flexor sublimis digitorum. It arises from the ulna, and like the superficial flexor muscle divides into four tendons, one to each finger. These tendons run underneath the superficial tendons as far as the second phalanx, where the superficial tendon splits into two; the deep tendon passes between the two slips, to be attached to the terminal phalanx of the finger. The deep flexor muscle can only act in sympathy with the superficial one, flexing the terminal phalanges when the superficial muscle flexes the joints between the first and second phalanges.

Bending the Thumb

In addition to these flexors of the fingers, the thumb has a special flexor muscle of its own which arises from the upper part of the radius and is attached to the last phalanx of the thumb. This muscle not only bends the thumb but helps to bend the wrist, so it must be included as one of the flexor muscles of the wrist joint.

The extensor muscles of the fingers lie on the back of the forearm, and are used to straighten the fingers when they have been bent. The chief of them arises from the outer side of the humerus, at its lower end, and is attached to the phalanges of the fingers by four tendons, one to each finger. At the wrist these tendons pass under the dorsal carpal ligament, which acts as a fulcrum upon which they can exert leverage; thanks to this ligament the long extensors of the fingers cannot only pull the fingers backwards, but can extend the wrist as well. Separate extensor muscles run from the group on the back of the forearm to supply the first finger, the little finger and the thumb. The long abductor

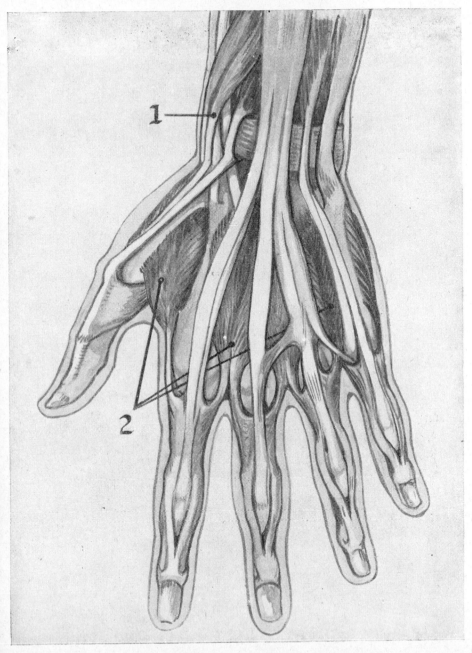

Fig. 20. *Muscles of hand: 1, Muscle used in stretching the thumb (extensor longus pollicis), 2, muscles lying between bones of the hand (interossei). Three of these, lying in the palm, are used in bringing the fingers together; the other four, at the back of the hand, spread them apart. There are altogether, in addition to the muscles of the forearm, which act on the fingers, twenty small muscles in the hand itself.*

muscle of the thumb runs from the back of the radius and ulna to the base of the thumb; it acts by drawing the thumb away from the mid-line of the hand and by helping to abduct and extend the wrist.

In spite of this fine array of muscles in the forearm, we have an additional battery of twenty small muscles in the hand itself (Figs. 19 and 20). Five of these form the swelling at the base of the thumb and four make up the swelling at the opposite side of the palm, at the base of the little finger; the rest are packed into the spaces between the metacarpals. The thumb muscles are attached to the bones of the wrist at one end and to various points on the thumb at the other, and are so well arranged that a most delicate variety of movements is made possible. The muscles attached to the little finger are comparatively weak. Of the small muscles lying between the metacarpals (the interossei), three lie in the palm of the hand and help to bring the fingers together; and the other four, their antagonists, lie on the back of the hand and spread the fingers apart. In addition there are four curious little muscles called the lumbricals which actually arise from the tendons of the deep flexor muscles supplying the fingers, and are attached to the joints between the metacarpals and the phalanges. They help to flex the fingers at these joints; but, by blending with the extensor tendons on the back of the phalanges, they also play a part in extending the fingers.

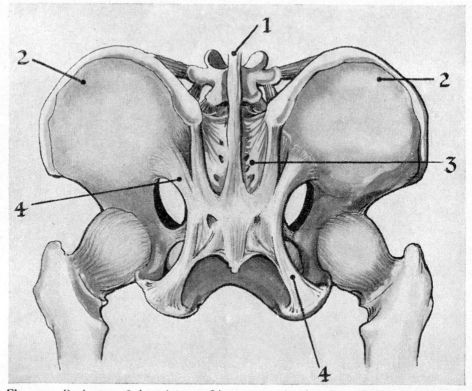

Fig. 21. *Back view of the pelvis. 1, Ligament running from base of spine (supraspinous ligament); 2, hip bones (ilium); 3 and 4, ligaments joining base of spine to hip (sacro-iliac ligament and great sacro-sciatic ligament). These ligaments are very strong, and make the back of pelvis almost solid. These great muscle masses are, however, very susceptible to rheumatism.*

Our arms are freely movable, but as our legs are designed chiefly for standing and walking, it might be thought that a simpler type of joint would suffice in the hip region. This is far from being the case. It will be remembered that the hip girdle, or pelvis (Fig. 21), is composed of the sacrum at the back, and the two innominate bones in front and at the sides; and that the innominate bones are each composed of three parts, the ilium, the ischium and the pubis. These three portions of each innominate bone are fused into one, but these two composite bones are fused neither with the sacrum behind nor with each other in front; so that there are three joints in the pelvis, one at each side of the sacrum, and one between the two innominate bones in front.

The sacrum is wedged in tightly between the two innominate bones, being jointed to both the ilium and the ischium, and is held in place by a number of powerful ligaments (Fig. 21). Strong bands of ligament run from the wing of the ilium to the sacrum, and other bands attach the sacrum to the ischial tuberosity. Another powerful band connects the crest of the ilium with the tuberosity of the ischium and so reinforces and strengthens the whole joint. On the front aspect of the sacrum, stout ligaments bind the bone to the two innominates and make this portion of the pelvis almost solid. Unfortunately these great strands of fibrous tissue are a favourite site for rheumatism, and once rheumatism has invaded the sacro-ischial joint it is difficult to get rid of.

Joints of the Pelvis

The joint at the front of the pelvis is not so rigid as the sacro-iliac joint; a pad of fibrocartilage separates the two pubic bones, which are in addition bound to each other by anterior and posterior, superior and inferior ligaments. This joint is important in women; during the birth of a child, the ligaments relax a little to allow the joint to ease slightly, so that the

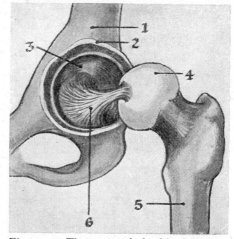

Fig. 22. *The parts of the hip joint.* 1, *Pelvis;* 2, *ligament of hip socket (cotyloid ligament);* 3, *hip socket (acetabulum);* 4, *head of the thigh;* 5, *thigh bone;* 6, *ligament tying thigh bone into hip socket (teres ligament)*

pelvic canal becomes a little less rigid. On each side of the mid-line, a ligament runs from the upper surface of the pubis to the crest of the ilium, forming a bridge beneath which several important muscles, vessels and nerves find their way over the brim of the pelvis to the leg. This is the inguinal ligament or ligament of Poupart.

The hip joint itself is formed by the innominate bone and the head of the femur (Fig. 22). The head fits into the acetabulum, a bony socket on the outer side of each innominate. This socket is very deep, and is made still deeper by a circular ligament, the cotyloid, which runs round the border of the bony socket and increases its capacity. There is a notch in the bone at the inferior margin of the acetabulum; across this margin the cotyloid ligament forms a bridge, and, under this bridge, vessels and nerves enter the joint. From the sides of the notch, two strong bands of ligament spring and unite to form a cylindrical cord, the teres ligament, which is attached firmly to the head of the femur, tying it into the acetabulum very much as a string ties the leg of a jointed doll into its socket. This strong

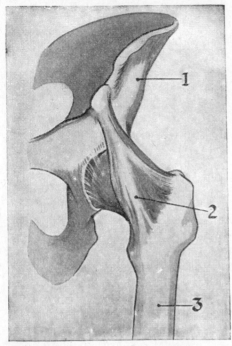

Fig. 23. *Reinforcement of the hip joint. 1, Pelvis; 2, Y-shaped ligament from upper edge of hip to front of thigh bone; 3, thigh bone.*

ligament is extremely difficult to rupture, and acts like a mooring rope to keep the head of the femur in place.

In addition, there is the usual strong capsule enclosing completely the head of the femur and the borders of the acetabulum; it is reinforced by a powerful Y-shaped ligament (Fig. 23) which runs from the upper margin of the ilium to the front aspect of the femur and which has been developed to this extent only in animals which use the erect position. When the hip is extended, that is to say, when we are standing upright, this ligament forms a strong, stretched band which prevents the pelvis from tilting backwards, and so preserves the muscles of the front of the thigh from strain; it is probably one of the most useful ligaments we possess. The capsule is reinforced by various other bands of ligaments.

The hip is a beautiful example of a ball-and-socket joint, and allows considerable movement. While we cannot extend the hip beyond a straight line, we can flex it so freely that we can bring the front of the thighs into contact with the abdominal wall, provided the knees are bent. We can also abduct the leg—a movement everyone uses when, in mounting a bicycle, the leg is swung out to the side in order to clear the saddle; or we can adduct the leg, bringing the thighs together. We find the adductor muscles especially useful when riding on horseback; they enable us to drive our knees well into the horse's sides and so help us to maintain our balance.

The chief muscles which flex the thigh (Fig. 24) arise inside the pelvis from the inner surface of the wing of the ilium and from the lumbar vertebræ. These muscles, the psoas and iliacus, form a thick band

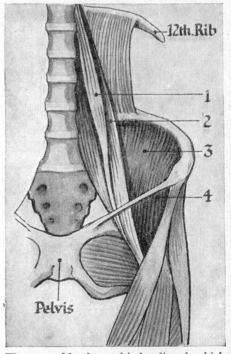

Fig. 24. *Muscles used in bending the thigh. 1, 2 and 3, Muscles running from pelvic cavity to the thigh bone (psoas minor, psoas major and iliacus); 4, ligament from pubic bone to hip (inguinal ligament).*

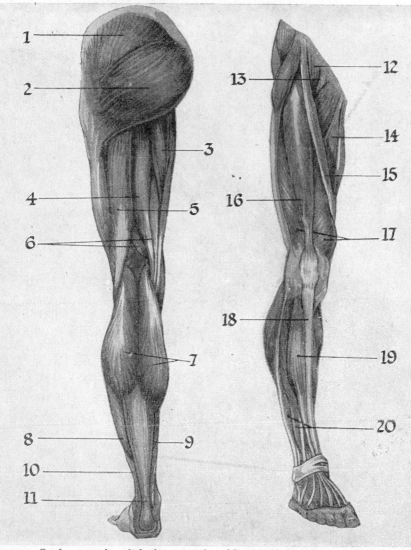

Fig. 25. *Surface muscles of the leg. 1 and 2, Muscles of the buttock used in straightening the leg (gluteus medius and gluteus maximus); 3, 12, 13 and 14, muscles used in moving thigh (adductor magnus, iliacus, psoas major and adductor longus); 4, 5 and 6, the hamstrings (semi-tendinosus; biceps and semi-membranosus); 7, 8 and 10, muscles of the calf, used in stretching leg (gastrocnemius, soleus and peroneus); 9, muscle used in bending toes; 11, tendon at back of heel (tendon of Achilles); 15, muscle used to bend hip and knee (sartorius); 16, muscle of thigh (rectus femoris); 17, muscles above knee (vastus muscles); 18, shin bone; 19, muscle at front of shin bone (anterior tibial); 20, muscles used in stretching toes.*

lining the pelvic cavity at each side and join together to slip over the pelvic brim beneath the inguinal ligament and attach themselves by a single tendon to the femur.

The two stout prominences on the femur situated just at the point where the neck joins the shaft are called the greater and lesser trochanters. Wherever bone is

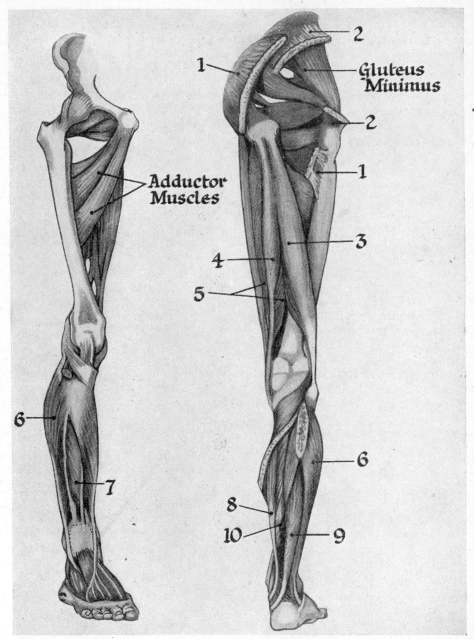

Fig. 26. *Deep layers of leg muscles. 1 and 2, Surface buttock muscles, cut away (gluteus maximus and gluteus minimus); 3, 4 and 5, the hamstrings (biceps, semi-tendinosus and semi-membranosus); 6, calf muscle (soleus); 7, muscles used in stretching toes (extensor muscles); 8 and 9, muscles used in bending great toe (long flexers of great toe); 10, muscle at back of shin bone (posterior tibial). Note fan-shaped adductor muscles attached to thigh bone. It is these muscles which give the curved appearance to the inner side of the thigh.*

subjected to the strong pull of a muscle it develops a projection in response to the strain. The trochanters of the femur are examples of bony prominences developed in this way. The single tendon of the psoas and iliacus muscles is attached to the lesser trochanter; when they contract they bring the femur up towards the abdomen. In a way they are acting at a mechanical disadvantage, because the lesser trochanter is so near the upper end of the femur that the psoas and iliacus muscles have hardly any purchase on that long bone; on the other hand, the brim of the pelvis provides them with a fulcrum and makes it possible for them to lever up the femur in spite of its great length.

Muscles of the Hip

The extensor muscles of the hip form the curve of the buttock (Fig. 25). The chief is the gluteus maximus, which arises from the crest of the ilium and the side of the sacrum, and is attached to the femur just below the great trochanter; the gluteus medius lies underneath it, arising from the ilium, and is attached to the top of the great trochanter. When these two muscles contract they pull the femur backwards so that the leg is in a straight line with the spinal column. If it were not for the Y-shaped ligament of the hip joint they would pull it still farther back and we should find ourselves in one of the ridiculous attitudes of those toy animals of which the legs, attached by elastic, can be twisted into the most extravagant poses. The gluteal muscles are in contraction when we are standing upright, and are two of the most hard-working and best developed muscles of the whole body.

The movement of adduction is carried out by a set of three adductor muscles (Fig. 26) which arise from a point near where the pubic bones join. Their fibres spread out fanwise to be attached to the inner border of the femur along its whole length. These powerful muscles give the characteristic curve to the thigh.

Abduction of the thigh is carried out chiefly by the gluteus medius (Fig. 27). When it acts as an abductor it is helped by the gluteus minimus (Fig. 26) which arises from the ilium beneath the other two gluteal muscles and is attached to the great trochanter of the femur. When these two muscles contract they pull the trochanter upwards and tilt the neck and head of the femur down, so that the head rotates downwards in its socket and the leg is

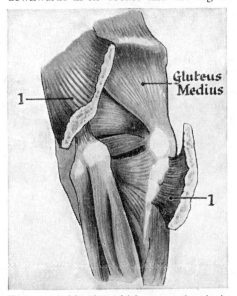

Fig. 27. *Muscles which move the thigh. 1, Gluteus maximus cut away. The gluteal muscles attached to the hip and the thigh are among the most hard working in the body.*

raised from the side. This movement has a limited application in everyday life but is a very useful addition to our repertoire of movements. We owe it to the fact that we spring from ancestors whose lives depended upon gymnastic feats in trees. Had we come of a stock which put its faith merely in fleetness of foot, our hind limbs would have been as specialized as those of the horse, and would have been equally incapable of the wide variety of sideways movement which are in their power.

Three bones take part in the knee joint (Fig. 28); the lower end of the femur, the upper end of the tibia and the patella which lies in front of them. The fibula takes no part in the joint, but is jointed to the tibia just below it. At the lower end of the femur are two rounded prominences called the condyles; towards the front of the bone these prominences melt into a common surface, but at the back they are separated by a deep groove. The top of the tibia bears two shallow saucer-like areas upon which these condyles move. They are not in direct contact with the tibia, however.

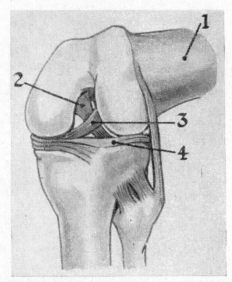

Fig. 28. *The knee joint. 1, The thigh bone; 2, 3 and 4, ligaments running from the shin bone to the thigh bone (posterior cruciate, anterior cruciate and transverse ligaments).*

A similar arrangement is found in the knee as obtains in the wrist joint, where a small triangular wedge of fibrocartilage fits in between the lower end of the ulna and the wrist joint. Lying on the upper surface of the tibia are two curved pieces of cartilage, the semi-lunar cartilages, thick at the outer border but narrowing to the thinness of a wafer towards the inside of the joint. The name is rather misleading, because they are shaped more like crescent moons or horseshoes than half-moons.

These two cartilages fit in between the condyles of the femur and the saucer-like surfaces on the top of the tibia, and not only play the part of shock absorbers but also make gliding movement possible. They have their drawbacks, for if they are torn from their attachments, as they may be by a sudden jerk, they are liable to become folded inside the joint and to give rise to such severe pain that walking is temporarily impossible. Footballers often experience this accident, and although the damaged cartilage can usually be put back into position it is always apt to become displaced again. In the end an operation for removal of one or both cartilages frequently becomes necessary. Curiously enough, the knee joint functions reasonably well even when both cartilages have been removed.

The Knee-cap

Inside the joint, two ligaments, the cruciate, run between the femur and the tibia, crossing each other as they pass. The whole joint is enclosed in a capsule, fairly thin in itself but reinforced by all the local ligaments and tendons, the chief of which is the patellar tendon. The patella (Fig. 29) is the rounded knee-cap lying in front of the joint; it is embedded in the tendon of the great quadriceps femoris muscle which lies on the front of the thigh. The tendon, after embracing the patella, travels on to be attached to the front of the tibia near its upper end. It is this short stretch of tendon between the top of the tibia and the lower border of the patella which the doctor taps when he examines the knee jerk.

The head of the fibula is attached to the side of the tibia just below the knee by a small capsule of its own lined with a synovial membrane entirely separate from that of the knee joint; a ligament runs from the lower end of the femur to the head of the fibula and helps to keep it in position. It will be clear from this that the leg has no power of supination and pronation equivalent to those found in the forearm because the fibula lacks a pivot joint at its upper end; it is, in fact, simply glued alongside the tibia like a kind of splint.

Movements at the knee joint are confined to flexion, extension and slight rotation, the muscles on the front of the thigh being the extensors and those on the back the flexors. The chief extensors are the thick bands of muscle which make up the quadriceps femoris. They rise partly from the front of the pelvis but chiefly from the front aspect of the femur itself, and unite to form the patellar tendon attached to the tibia. They are immensely powerful; if we throw them into action when the knee is bent, they first bring the patella into contact with the front of the knee and then lever the tibia forwards by means of the tension which is exerted through the lower part of the tendon.

Running across the quadriceps muscle diagonally is a narrow strap-like muscle, the sartorius or tailor's muscle (Fig. 30). The sartorius is the longest muscle in the body;

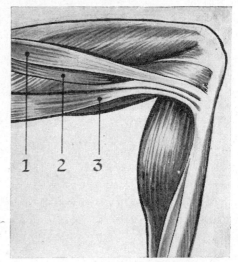

Fig. 30. *Muscles which contract to bend the knee. 1, Muscle which bends hip and knee and turns thigh outwards (the tailor's or sartorius muscle); 2 and 3, hamstrings (semi-membranosus and semi-tendinosus).*

it rises from the front of the crest of the ilium and is attached to the upper part of the tibia on its inner side. When it contracts, it flexes both the hip and knee and at the same time rotates the thigh outwards and abducts it. This sounds more complicated than it is. It is the movement we employ when we sit cross-legged upon the floor, as tailors used to do in the old days.

Opposing the action of these muscles are the hamstrings, which form the muscular mass at the back of the thigh. There are three hamstrings: the biceps (Fig. 25), the semi-membranosus and the semi-tendinosus. The biceps, like the biceps in the arm, rises by two tendons, one from the ischium and the other from the shaft of the femur itself, and is attached to the head of the fibula. The semi-membranosus and the semi-tendinosus also rise from the ischium, but they are attached to the tibia on its inner side; so that the hamstring muscles divide at the back of the thigh, and their tendons can be felt running down as stout cords at either side of the knee joint, one going to the outer side and two to the inner.

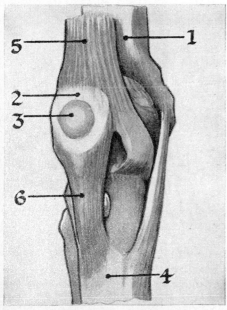

Fig. 29. *Ligaments of the knee joint. 1, Thigh bone; 2, knee-cap (patella); 3, sac between the muscles which lessens friction; 4, shin bone; 5, stretching muscle (quadriceps extensor); 6, ligament below knee-cap*

When they contract they pull the tibia and fibula up towards the pelvis, bending the knee. In medieval times it was not uncommon to punish offenders by hamstringing, that is to say, by cutting the hamstring tendons behind the knee so that the man could no longer bend his leg.

At their lower ends, the tibia and fibula are bound together by ligaments, and at either side are prolonged downwards to grip the astragalus like a pair of tongs (Fig. 31). Anterior and posterior ligaments unite to make a firm capsule to this joint, with extra bands reinforcing the sides and binding the tibia and fibula to the other tarsal bones. When the ankle is sprained the sole of the foot is usually turned inwards; the outer part of the capsule is strained and very often a few of its fibres are torn; pain and swelling are present for a few days but the capsule quickly mends and the disability is seldom great. On the other hand, the jerk may be so sudden that the fibres of the ligament tear off with them a flake of bone from the lower end of the fibula. This accident can be detected only by X-ray examination, and this is why, in the case of a severe sprain, the doctor usually insists upon a radiograph being taken.

The tarsal bones are bound to each other and to the metatarsal bones by liga-

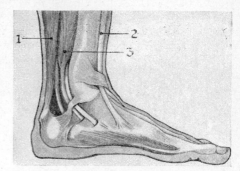

Fig. 32. *Tendons of the ankle joint. 1, Tendon of Achilles; 2, muscle at front of shin bone (anterior tibial); 3, muscle used in bending toes (flexor longus digitorum).*

mentous bands running in all directions. The chief movements at the ankle joint are flexion and extension, the former occurring when we bend the foot up towards the shin and the latter when we stretch the toes downwards.

Muscles of the Calf

Extension is carried out by the powerful group of muscles which give that handsome curve at the back of the calf. The chief of these are the gastrocnemius, the soleus and the posterior tibial (Figs. 25 and 26). The gastrocnemius rises by two bands, one from each side of the lower end of the femur, and the soleus from the back of the tibia and fibula. The fibres of both muscles unite to form a thick strong tendon, the tendon of Achilles (Fig. 32), which is attached to the back of the heel bone. According to the legend, when the hero Achilles was a baby, his mother dipped him in the waters of Styx and so made him proof against all mortal weapons. But she picked him up by the heel and so unfortunately omitted to submerge this, so Achilles had still one vulnerable spot in his body. In the end it was a wound in the heel which slew him.

The posterior tibial muscle rises from the back of the tibia and fibula; its tendon does not join the tendon of Achilles, but passes behind the inner side of the ankle

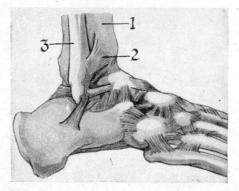

Fig. 31. *Ligaments of the ankle joint. 1, Shin bone (tibia); 2, smaller bone of lower leg (fibula); 3, ligament binding these bones together (tibio-fibular ligament).*

joint to be attached to the scaphoid bone of the tarsus. When these three calf muscles contract they pull on the heel bone and tarsus, tilting the foot downwards so that the weight falls on the ball of the toe. Every time we take a step, we perform this movement, and we use it in springing, leaping and running. At the end of each step we lower the heel so that the weight is transmitted to the whole foot; this action is performed by the muscles on the front of the leg, especially the anterior tibial, which arises from the front and side of the tibia and is attached to the first metatarsal. It is helped by the extensor longus digitorum (Fig. 33), which rises from both the tibia and the fibula and divides into four tendons which are attached to the phalanges of the four outer toes. The great toe has its own extensor muscle, arising

from the fibula. This arrangement resembles that of the tendons in the hand, and reminds us that our remote ancestors had a great toe which they could use for grasping just as we use the thumb.

Flexor muscles are attached to the toes on their under side. The flexor digitorum longus (Fig. 34) rises from the shaft of the tibia at the back and is covered by the soleus and gastrocnemius muscles. Like the extensor muscle, it has four tendons which run to the four outer toes; and the great toe has a separate flexor, also arising from the back of the tibia. These muscles are much less important than those in the hand, because we need to bend our toes comparatively little. They help to bend and straighten the ankle, in the front of which three bands of ligament form a Z-shaped strap, the upper band crossing the

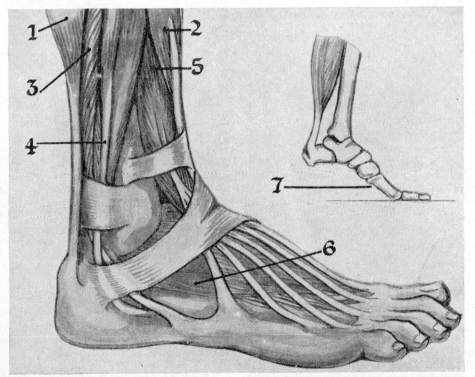

Fig. 33. *Muscles used in stretching ankle and foot. 1, 3 and 4, Muscles at back of calf (gastrocnemius, soleus and peroneus); 2, shin muscle (tibial); 5 and 6, toe stretching muscles (extensor longus digitorum and extensor brevis digitorum); 7, strong bone of the foot.*

tendons above the ankle, the lower below, and the third band joining the other two diagonally. When the extensor muscles have straightened the toes, this third ligament holds the tendons fixed at the ankle joint, and any further contraction of the muscles merely helps to bend the foot up towards the shin. A similar band of ligament crosses the back of the ankle joint and encloses all the tendons there except the tendon of Achilles. In this way, when the flexor muscles have caused the toes to curl up they can continue their action, using this ligament as a fulcrum, and helping the calf muscles in the process of turning the foot downwards.

Moving the Foot

Notice that the terms flexion and extension become a trifle inaccurate when we speak of the foot. The extensor muscles extend, that is straighten, the toes; but if their action is continued they help to bend the foot upwards on the ankle, that is, to flex it. In the same way, the flexor muscles, pulling on the under surfaces of the toes, can make them curl up; but when they act further they help to straighten, or extend, the ankle. The reason for using the terms thus becomes clear if we remember that the sole of the foot corresponds to the palm of the hand, and that extension of the foot corresponds to bending, or flexion, at the wrist; whereas the movement of bending the foot upwards towards the shin (flexion) is identical with extension in the hand.

In the hand, the interest centres in the movements performed with the fingers; in the foot, the toe movements are unimportant compared with those performed in walking. The chief muscles used in walking lie in the calf. The bones of the foot form a longitudinal arch (Fig. 33), the posterior pillar being formed by the heel bone and the anterior pillar by the base of the great toe; the keystone of the arch is the astragalus. All the bones taking part in this arch are bound together by strong, resilient ligaments; one of these, the spring ligament, attaches the under surface of the heel bone to the front of the tarsus and helps to support the astragalus, so that it acts as a kind of tie to keep the pillars of the arch from spreading.

The long plantar ligament, fulfilling the same purpose, is also attached behind to the heel bone and, in front, to the metatarsal bones, thus acting as a second and a longer tie. In addition, the arch is held up by the tendons of two strong muscles, the flexor digitorum longus and the long flexor of the big toe, which lie at the back of the calf. Their tendons pass behind the ankle on the inner side, and then hook themselves under a stout little wing of bone which projects from the side of the heel bone. This little prominence, the sustentaculum, helps to carry the astragalus on its upper surface; the two tendons, passing beneath it, act as cables receiving some of the weight of the astragalus, which in turn takes the full weight of the body.

The arch is further reinforced by the tendon of the anterior tibial muscle (Fig. 32), which curves round from the upper surface of the foot to be attached to the under surface of the tarsus; and by the tendon of the posterior tibial muscle which, after passing round the inner side of the ankle to be attached to the under surface of the scaphoid, sends fibres to most of the other bones of the tarsus and to some of the metatarsals as well.

Muscles of the Sole

The small muscles in the sole of the foot spring into action when we stand, and help to maintain the arch. These include the short flexor of the toes, flexor brevis digitorum (Fig. 34), which arises from the heel bone, forms a stout little pad of muscle under the middle of the sole and sends a tendon to each of the four outer toes; and the lumbrical and interosseous muscles which have attachments corresponding to those of their counterparts in the hand (Figs. 18 and 20).

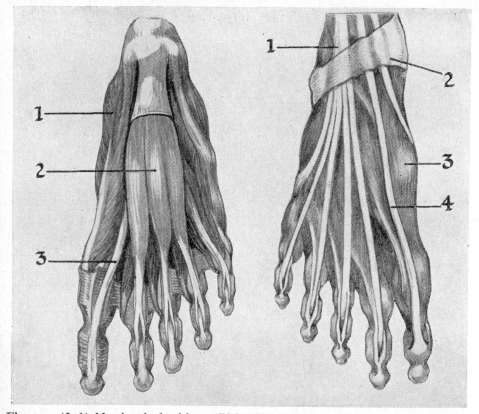

Fig. 34. *(Left) Muscles of sole of foot. (Right) Muscles of foot. (Left) 1, 2 and 3, Muscles used in bending the toes (abductor pollicis, flexor brevis digitorum, flexor digitorum longus). (Right) 1, Muscle used in stretching toes (extensor longus digitorum); 2, strong band of ligament encircling the ankle (annular ligament); 3, bones of the foot (metatarsal); 4, muscle used in stretching the great toe. Notice that the stretching muscles of the toes, when they continue their action, beyond straightening the toes, help to bend the foot upwards on the ankle, and the bending muscles of the toes stretch the foot after their bending action is complete.*

It will now be clear what an admirable springy device the longitudinal arch of the foot should be. Acting as a natural shock absorber, it takes the weight of the body much as the springs of a car take the weight of the chassis. The longitudinal arch, however, is not the only arch in the foot: there is a transverse arch also near the front of the foot, running from the base of the big toe on the inner side to the base of the little toe on the outer side. The heads of the three middle metatarsal bones lie between these two points, and in the normal foot these heads never touch the ground but are raised above it, forming the transverse arch. In young children it is easy to see that this arch is present; there is a slight hollow in the sole, just behind the bases of the toes, which is soft and flexible when pressed. In grown people, unfortunately, this flexible hollow is often replaced by a hard horny swelling —almost a corn. The pressure of such a hard area in the middle of the front part of the sole is a sign that the anterior arch of the foot has collapsed; the heads of the middle three metatarsal bones are resting upon the ground, and usually causing their owner considerable pain. High heels help to induce collapse of the anterior arch because they throw the weight of the body on to the front part of the foot, which was not meant to bear it.

The foot is not designed as a passive weight bearer, but as an active machine for transport. If we stand long in one position the muscles supporting the arch of the foot become tired and the strain is transferred to the ligaments. Ligaments cannot lengthen and contract like muscles; though they are to some extent elastic, they will stretch if kept at strain, and once stretched cannot be shortened again. People, such as nurses and policemen, who have to stand for long hours often find that the ligaments of the feet have given way and their feet have become flat. Usually the anterior arch goes first and the longitudinal arch follows suit. This makes walking laborious and standing painful. Growing children who are kept too much on their feet are apt to lose their arches. It should be borne in mind that all feet, young and old, work best if they are given alternating movements to perform. When we are walking the strain is thrown alternately on opposing groups of muscles so that each set has a period of action followed by a period of rest. So long as this process is continued the arch is well supported, and not likely to break down.

Turning the Ankle

Running down the outer side of the leg is a group of three muscles. These are the peroneal (Fig. 25), which arise from the fibula one above the other; their tendons pass behind the outer prominence of the ankle. Two of them are attached to the fifth metatarsal bone; they help to extend the ankle joint and to turn the sole of the foot outwards—a very limited movement. The third peroneal tendon slips round the outer border of the foot and then runs diagonally across the sole, to be attached to the first metatarsal. It acts as a sort of extra support to the arch of the foot, form-

ing a cross strap, so to speak, with the long flexor tendons which are crossing the foot diagonally from the opposite direction. Like the other two peroneal muscles, it helps to extend the ankle joint and to turn the foot outwards. When we wish to turn the sole of the foot inwards, we use the anterior tibial and its fellow on the back of the leg, the posterior tibial.

Other Foot Movements

If you run your fingers down the outer side of the leg from the knee to the ankle your fingers encounter the anterior tibial muscle. Its tendon passes beneath the Z-shaped ligament on the front of the ankle joint and crosses to the inner side of the foot to be attached to the under surface of the inner cuneiform bone and the first metatarsal; so that this muscle, too, acts as an extra support to the arch of the foot. When it contracts it tilts the sole of the foot inwards and helps to flex the ankle. The posterior tibial muscle (Fig. 26) rises from the back of the tibia and fibula and passes behind the inner side of the ankle joint to be attached to the under surface of the tarsus. When it acts with the gastrocnemius and soleus it helps to extend the foot, but when the anterior tibial and the posterior tibial act together they turn the sole of the foot inwards. This movement can be seen to advantage in the well-known statue of the boy with the thorn : he sits scrutinizing his foot, with one ankle crossed over the opposite knee, and with his foot twisted round so that he can examine the sole.

During the last thirty years, the cinematograph has put the muscles of expression (Fig. 35) in a class by themselves. On the stage, actors playing to large theatres know that their faces are visible merely as pink blobs to the greater part of their audiences, and they base their work on the assumption that emotion must be expressed by the rest of the body rather than by the face. But the cinema puts every face under the microscope, so to speak, and

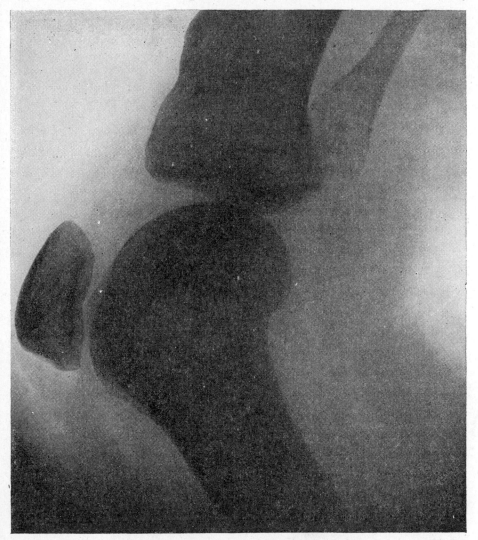

RADIOGRAPH OF THE KNEE

Notice the strong rounded prominences at the lower end of the thigh bone, which lies in a saucer-like surface at the upper end of the shin bone. Between the two bones is a curved piece of cartilage, which makes possible the gliding movement of the leg.

exposes even the minute details of facial expression. The result has been a great advance in facial acting.

What are the muscles that make these shades of expression possible ? What gives Garbo her sulky smile, Francoise Rosay her quizzical eyebrow, or Eddie Cantor his air of surprise ? Expression is achieved mainly by movements of the mouth (Fig. 36) and eyebrows. A circular muscle, the orbicularis oris, surrounds the mouth, helps to keep the lips closed and can also be used to compress them, thus giving the face an expression of determination, or to protrude them, giving an agreeable —or disagreeable—pout. When we smile,

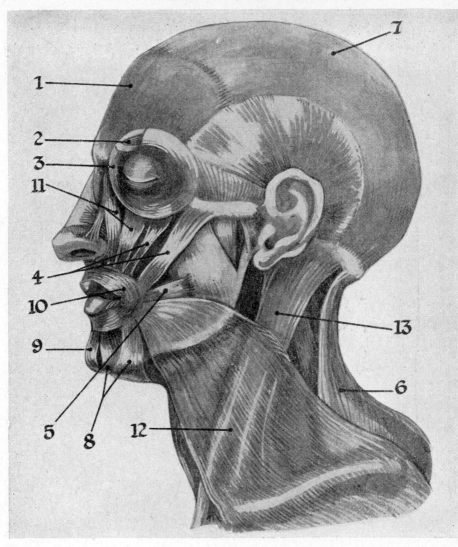

Fig. 35. *Muscles of the head and face. These are the muscles used in changing expressions so as to indicate feelings and emotions. 1, Muscles of the forehead (frontalis muscles), which produce the transverse furrows across the forehead; 2, muscle used in frowning (corrugator); 3, circular (orbicular) muscle round the eye, which closes the eye or screws it up tightly; 4, muscle running from cheek bone to the angle of the mouth (zygomatic muscle); 5, muscle used in pulling angles of mouth outwards; not really used in laughter, though called the laughing muscle (risorius); 6, diamond-shaped muscle of back of neck (trapezius); 7, muscles of back of head, used in moving skin of the scalp (occipital muscles); 8, muscles used in pulling down lower lip; they blend in the middle, but each can act separately (depressor muscles); 9, muscle used in pushing upwards and protruding lower lip (mentalis muscle); 10, circular muscle surrounding mouth, which helps to close and compress lips (orbicular oris); 11, muscles used in deepening furrow at side of mouth (levators); 12, muscle used in drawing down corner of the mouth (platysma); 13, muscle running from mastoid to breast bone (sternomastoid).*

we use the zygomatic muscles which rise from the cheek bone and are attached to the angle of the mouth; they draw the angle of the mouth upwards and outwards. Some people are able to use one zygomatic muscle only at will and thus to produce a rather attractive one-sided smile. Another muscle rises from the sheath over the parotid gland and is attached to the corner of the mouth; it is called the risorius, or laughing muscle, though it acts by pulling the angles of the mouth outwards in a strange sardonic grin and is not a muscle used in ordinary genial laughter. In persons suffering from tetanus, or lock-jaw, this muscle is among those thrown into spasm, so that the patient carries a ghastly expression of amusement on his face.

The depressor muscles of the lower lip rise from the lower maxilla and are attached to the skin at each side of the lip. The two muscles blend in the middle line, but when either acts separately it pulls the lower lip downwards, giving the mouth an ironic expression.

Expressing Surprise

Another muscle, the platysma, by drawing down the lower lip and the corner of the mouth, helps to lend the face an expression of horror and surprise. This strange muscle is a broad thin sheet arising from the sheath of the pectoralis major and the deltoid muscles. Its fibres sweep across the clavicle and cross the side of the neck obliquely to be attached partly to the skin of the lower part of the face and partly to the muscles round the mouth, with which its fibres blend. In man, the platysma can merely wrinkle the skin of the neck and produce the movements of the lip already described, but in horses and many other animals this muscle is much more important. It spreads over nearly the whole body and enables the animal to twitch any isolated portion of its skin it likes. Thus you will often see a horse dislodge a fly from its belly or back by shrugging the skin in that

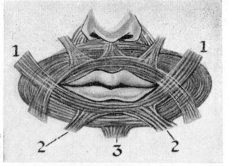

Fig. 36. *Muscles of the mouth. 1, Muscle used in smiling (zygomatic); 2 and 3, muscles used in lowering and raising the lip (depressor and mentalis muscles).*

region. The movement is brisk and local and can be carried out more quickly than a swish of the tail.

The levator muscle, running from the side of the nose to the upper lip, helps to deepen the furrow at the side of the mouth, and so gives an expression of sadness. This muscle is joined from above by another, which rises from the corner of the eye socket and sends slips to the wing of the nostril; when it acts, it pulls the lip upwards and twists it outwards, and simultaneously dilates the nostril on the same side. The result is the well-known sneer of Charles Laughton as Captain Bligh. Finally, the mentalis muscle pushes the lower lip upwards and protrudes it, giving an expression of doubt or disdain.

The muscles round the eyes are no less active. An orbicular muscle, similar to that of the mouth, surrounds each eye and can be used either to close it gently or screw it up tightly. This screwing up movement produces folds at the angles of the eyelids which eventually form the crows' feet of old age. A levator muscle which has the power of raising the upper lid runs forwards from the back of the eye socket to be attached to the lid itself; this too is a muscle of expression, since it can pull the lid away from the eyeball to leave the staring iris surrounded by a rim of white. Every actor uses this muscle in registering terror.

At the inner angle of the eye is a small muscle, the corrugator, which pulls the eyebrow downwards and inwards, giving the vertical furrows of a frown. The transverse furrows across the forehead are produced by the frontalis muscles which blend in the mid-line of the forehead, and are attached to a smooth sheet of tendon running across the vault of the skull; the occipital muscles are attached to the other side of this tendinous sheet, and a sort of see-saw movement of the skin of the scalp is produced when the frontalis and occipital muscles act alternately. It is hardly an expressive gesture and actors rarely use it, but it has made many a man popular among his nieces and nephews.

Three muscles which in man have little purpose, if any, are active in other animals. These are the small muscles attached to the ear, one above it, one behind and one in front. A few people can use them to wag their ears; the accomplishment has entertainment value but registers no particular emotion. Animals, however, can convey fine shades of opinion with their ears; a horse can twitch them in most sinister fashion, as every novice in the riding school knows very well.

Filling Up Spaces

The framework of the body consists of a strong bony skeleton to which the muscles are attached, and upon which they act to produce movement. Inside the skeleton a system of packing has been adopted which gives every organ its appropriate cranny. But any one who has packed a parcel of china knows that padding is necessary to keep the various items in place. In the body there are two packing materials available, as well as a tough wrapper in the form of the skin. Connective tissue acts as adhesive material between surfaces which lie close to each other, and fat fills up the corners which are not otherwise occupied.

The muscles are enclosed in sheaths which become thickened at either end to form tendons; in between the muscles lie thin sheets of connective tissue, made up of cells and elastic fibres. These form a pliable packing material between the various muscle layers. Covering the muscles and lying between them and the skin is a layer of fat of variable thickness, which not only acts as a protection and buffer but also plays a part in conserving heat.

Value of Fat

Fat consists of cells distended with oily material, liquid in the living person but solidifying when the body becomes cold in death. As we advance in years we develop a distressing ability to produce fat; it may also be formed in excess in certain diseases. But in spite of these disadvantages it is a valuable component of the body, and we should be badly off without it. In the abdominal cavity, for example, each kidney nestles comfortably in a bed of fat; and a thick curtain of fatty tissue hangs down from the lower border of the stomach covering the organs in the abdomen like an eiderdown. Fat forms the padding round the eyeball; fat is tucked round the big blood vessels where they come dangerously near the surface; and the fat which forms the pads over the ischial tuberosities results in sitting being a pleasure instead of a penance.

Ensheathing our whole complicated mechanism, neatly and tightly, is the skin, our final defence against a hard world. In most places it is attached only loosely by means of a connective tissue to the fatty layer beneath it, but here and there it is tied down; for example, on the palms of the hands and the soles of the feet a stout layer of fibrous tissue is interposed between the skin and the structures which lie beneath. An intact skin is one of our best defences against invading micro-organisms; and if it is not such a good defence against direct injury as, say, the shell of the tortoise, it is much less hampering and allows us to follow that taste for active pursuits which we inherit from the remote days when our ancestors lived in trees.

CHAPTER III

THE BLOOD AND ITS CIRCULATION

CIRCULATION OF THE BLOOD: CONSTRUCTION AND MECHANISM OF THE
HEART: ARTERIES, CAPILLARIES AND VEINS: BLOOD PRESSURE: THE MAIN
ARTERY AND ITS BRANCHES: ARTERIES AND VEINS OF THE ABDOMEN:
COMPOSITION OF BLOOD: CONTROL OF BLOOD SUPPLY: UNIFORMITY OF
INTERNAL BODILY CONDITIONS: BLOOD TRANSFUSION AND ITS EFFECTS

ALMOST FROM the earliest times of which we have any record, the scientifically minded have been attracted by the sensations of the beating heart and the throbbing pulse. Yet it was not until a few hundred years ago that any one put forward in coherent form the doctrine of the circulation of the blood accepted today.

It was in 1628 that an English physician, William Harvey, in a book entitled *An Anatomical Disquisition on the Motion of the Heart and Blood in Animals*, first explained scientifically how the blood circulates through the body.

Discovery of Blood Circulation

This discovery of Harvey's was a very great achievement, for in his day science lacked knowledge of many physical and chemical facts necessary for the proving of his theory, while the microscope, which alone could substantiate some of his conclusions, was still in its infancy. Harvey was quite unable to prove by demonstration, for example, how the blood passes from the smallest arteries visible to the naked eye into the smallest visible veins, nor could he show conclusively what happens in the lungs; yet by pure scientific genius he deduced correctly the facts.

The real significance of Harvey's great discovery that the blood circulates constantly through our bodies, forming the true internal environment of all our inward parts—just as the air forms our immediate external environment—has only become clear as scientists have come, largely through the aid of the microscope, to a truer understanding of what we may call the minute anatomy of the body.

Followers of Harvey

In the decades following the publication of Harvey's great work, a series of improvements was made in the simple forms of microscope hitherto employed. Shortly after the middle of the seventeenth century an Italian, Marcello Malpighi, discovered under the microscope the capillaries connecting the smallest arteries with the smallest veins. Malpighi's description of the capillary circulation was not very clear or explicit, but a few years later a Dutch microscopist, Anthony van Leeuwenhoek, gave a detailed account of the capillaries as seen by him in various parts of a number of animals, and established the fact that the circulatory system is a closed one. In the early part of the next century the Rev. Stephen Hales, famous for his researches into the subject of blood pressure, drew attention to the changes that take place in the size of the smaller arteries and capillaries according to the local demands on them for blood.

The microscope has revealed to us the

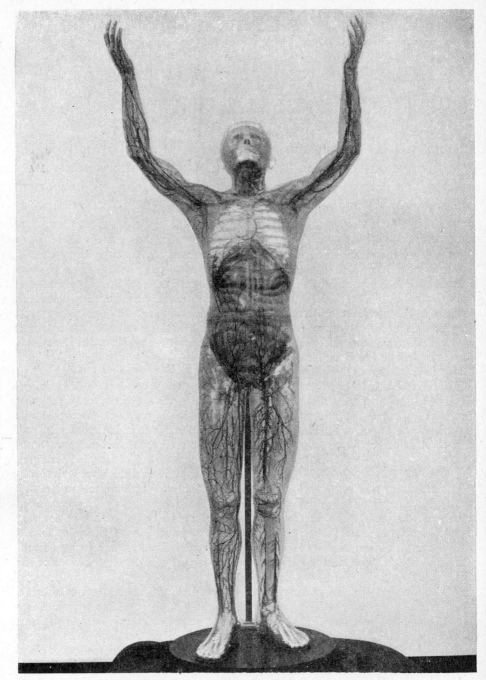

CIRCULATION OF BLOOD THROUGHOUT BODY

Notice how the large blood vessels branch into smaller and smaller ones until the blood is flowing through minute tubes and reaching every part of the body.

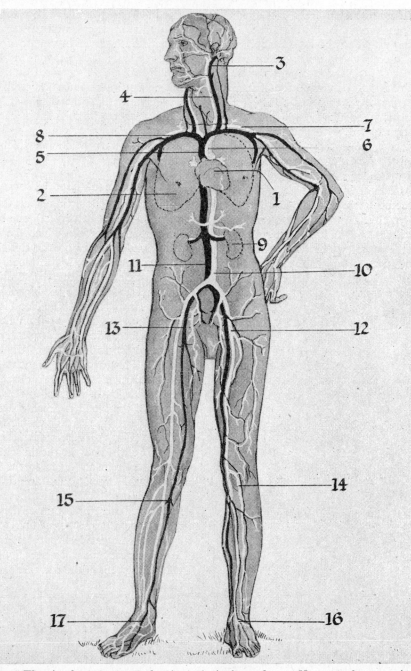

Fig. 1.   *The circulatory system, showing principal vessels. 1, Heart; 2, lungs; 3, jugular vein; 4, carotid artery; 5, superior vena cava; 6, ascending aorta; 7, subclavian artery; 8, subclavian vein; 9, kidney; 10, descending aorta; 11, inferior vena cava; 12, iliac artery; 13, iliac vein; 14, popliteal artery; 15, popliteal vein; 16, arterial arch of foot; 17, venous arch of foot.*

important and significant fact that our body, in common with that of nearly all animals visible to the naked eye, is made up of a conglomerate of millions of tiny organisms which we call cells, each of which has a physiological life of its own. Each one of these living cells, like any other animal or plant, has to be kept adequately supplied with nutriment and air; and waste products resulting from its vital activity have to be cleared away. All organisms consisting of a single cell live in a fluid medium, and the cells of which we are composed are no exception. The blood and lymph surrounding them form a sort of artificial sea; and it is an interesting fact that the composition of the blood is not very different from that of the primal sea from which our earliest evolutionary ancestors emerged.

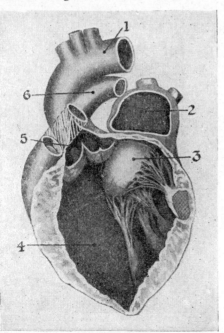

Fig. 2. *Inside of left side of heart. 1, Arch of the main artery (aorta); 2, ear-shaped cavity (auricle); 3, valve preventing blood from flowing back (mitral valve); 4, large cavity (ventricle); 5, main artery (aorta) split so as to show valves; 6, artery running from heart to lungs (pulmonary).*

The blood, then, serves in our internal economy the same essential part that the watery medium served in the life of those remote ancestors; it carries to the millions of individual cells a constant supply of utilizable nutriment and takes away from them the waste that otherwise would clog and poison them. Its constant circulation is therefore necessary to life.

What, briefly, is the course which that circulation takes?

Direction of Blood Flow

Let us choose, as starting point, the left ventricle of the heart (Fig. 2), one of the four compartments into which the heart is divided. We will suppose that this chamber has just been filled with blood from the left auricle, and is thereby stimulated to contract and squeeze the blood out of itself, that is to "beat." The blood is prevented by valves (Fig. 3) from flowing back into the auricle. Consequently it is forced into the main artery of the body, the aorta. This great tube branches, and each branch divides into smaller branches, which divide into still smaller ones, and so on until the blood is flowing through quite tiny arteries scarcely visible to the naked eye (Fig. 4). These branchlets go to every part of the body, to the muscles, the glands, the brain and even to the heart muscle itself. The smallest arteries ultimately end in still more tiny tubes which we call capillaries. The walls of these are more or less porous, enabling fluid to pass through them and so yield supplies of oxygen and nourishment to the liquid in which all the cells of the body are actually bathed—the lymph.

The blood having discharged its cargo and taken up various waste products, including the gas carbon dioxide, continues its flow through the capillaries, which now join together to form small veins, which join to form bigger ones, ending in two great veins that open into the right auricle of the heart (Fig. 3). From the right auricle the blood passes into the right ventricle.

Just as did the left ventricle, so now does the right ventricle, filled with venous blood, contract and squeeze out its contents. Just as on the left side of the heart, so here, valves prevent the blood from flowing back into the auricle. The blood is driven into large tubes called the pulmonary arteries, through which it is taken to the lungs. There it gives up the carbon dioxide gas it has collected, and takes in a fresh supply of oxygen. From the lungs, the blood is returned to the pulmonary veins, and by these to the left auricle, from which in due course it passes to the left ventricle, which was the point from which the whole cycle started.

Heartbeats

The heart (Fig. 2) is a roughly conical organ, which, in an average adult, is about three and a half inches wide at the base, about five inches from base to apex and about two and a half inches thick. It lies with its base obliquely upwards, almost in the middle, but slightly to the left, of the chest cavity. At its higher and broader end it is, as it were, suspended from the big arteries, itself hanging somewhat loosely in a sac, called the pericardium. It is made up of four chambers or compartments—two receiving ones and two expulsive ones, called respectively the auricles and the ventricles. The muscles of which the walls of the ventricles are largely composed are interconnected, so that the two ventricles contract together. This contraction for the time being alters the shape of the heart, drawing the top and bottom more nearly together, a cross-section at this stage being almost circular, instead of elliptical, as would be the case with the heart at rest. Owing to the pressure of the blood on the apex when the ventricles contract, the base is drawn down towards the apex during contraction more than the apex is drawn up. The contraction of the ventricles tends to bring the apex of the heart round to the front of the chest wall. In most individuals the thump of the heart's contraction can

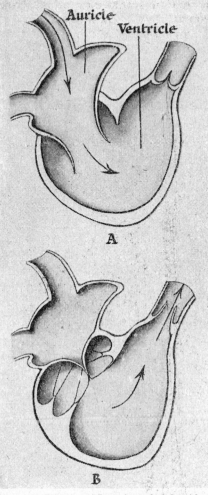

Fig. 3. *Diagram of section of right side of heart. The arrows show direction of blood flow. Blood passes from auricle into ventricle (A). The valve between auricle and ventricle prevents a backward flow, and so, when the ventricle is filled, blood is squeezed out of it and flows into the artery (B).*

easily be felt through the chest wall by the hand; the beat is, indeed, often visible to the eye. This "apex beat" is normally most obvious just below the fifth rib on the left side of the body.

The outer surface of the heart is covered by a double membrane, the pericardium, the two layers of which are able to move over one another when the heart expands or contracts. A small quantity of a lubricating fluid makes this movement easier and smoother. On occasion the pericardium is liable to become inflamed, giving rise to the serious condition called pericarditis. The two inflamed layers of the pericardium move over one another with a

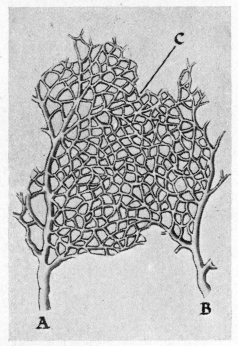

Fig. 4. *Diagram, highly magnified, showing how blood flows from great artery* (A) *through smaller and smaller branchlets, into tiny tubes (capillaries)* (C) *which join together to form, first, small veins and eventually great veins* (B), *so returning to the heart.*

good deal of friction, to lessen which an excess of pericardial lubricating fluid is provided. This produces the condition called pericarditis with effusion, which often causes hindrance to the regular expansion and contraction of the heart itself.

The inside of the heart, that is, of its separate compartments, auricles and ventricles, is lined with a delicate membrane called the endocardium, which plays a considerable part in the structure of its several valves. The endocardium is composed of endothelial cells; these also cover the fibrous tissue of which the various heart valves are composed. This endothelial lining is of special interest to doctors because it is the part specially liable to be infected and inflamed in the course of those diseases especially responsible for the conditions which are known as valvular disease of the heart and endocarditis.

The heart is far from being of uniform structure and consistency. The auricles, which have only to empty themselves into the adjacent ventricles, need but little muscle in their walls. Consequently they are, as compared with the ventricles, relatively flabby structures. The ventricles, on the other hand, having to force the blood considerable distances, are furnished with powerful muscles.

Action of Valves

On the inner surface of the wall of the ventricles may be seen small projections, to which are joined tendinous chords which, at their farther end, are joined to flaps, which act as valves between the ventricles and the auricles (Figs. 2 and 3). These chords contract and relax coincidently with the contraction and relaxation of the ventricular muscles. When the chords contract they pull the valves taut, so that blood cannot be forced back from the ventricle into the auricle; during relaxation the flaps of the valves lie open whilst the blood flows into the ventricles. The valves between the left auricle and the left ventricle, known as the mitral valves, have two flaps, or cusps; those between the right ventricle and the right auricle have three, and are known as the tricuspid valves. Valves are necessary also between the ventricles and the great arteries proceeding from them to prevent a back-flow. These, on account of their shape, are known as the semilunar valves. They are not unlike pockets.

In valvular diseases of the heart the usual sequence is that the damaged covering membrane of the valves, or of the doorways which they protect, becomes inflamed; and then, in the process of healing, becomes tough, contracted and inelastic, just as hard scar tissue replaces our springy natural flesh when an ordinary wound heals. The result may be either that the opening between one of the auricles and its corresponding ventricle, or between a ventricle and the artery proceeding from it, becomes contracted, thus hindering a free passage of blood, a condition known as stenosis, or that the valves themselves become contracted and no longer fit the opening, in which case a back-flow of the blood or regurgitation is likely to occur. Mitral stenosis, mitral regurgitation, aortic stenosis and aortic regurgitation are unfortunately not uncommon medical diagnoses.

Action of Ventricle

During the resting period, or diastole (Fig. 3, B), of the heart muscles, blood flows freely through the big veins into the auricles and through the auricles into the ventricles. When the ventricles are almost full of blood the auricular muscles begin to contract. Then, the ventricles being practically full of blood and their walls being under pressure, the auricular contraction ceases and the valves between the ventricle and the auricle are forced upwards into a closed position. When the muscles of the ventricles have expended their force and have squeezed practically all the blood they contained into the great arteries leading from them—the aorta on the left and the pulmonary on the right (Fig. 2)—the pressure in the arteries is greater than that within the ventricles themselves, and the semilunar valves come into operation and prevent blood being forced back into the ventricles by the elastic recoil of the arterial walls. The ventricular muscles continue to relax, so that the pressure of the accumulating blood in the auricles soon exceeds the pressure in the ventricles. The valves of the orifices between the auricles and the ventricles accordingly open, and blood

begins to flow into the relaxed ventricular cavities. This cycle is complete in something like four-fifths of a second. It seems that the local nerve centre regulating or originating this series of impulses is located in a particle of specialized tissue, called the sinoauricular node, situated near the point where the great vein, the superior vena cava (Fig. 18), joins the left auricle.

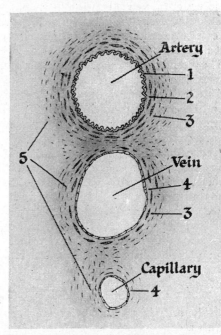

Fig. 5. *Diagram of sections of artery, vein and capillary. 1, Delicate inner layer of cells (endothelial cells) and layer of elastic membrane; 2, layer of muscular cells, which help to propel blood (contractile fibre); 3, outer wall of fibrous tissue; 4, endothelial cells, the capillary's only covering; 5, connective tissue.*

Every one knows that in the course of a careful medical examination the doctor applies his stethoscope to the chest wall over the region of the heart. He does this to ascertain whether the beating of the heart is normal or unusual. If the heart is a healthy one he hears two sounds during the cardiac cycle, rather like the sounds symbolized by the words "lubb-dup"; these are heard at each beat of the heart, that is, in a normal healthy person at rest, about seventy times a minute. The first sound is dull and low pitched, the second, which comes quickly after it, is rather sharp and high pitched. The two sounds are followed by a pause somewhat longer than that between them.

The first of these sounds, known as the systolic sound, results from the sudden closure of the valves between the auricles and ventricles at the climax of systole, or ventricular contraction (Fig. 3, A), and by the outrush of blood into the big arteries. The second sound, called the diastolic because it coincides with the beginning of diastole, is caused by the sudden tension on the semilunar valves between the arteries and the ventricles when the latter have ceased contraction and the elastic rebound of the arteries begins. If there is any obstacle to the efficient closing of the valves, or if the outflow of the blood is in any way hindered, the sounds are modified. These modifications are technically spoken of as murmurs. Doctors speak of systolic, presystolic and diastolic murmurs, each indicating a definite lesion at one of the heart's openings.

Lining of Arteries

The arteries, like the heart, are lined with a delicate inside layer of cells, the endothelial layer (Fig. 5). Surrounding this are layers of elastic and of muscular cells, whilst the outer wall is fibrous, containing little or no elastic or muscular tissue. In the bigger arteries, the elastic layers altogether out-measure the muscular ones; as the arterial branches get smaller the walls become relatively more muscular and less elastic, though in the smallest, the arterioles, there is very little muscle at all. The reason for this variation is that the impulse of the heart's contraction carries the blood over the first part of its journey, the elastic rebound of the walls of the big arteries sufficing to distribute the force over a good length of the arterial course. As the arteries approach the capillaries, a large part of the original cardiac impulse is spent, and the muscles in the walls of the arteries are needed to supplement it. Moreover, the contractibility of the smaller arteries enables the available blood to be rationed according to the temporary needs of this or that part of the body.

We have not enough blood in us to keep all our tissues on a maximum supply at once. When we are running or doing hard physical work all the blood possible is pumped into our muscles, because they need fuel and oxygen in abundance. Conversely, when we have had a good meal it is our digestive organs that want a liberal supply of energy-yielding materials, and the muscles of our limbs have to take things easy. Hence the unwisdom of violent exercise directly after a meal.

The Capillaries

The capillaries, into which the smallest arterioles empty their blood, are very thin-walled microscopic tubes, their covering apparently being composed of but a single layer of cells, between the joins of which both the fluid part of the blood and the white corpuscles can pass in either direction. It is while it is passing through the capillaries that some of the liquid part of the blood, the plasma, exudes from the blood stream into the intercellular spaces, where it constitutes the so-called lymph. This is really the sea or ocean in which the active cells of the body live. From it they take their nourishment and into it they empty their waste products. The capillaries are thus in a way the most important part of the blood transport system. While passing through them the blood takes up oxygen from the air cells of the lungs and food products from the alimentary canal; and delivers up these necessities to the tissues. Through the walls of the capillaries, the white blood cells, or leucocytes (Fig. 24), worm their way when any part of the body is injured, or if it is invaded by hostile germs.

Compared with those of the arteries,

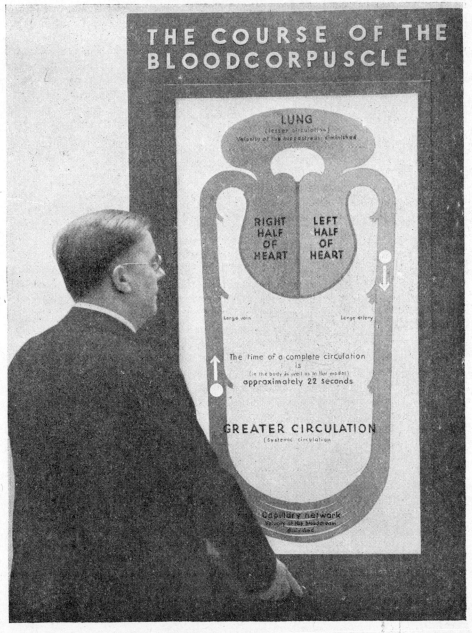

MODEL SHOWING BLOOD CIRCULATION

The blood which starts from the left side of the heart is squeezed out by the heart's contraction into the arteries, thence into the whole system of the circulation; it passes through the capillaries into the small veins, thence into the larger veins and so back to the right half of the heart. Passing through the lungs, it is cleansed and reoxygenated, and so recommences its journey, which from start to finish takes approximately twenty-two seconds.

the walls of the veins (Fig. 5) are relatively thin, unmuscular and inelastic, though the veins themselves are rather more roomy. It is estimated that the total capacity of the veins is about half as much again as that of the arteries. The original force of the heart-beat and that supplied by the elastic rebound and muscular contraction of the arteries are almost

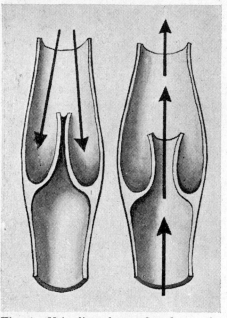

Fig. 6. *Vein slit and opened to show action of valves. These are contained at short intervals in the smaller veins; they permit blood flow in one direction only, towards the greater veins and so to the heart.*

used up in forcing the blood through the "capillary lake," the total area of the capillaries arising from a single arteriole being at least five hundred times the area of the vessel from which they arose. Consequently, were much resistance offered to the return flow of the blood to the heart (as would be, had the veins less capacity than the arteries), this return would be difficult without a great deal of supplemental aid.

As it is, aid has to be given, though there still remains a little of the original

cardiac and arterial impetus. A small supplemental impulse is given by the muscles in the walls of the veins themselves, and, most important, pressure is exercised on the veins by the movements of the muscles between which they pass. This is especially marked in the arms and legs. This pressure, however, would be as likely to force the blood back towards the capillaries as towards the heart, were it not that the smaller veins are furnished at short intervals with valves (Fig. 6) which permit a free flow in one direction only. If we bare an arm, grasp it below the elbow, and exercise pressure to obstruct the venous flow, the veins stand out clearly and numerous little enlargements in their course will show themselves owing to distension of the veins where the blood is obstructed by the valves. The movements of the chest in respiration also contribute to the venous flow.

Rate of Flow

The total amount of blood in the adult body averages between three and four quarts. At each contraction of the ventricles, some two and a half ounces (about one-eighth of a pint), is pumped into the aorta for distribution over the body, and two and a half ounces into the pulmonary arteries to be re-aerated. During the diastole a corresponding amount of blood reaches the ventricles from the auricles. The heart beats, that is, the ventricles contract on an average in an adult man at rest about seventy-two times a minute, the ventricular systole occupying about three-tenths of a second, and the diastolic interval about half a second. The rate is considerably faster in children, and somewhat more rapid in young women. Some 4,000 gallons are thus pumped out of each ventricle daily. It is estimated that the time taken for a drop of blood to travel round the body from left ventricle to right auricle is between one-third and one-half of a minute, that is, the time occupied by twenty-five to thirty beats of the heart.

The blood sent to the lungs through the pulmonary arteries by the right ventricle has a much shorter journey to make, and manages the complete tour from right ventricle to left auricle in about a quarter of this time, that is in the course of between six to eight beats of the heart. The blood, it should be added, does not travel at uniform velocity round the body. But for the muscularity and elasticity of the walls of the arteries, the circulation would be spasmodic, the blood spurting along each time the heart beats, but remaining stagnant in the intervals. As it is, the flow is continuous, though it experiences different degrees of pressure from second to second, and from inch to inch, in its course. We know that when a stream suddenly widens out and then again narrows, the speed of the water through the wide part is much less than that of the water in the narrow. As the area of the capillaries fed by a single small artery is at least five hundred times as great as the area of that artery, the speed of the circulation through the capillaries is correspondingly slower. The length of each capillary is, however, trifling compared with that of the arteries, and so interferes but little with the total of time occupied by the circulation, though the capillaries make up in number what they lack in length, and are estimated to measure altogether about 100,000 miles.

Blood Pressure

This brings us to a consideration of a problem about which we nowadays hear a good deal: the problem of blood pressure. When we consult a doctor, almost always one of the first things he does is to feel our pulse. From the impressions he derives from this procedure he can draw a number of significant conclusions. He will learn whether our heart is beating quickly or slowly; whether it is beating regularly or irregularly; whether the tension in the arteries is high or low.

When fluid is pumped into a system of tubes, a certain amount of pressure is exercised on the walls of the tubes, the amount of pressure depending on the power of the original force, the resistance offered by the walls of the tube, and how free the outflow is at the other end of the system. If fluid is impelled with great force into non-resilient tubes with no outlet and there is a weak spot anywhere, a burst is liable to occur, as happens to water pipes in time of severe frost. If the tubes are resilient, the pressure within them can, by their stretching, be lessened or distributed. The arteries, capillaries and veins constitute such a closed system of tubes, and the contraction of the heart supplies a powerful initial force.

Normal Pressure

Happily, these tubes are highly resilient, and in health they are not liable to burst even when the heart beats with abnormal vigour. Still, there is always an internal pressure being exercised upon their walls, greatest when the ventricles have just contracted and forced additional blood into them, least at the end of the interval between one heart-beat and another. Normally, the pressure in the aorta during systole is about four pounds per square inch, in the arteries about one pound, and in the capillaries less than half a pound.

People often speak of blood pressure as though it were a disease. They might just as sensibly speak of the circulation of the blood as a disease. It is abnormal blood pressure or abnormalities in the circulation generally, which often gives evidence of those irregularities in the body's working which we call disease.

"Blood pressure" is necessarily universal among living animals with a circulatory system. The desirable thing is to have a pressure approximating to the normal; much higher or much lower pressure is an indication of some more or less grave physical disturbance. When people speak of blood pressure as if it were a disease they generally mean high pressure;

though as a matter of fact very low blood pressure is a more sinister symptom.

The factors which go to the creation of blood pressure essentially resemble those which cause pressure in any other system of closed tubes through which fluid is being impelled. First, there is the impulsive force of the pump. Some seventy-two times a minute the heart closes down on itself and squeezes the contained blood into the big arteries which lead from it. Second, there is the ratio of the volume of the blood to the capacity of the vessels through which it circulates. Third, there is the elasticity or rigidity of these tubes or arteries; and last, there is the total resistance at the outlet, that is, at the ends of the small arterial branches.

Varying Pressure

From this, one can easily see how blood pressure may be raised or lowered by various circumstances. If as the result of hæmorrhage the volume of blood in the body is lessened, the pressure must fall. This explains the prevalence of the old medical custom of blood letting or bleeding, for the relief of conditions in which the blood pressure was probably dangerously high. A lowered pressure also may result from a weakened heart-beat; whilst the condition known as surgical shock may cause an alarming drop in the arterial pressure, owing to the dilatation of the capillaries and the small arteries, with consequent diminished resistance to the onward flow of blood.

It was in the early part of the eighteenth century that the notion of blood pressure as a measurable factor was brought to the notice of physiologists, and it is to a clergyman, the Rev. Stephen Hales, curate of Teddington in Middlesex, that we owe our earliest knowledge of it. He discovered the primary fact by means of an unpleasant and somewhat cruel experiment; namely, by tying down a horse on its back, and then making an opening in the great artery of the thigh, inserting into the open-

ing a brass pipe, one-sixth of an inch in diameter, to which was closely fitted a glass tube about nine feet long. He found that, when he released the ligature which he had tied round the artery, the blood rose in the tube to a height of over eight feet. A hundred years later an essentially similar experiment was performed on a patient whose arm had to be amputated, when it was found that the blood rose in the tube with such pressure as to force upwards a column of mercury to a height of 120 millimetres (about five inches), which is the equivalent of a column of water five feet high. The blood pressure in the great artery of the arm of a normal man was thus found to be equal to that required to raise a mercury column 120 millimetres; and that is what is meant when it is said that a man's systolic blood pressure is 120.

Hales found that the pressure varied during the interval between one beat of the heart and the next, the greatest pressure being exercised when the ventricle contracts, the least at the end of the interval between the beats. We now speak of the former as the systolic, and the latter as the diastolic pressure. A fairly good idea of the blood pressure can be formed by an experienced doctor by applying the fingers at two different levels of the radial artery in the forearm. By this means he ascertains the amount of pressure needed at the higher level, in order to abolish the pulse at the lower.

Measurement of Pressure

Nowadays, the pressure may be much more accurately and easily gauged by the use of an instrument called the sphygmomanometer (Fig. 7). When sufficient pressure is applied to the great artery of the upper arm, the brachial (Fig. 9), to stop the flow of blood through it, the pulse at the wrist can no longer be felt. The sphygmomanometer shows exactly what force is necessary for this purpose in each individual instance. The appliance consists essentially of an inflatable bag, capable of being wrapped round the upper arm, and then of being filled with air by means of a hollow rubber ball and tube, until it exerts enough pressure on the brachial artery to obliterate the pulse at the wrist. The cavity of this bag is connected, by means of a rubber tube, either with a mercury gauge, or with a recording mechanism indicating the tension.

The method of using this instrument is as follows. The bag having been wrapped round the upper arm, the observer inflates it by pressing the ball with his left hand, the right hand being applied to the pulse the while. Inflation continues until the pulse can no longer be felt. By means of a valve, air from the bag is then very slowly released, until the pulse can just be felt. The figure shown by the indicator, or by the mercury gauge, at this moment is the measure of the systolic pressure. If the air is then further slowly liberated, a

point occurs at which the full pulse comes through, and the needle on the dial of the indicator suddenly oscillates widely, or the column of mercury moves in jerks. The figure shown at this moment indicates the diastolic pressure. The appropriate moments for the readings can be more accurately determined by the use of a stethoscope applied to the artery, just below the bend of the elbow.

The average systolic pressure in the brachial artery of healthy young adults is about 120. As we get older, the blood pressure usually rises, though some people in perfect health maintain their youthful level through middle age. Abnormally high blood pressure is usually indicative of undesirable changes in the heart or in the blood vessels, though some individuals with a blood pressure of 180 or over show no signs of disease, and are apparently in the pink of condition.

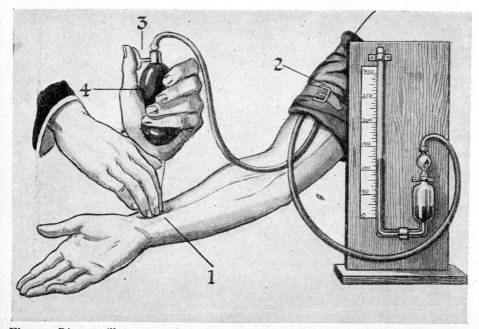

Fig 7. *Diagram illustrating sphygmomanometer, instrument for measuring blood pressure. The pulse (1) is pressed while an inflatable armlet (2) is wrapped round the upper arm and connected to a mercury pressure gauge. The armlet is inflated by pressure on a rubber bulb (4) until the pulse cannot be felt. Air is then released from the armlet by means of a valve (3) until the pulse can just be felt. The pressure can then be read on the indicator.*

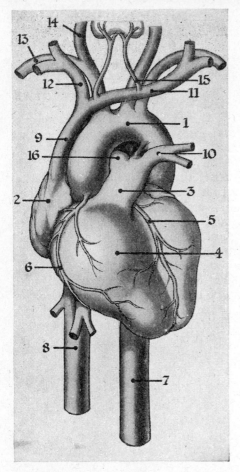

The great artery through which the blood flows out of the left ventricle is called the aorta (Fig. 8). It is about one inch in diameter. From the heart it arches upwards, curving towards the right. First of all, it feeds two arterial branches, the so-called coronary arteries, which run to the muscle of the heart itself, this muscle needing fuel and oxygen as does every other tissue in the body. One of the most serious conditions with which doctors have to deal is a blockage in one of the branches of a coronary artery. The next great artery to branch off from the aorta is

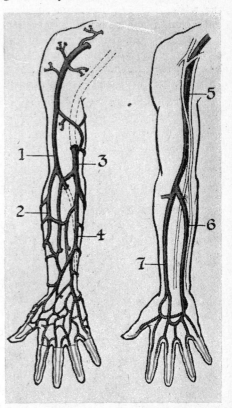

Fig. 8.   *Arch of the main artery of the body (aorta) and its branches.   1, Arch of aorta; 2, right auricle; 3, artery connecting with lungs (pulmonary artery); 4, right ventricle; 5 and 6, branches leading to muscle of the heart (left and right coronary arteries); 7, artery of the chest (thoracic aorta); 8 and 9, large veins, running parallel with aorta (inferior and superior vena cava); 10, left artery of lung (left pulmonary artery); 11 and 12, branches of superior vena cava; 13, artery supplying blood to arm (subclavian artery); 14, artery supplying blood to head and neck (common carotid artery); 15, artery of the thyroid; 16, right artery of lung (right pulmonary artery). The main artery, which is about one inch in diameter, carries the blood from the heart, and through its branches eventually supplies the whole body.*

Fig. 9.   *Blood circulation of the arm.   Left, veins; right, arteries.   1, Principal vein of the arm (cephalic); 2 and 4, veins parallel with bones of forearm (radial and ulnar veins); 3, large vein starting at elbow (basilic); 5, artery of the upper arm (brachial artery); 6 and 7, arteries parallel with bones of forearm (radial and ulnar arteries).*

a short one, which quickly subdivides into two, one called the right subclavian, which supplies the right arm with blood, and the other the right common carotid artery, which supplies the right half of the head and neck. A very little farther on the left common carotid branches off, and a fraction of an inch later, the left subclavian artery.

Having given off many branches to various tissues on its way, the subclavian artery on each side reaches the armpit, at the top of which it changes its name to the axillary artery. At the bottom of the armpit, or axilla, it is renamed the brachial artery (Fig. 9), and continues until the bend of the elbow is reached. There the brachial artery divides into two great branches, the radial and the ulnar arteries,

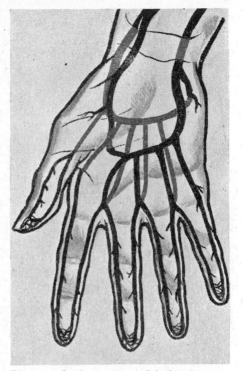

Fig. 11. *Surface arteries of the hand (superficial palmar arch); a continuation of the ulnar artery, lying above the tendons. The finger arteries are branches of this arch.*

the former supplying the thumb side of the forearm, the latter the other side. The ulnar and the radial arteries both contribute to the blood supply of the hand.

At the bottom of the forearm, the radial artery moves round to the back of the wrist and then passes forwards, between the first and second metacarpal bones, towards the palm, which it crosses under the tendons, and with a branch of the ulnar artery constitutes the deep palmar arch (Fig. 10). The ulnar artery also crosses the palm but above the tendons, forming, with a branch from the radial artery, what is called the superficial palmar arch (Fig. 11). The arteries that run up the sides of the fingers are branches of this arch. Between the deep and the superficial arteries there is direct communication; this explains why a wound in the

Fig. 10. *Deep arteries of the hand (deep palmar arch); a continuation of the radial artery lying under the tendons of the palm. It has direct communication with the arteries which lie nearer the surface.*

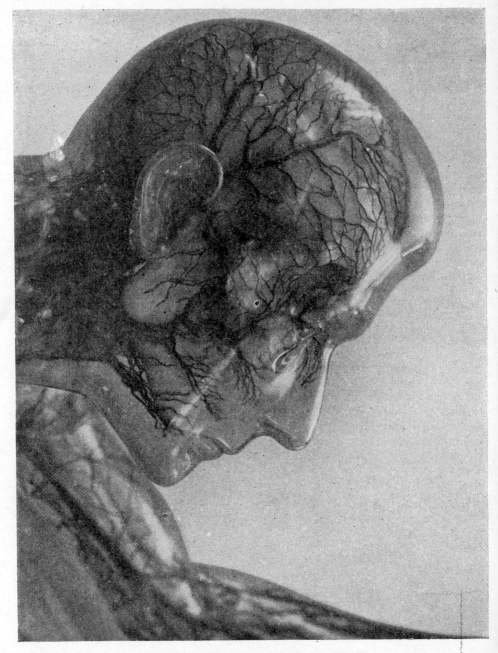

CIRCULATION OF BLOOD IN HEAD

Notice the great system of blood vessels in the neck and throat, which gradually extends throughout the whole of the head. A whole subsidiary system runs to the base of the brain; another system to the back of the head, and yet another to the eye. Smaller branches run off to each of the organs and to every part both of the surface and the deep sections of the face.

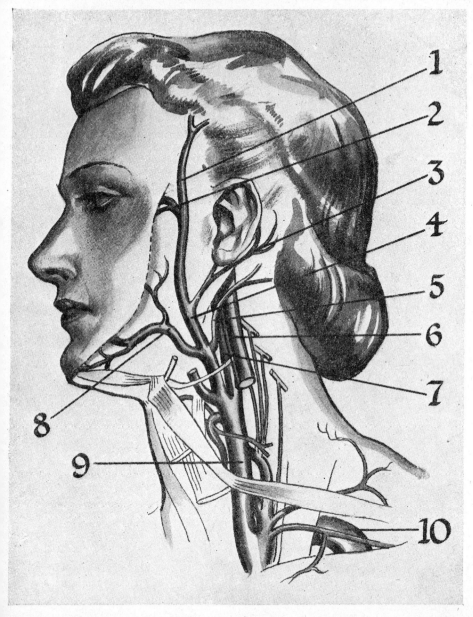

Fig. 12. *Arteries of the face and neck. 1, Artery of the temple (temporal artery); its position is indicated by the pulse that can be felt on the temple; 2, artery which supplies blood to deep part of face, nose and dental sockets (maxillary); 3, artery which supplies the ear (auricular); 4, artery supplying external tissues of neck and scalp (external carotid); 5, artery connecting with back of head (occipital); 6, big veins of the neck (jugular); 7, artery which supplies internal parts of neck and scalp, including brain (internal carotid); 8, branch of carotid artery supplying face (facial carotid); 9, main artery leading to head and neck and supplying branches to brain, eyes, and ears (common carotid); 10, artery supplying arm (subclavian).*

palm sometimes gives rise to very serious bleeding. Blood may be issuing from both the ulnar and the radial arteries.

The carotid artery (Fig. 12) on each side subdivides into an external and an internal carotid artery—the former supplying the external tissues of the neck and scalp and head, the latter the internal parts, including the brain (Fig. 13). The pulsation which we can feel by placing our finger on the temple indicates the position of the temporal artery, one of the terminal vessels into which the external carotid branches. The other terminal branch of the external carotid is called the internal maxillary artery. This supplies the deep parts of the face with blood. Most of the blood supply of the nose, the pharynx and the dental sockets comes from this artery.

Course of Aorta

Having given off these important vessels, supplied intercostal branches to the muscles between the ribs, and bronchial arteries to nourish the tissues of the lungs (these last not to be confused with the pulmonary arteries, of which mention will be made later), as well as vessels to the outer covering of the heart and to the œsophagus, or gullet, the aorta passes through the diaphragm. In its course through the abdomen (Fig. 14), it supplies branches for the nourishment of the stomach, intestines, pancreas, kidneys, liver, spleen, for the sex glands, the lumbar muscles and the muscles of the abdominal wall.

The abdominal aorta then divides into two great arteries, known as the right common iliac and the left common iliac (Fig. 14). Each of these soon subdivides into an internal and external iliac (Fig. 15). The internal iliac supplies with blood all the organs in the pelvis, except the sex glands, and also the perineum. There is a great deal of intercommunication between the various pelvic arteries, which accounts for the extensive hæmorrhage which so often results from even a small wound in this area.

The external iliac artery supplies all the tissues of the leg with blood. After its initial stage, in which it gives off a few branches, it is known as the femoral artery (Fig. 15). This is the great vessel of the thigh. Its branches run to every part of the thigh and its coverings, and also supply the skin of the lower part of the abdomen. When the femoral artery reaches the hollow space behind the knee, the popliteal space (Fig. 15), it again changes its name to the popliteal artery. Having furnished the knee joint and the tissues at the front and back of the knee with blood, the popliteal artery divides into two vessels: the anterior tibial, which supplies the front of the leg and the upper part of the foot, and the posterior tibial, which supplies the back of the leg and the sole of the foot.

The above summarizes the outstanding facts relative to the outward flow of the blood from the heart. There remains to be considered the return flow.

Return Flow

Having given to the living cells of the body a fresh supply of oxygen and such other nourishment as they severally need, and having taken up the waste resulting from the activity of the cells, the blood proceeds through capillaries to enter the tiny tubes which are the smallest branches or tributaries of the veins. The little veins join up with one another, forming bigger veins, which repeat the process. The deeper veins for the most part run alongside the corresponding arteries, but other veins take a more superficial course.

The names given to the veins are in many cases identical with those given to the arteries which they accompany. Thus, we have, beginning at the foot, an anterior and a posterior tibial vein (Fig. 15). These unite to form the popliteal vein, which later becomes the femoral vein (Fig. 15), which in turn becomes the exterior iliac vein. The blood from the more superficial tissues of the foot and leg is collected into

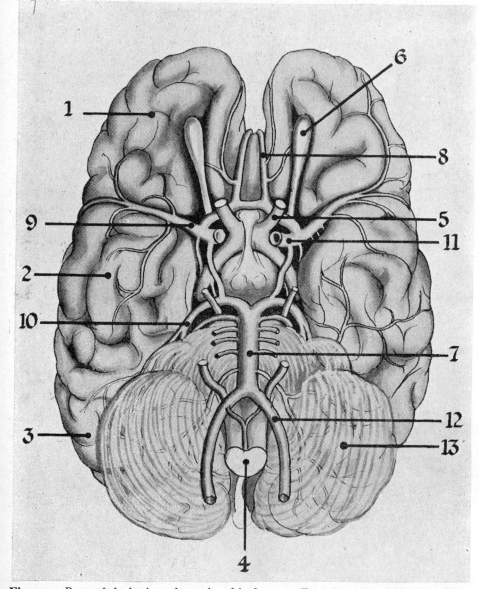

Fig. 13. *Parts of the brain and arteries of its base. 1, Front (anterior) lobe of the brain; 2, middle lobe; 3, back (posterior) lobe; 4, small portion of brain at upper end of spinal cord where nerve centres are found (medulla oblongata); 5, nerve of the eye (optic nerve); 6, nerve of smell (olfactory nerve); 7, artery of the base of the skull (basilary artery); 8, front artery of the brain (anterior cerebral artery); 9, middle cerebral artery; 10, posterior cerebral artery; 11, branch of main artery of head (internal carotid); 12, artery connecting with spine (vertebral); 13, nervous matter at the back of the brain (cerebellum). The blood supply of the brain is derived from the internal carotid artery. This is a branch of the common carotid artery, which itself springs from the aorta, the main artery of the body. From the internal carotid artery, smaller branches run off to feed every part of the brain.*

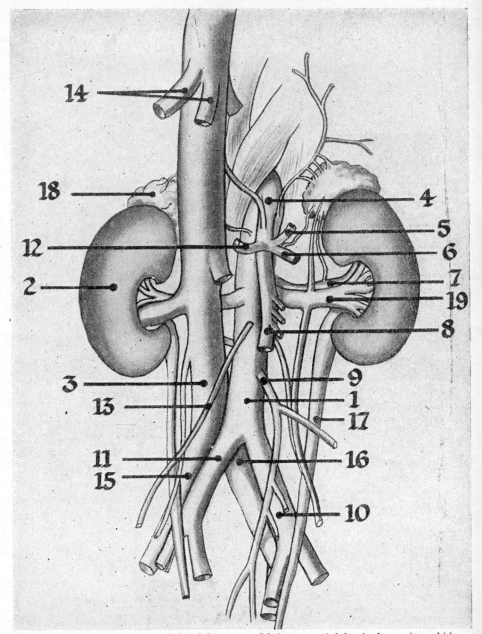

Fig. 14. *Arteries and veins of the abdomen. 1, Main artery (abdominal aorta); 2, kidney; 3, main vein (inferior vena cava); 4, artery of diaphragm (phrenic); 5, artery of stomach (gastric); 6, artery of spleen (splenic); 7, artery of kidney (renal); 8 and 9, arteries of the intestines (mesenteric); 10 and 11, arteries of the hip (common iliac); 12, artery of liver (hepatic); 13, artery of ovaries (spermatic); 14, veins of liver (hepatic); 15 and 16, veins of hip (common iliac); 17, tube from kidney to bladder (ureter); 18, gland above kidney (suprarenal); 19, vein of kidney (renal).*

two veins known as the great and the small saphenous veins (Fig. 15) which empty respectively into the femoral vein and the popliteal vein. It is these branches of veins which often become varicosed. The veins from the pelvic region unite and empty into the internal iliac vein which, on each side, joins with the external iliac vein to form the common iliac. The two common iliac veins, a little farther on, join together to constitute a large vessel known as the inferior vena cava. This important vein passes upwards, through the abdomen by the side of the aorta, just in front of the spine.

The Liver

At this point there occurs a divergence from the steady heartward flow of the venous blood. The blood collected from the stomach, intestines, spleen and pancreas, which is loaded with all sorts of nourishment resulting from the digestion of our food, is poured into a rather large vein, called the portal (Fig. 16), and conveyed, not directly to the heart, but to that great chemical factory and storehouse, the liver. The liver receives for the nourishment of its own tissue, through the hepatic artery, a supply of fresh oxygenated blood (Fig. 14), and both the blood brought to the liver by the portal vein and that brought by the hepatic artery is collected by the hepatic veins, which empty into the higher part of the inferior vena cava. This leads to the right auricle of the heart, into which its contents flow.

The blood from the head, arms and chest is collected in similar manner, the resulting great vein, known as the superior vena cava (Fig. 18), also emptying into the right auricle. The names of the important veins here, as elsewhere, correspond closely with those of the arteries; but the big veins of the neck running parallel to the carotid arteries are called the jugulars (Fig. 17).

The blood has now completed the circuit of the body. For cleansing and re-

oxygenation it passes from the right auricle into the right ventricle (Fig. 19), which pumps it through the great pulmonary arteries to the lungs. Whilst on its passage through the walls of the tiny air cells which make up the bulk of the lungs, the venous blood gives up much of its waste carbon dioxide gas, and takes on board a fresh cargo of oxygen. The recharged

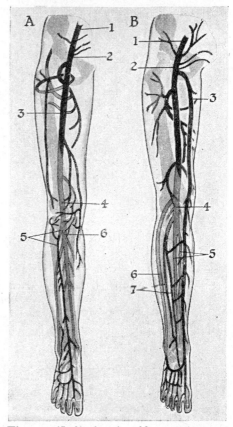

Fig. 15. (Left) Arteries of leg. 1, Artery of hip (exterior iliac); 2 and 3, artery of thigh (common femoral and superficial femoral); 4, artery of hollow behind knee (popliteal); 5 and 6, arteries of shin (anterior and posterior tibial). (Right) Veins of leg. 1, Vein of hip (exterior iliac); 2, vein of thigh (femoral); 3, vein running from ankle joint to thigh (saphenous); 4, vein of knee (popliteal); 5 and 6, veins of shin (posterior and anterior tibial); 7, vein running from foot to knee (small saphenous).

blood is then collected into the numerous branches of the pulmonary veins, which lead it back to the heart. The pulmonary veins open into the left auricle, from which, in due course, it passes to the left ventricle, whence it once more commences its round of the body. This is what is meant by the circulation of the blood.

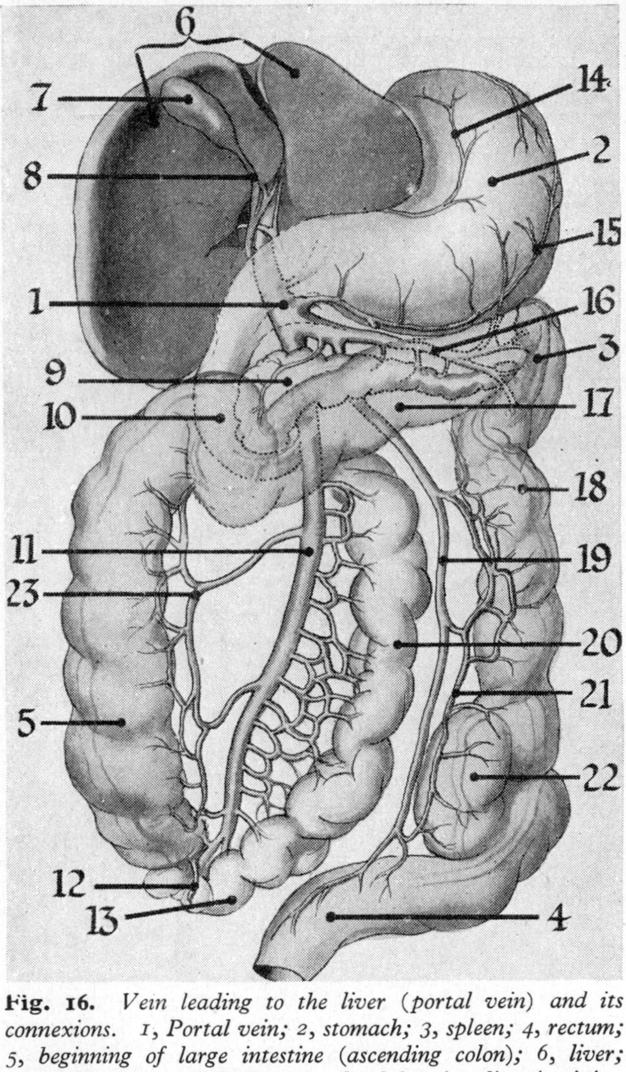

When the ventricles contract and expel the blood in them, the walls of the aorta are suddenly distended. The wave of distension passes down the walls of the arteries, so that they are all in succession momentarily dilated, their elasticity quickly restoring them to their normal calibre. This produces the throbbing we call the pulse. Feeling the pulse is traditionally one of the first diagnostic acts of the physician. Nowadays, a more precise examination is possible by means of an instrument called the sphygmograph.

A small metal pad, or button, is placed over the radial artery at the wrist and held in place by a rubber band. This pad is one end of a delicate lever so adjusted as to rise and fall with the dilation and recovery of the artery. This lever is jointed to another with a stilet or needle at its farther end. The stilet comes lightly into contact with a long strip of blackened paper which is carried along by means of attached clockwork at a uniform rate, generally about four inches in ten seconds. On this blackened surface the

Fig. 16. *Vein leading to the liver (portal vein) and its connexions. 1, Portal vein; 2, stomach; 3, spleen; 4, rectum; 5, beginning of large intestine (ascending colon); 6, liver; 7, gall-bladder; 8, bile duct; 9, gland forming digestive juices (pancreas); 10, beginning of small intestine (duodenum); 11 and 19, veins of intestines (mesenteric veins); 12, appendix; 13, third part of small intestine (ileum); 14 and 15, veins of stomach (gastric and gastro-epiploic); 16, vein of spleen (splenic); 17 and 18, parts of intestine (transverse and descending colon); 20, second part of small intestine (jejunum); 21 and 23, veins of large intestine (colic veins); 22, end of large intestine (sigmoid flexure).*

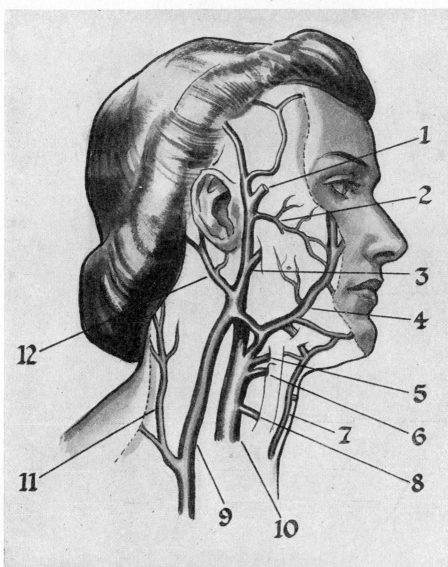

Fig. 17. *Veins of the face and neck. The veins run roughly parallel with the arteries, and usually bear the same names as the arteries to which they correspond. 1, Vein of the temple (middle temporal); 2, vein running across the face (transverse facial); 3, vein running from deep parts of the face (internal maxillary); 4, main vein of face (facial); 5, vein running from tongue (lingual); 6, vein running from larynx (laryngeal); 7, vein of front of neck (anterior jugular); 8, vein from thyroid gland (superior thyroid); 9, large vein of neck, collecting blood from surface parts of head (external jugular); 10, large vein of neck, collecting blood from deeper parts of head (internal jugular); 11, tributary of external jugular vein, running from back part of head (posterior external jugular); 12, vein running from ear into the external jugular vein (posterior auricular).*

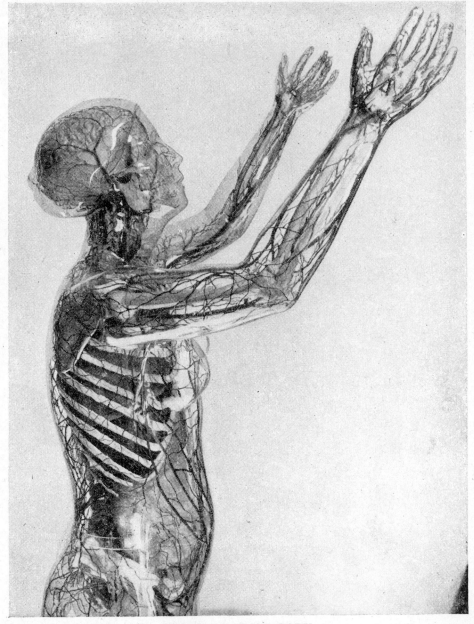

UPPER HALF OF BODY

This reconstruction of the human body shows not only the blood circulation system, but its relationship to the bones, muscles, organs, and other parts of the system. It is part of the famous "transparent woman" constructed by an American scientist, and exhibited in New York. The reconstruction has been so skilfully and accurately carried out that the model is able to carry through the actions of walking, dancing and running with perfect precision. Notice the large blood vessels running to and from the heart, with their many tiny branches.

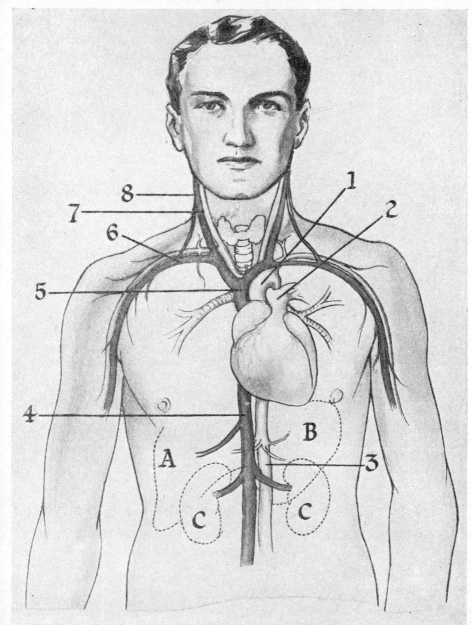

Fig. 18. *Heart and principal arteries and veins of the upper trunk. The arteries, through which the blood flows outwards, are unshaded, and the veins, through which it returns, are shaded dark.* (A) *Liver.* (B) *Stomach.* (C) *Kidneys.* 1, *Main artery of the body (arch of the aorta); 2, artery connecting with the lungs (pulmonary artery); 4 and 5, main veins of the body, running parallel with the aorta (inferior and superior vena cava); 6, artery leading to the arm (subclavian artery); 7, main vein of neck (jugular vein); 8, main artery leading from the aorta, and possessing branches which supply every part of the head (common carotid).*

movements of the stilet, and therefore of the pulse, are recorded (Fig. 20). A tracing of the normal pulse shows that the pulse wave consists of a sudden up stroke, and then of a gradual decline interrupted by two minor uprisings. The first up stroke is caused by the sudden forcing of additional blood into the arteries by the

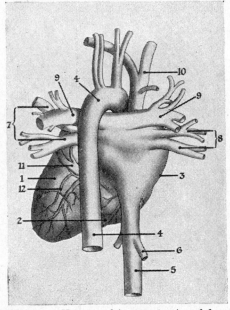

Fig. 19. *Heart and its vessels viewed from behind. 1 and 2, Left and right ventricles; 3, right auricle; 4, main artery (aorta) and its branches; 5, large vein of lower part of body (inferior vena cava); 6, vein of the liver (hepatic vein); 7, veins of left lung (left pulmonary veins); 8, veins of right lung (right pulmonary veins); 9, arteries leading to lungs (pulmonary arteries); 10, large vein of upper part of body (superior vena cava); 11, artery of heart muscle (coronary artery); 12, vein of heart muscle (coronary vein).*

contraction of the left ventricle of the heart; the gradual decline is due to the elastic recoil of the arterial wall. When the condition of high blood pressure is present, the up stroke reaches an abnormal height and remains at near that height for a while before descending to the base line.

The course which the blood takes in the as yet unborn child (Fig. 22) differs in several ways from that of the circulation in the individual after birth. Instead of absorbing the nourishment which its developing parts require from the intestine, and the oxygen which they need from its lungs, the embryo receives its blood, fully charged with both oxygen and nutriment, direct from its mother through the blood vessels contained in the umbilical cord connecting the fœtus with the placenta, the fleshy sponge-like mass attached to the walls of the maternal uterus.

Fœtal Circulation

At the stage reached within a month of being born, the circulation in the child proceeds roughly as follows. The maternal blood enters the child's body at the umbilicus, or navel (Fig. 22). Part of this purified blood goes to the liver; but the main part joins the inferior vena cava, where it meets and mingles with the impure blood returning from the lower half of the child's body. This mixed blood in the inferior vena cava passes into the right auricle of the heart. At this stage of development there is an opening between the two auricles known as the foramen ovale (Fig. 22). From the right auricle most of the blood which comes to it from the inferior vena cava is directed through the foramen ovale to the left auricle. Thence it flows into the left ventricle, and from there, is propelled into that branch of the aorta which supplies the head, neck and the upper limbs. The venous blood brought from the upper part of the body through the superior vena cava also enters the right auricle, where it is to a small extent mixed with the blood from the inferior vena cava, the greater part of it proceeding into the right ventricle. Thence it flows in small measure to the lungs through the pulmonary arteries, and in greater measure into the descending aorta, by which it is distributed to the lower parts of the body and to the umbilical arteries through which it reaches the placenta and rejoins the maternal circulation.

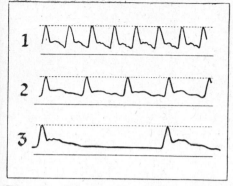

Fig. 20. *Diagram of recordings showing variations of heart-beat. 1, Rapid pulse (tachycardia), showing insufficient pause between beats; 2, normal pulse; 3, slow pulse, indicating some blockage of normal system.*

As soon as the child is born and breathing starts the umbilical cord is cut and tied, the umbilical vessels become obliterated and within a week or so the foramen ovale closes so that blood can no longer pass from the right auricle to the left. Coincidently, the pulmonary arteries and veins undergo rapid enlargement, because henceforth through them all the blood in the body must constantly pass in order to receive supplies of oxygen.

Nature of Blood

Human blood is a reddish, opaque, rather viscid fluid. Arterial blood is bright red, venous blood has a dark, bluish-red colour. Examined under the microscope, blood is seen to consist in nearly equal parts of a clear, almost colourless fluid, known as plasma, and an enormous number of small solid bodies, the red and white corpuscles (Fig. 21).

The red corpuscles, which are about 500 times as numerous as the white ones, are biconcave discs about one three-thousandth of an inch in diameter. In every cubic millimetre of blood (a millimetre is about one twenty-fifth of an inch) there are some five million red corpuscles, the total number in the blood of an average man being about 30,000,000,000. These are

produced in the red marrow of the bones, and as about one-twentieth of the number of red corpuscles are destroyed and have to be replaced every twenty-four hours, a rapid rate of production is required.

Hæmoglobin

The most important constituent of the red corpuscles is a substance called hæmoglobin. Hæmoglobin contains a pigment, hæmatin, to which the colour of the blood is due. An important ingredient of hæmatin is iron, and it is well known that a deficiency of iron in the body leads to a notable loss of colour in the blood, manifested in various forms of anæmia. In some forms of anæmia, the number of red blood corpuscles may be reduced even to one-fifth of the normal number.

The capacity of the blood to carry a constant supply of oxygen to every cell in the

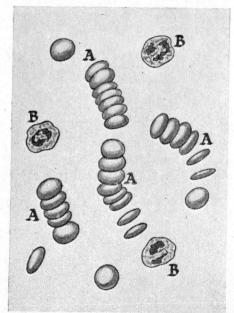

Fig. 21. *Human blood cells, highly magnified. (A) Red corpuscles, biconcave discs about one three-thousandth of an inch in diameter. The body contains about 30,000,000,000 of them. (B) Leucocytes, one form of white, or colourless, corpuscles.*

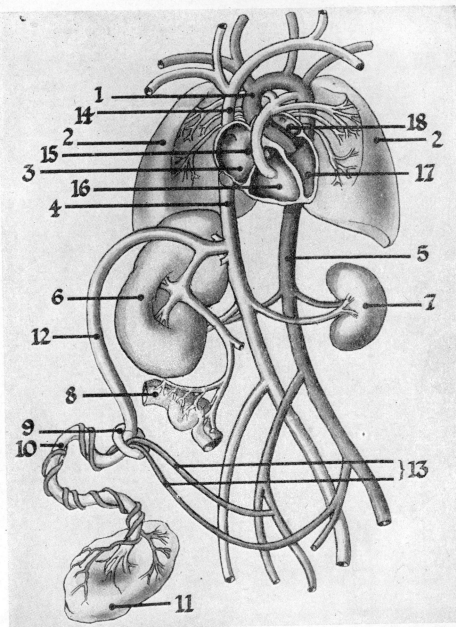

Fig. 22. *Circulation of the blood in the unborn child. 1 and 5, Main artery (aorta); 2, lungs; 3, right auricle of heart; 4, lower main vein (inferior vena cava); 6, liver; 7, kidney; 8, intestine; 9, navel (umbilicus); 10, cord (umbilical cord) connecting fœtus with (11) fleshy, sponge-like mass attached to wall of maternal uterus (placenta); 12, vein of the navel (umbilical vein); 13, arteries of the navel (umbilical arteries); 14, upper main vein (superior vena cava); 15, opening between right and left auricles (foramen ovule); 16 and 17, right and left ventricles; 18, left auricle. The embryo receives both oxygen and nutrient from its mother's blood vessels.*

body depends entirely on the amount of hæmoglobin present. As the blood passes through the walls of the air cells of the lung, the oxygen in the air forms a loose combination with the hæmoglobin called oxyhæmoglobin, from which it is readily detached when it reaches the tissues. The addition of oxygen brightens the colour of the hæmoglobin, hence the difference between the almost scarlet redness of arterial blood and the purplish red of venous blood. If a little venous blood be shaken up with air, it quickly becomes lighter and brighter in colour.

Hæmoglobin also unites readily with carbon monoxide, but the resulting compound, known as carboxyhæmoglobin, is a much more stable and permanent combination than the oxygen compound, and does not readily part with its gaseous ingredient. That is why carbon monoxide is so deadly to human beings. If inhaled, it loads the hæmoglobin with a gas which it cannot get rid of, and thus makes it incapable of taking up oxygen and distributing it through the tissues.

Iron in the Blood

Although but a very small proportion of iron enters into the composition of the red corpuscles, the total amount in the blood is far from inconsiderable. As well over a billion corpuscles are destroyed daily in the blood of each person, and a billion fresh ones have to be manufactured to replace them, it might be thought that a large amount of iron needs to be taken every day in the form of food or medicine. Actually, nothing like the amount is needed which would be necessary if the iron in the destroyed corpuscles were lost to the body. Considerable economy is exercised, the corpuscles put out of action being disintegrated largely in the liver, and the bulk of the iron is carefully saved. This is used again and again in the manufacture of fresh corpuscles, only a little addition being required to make good the small amount of wastage which takes place.

A fact sometimes made use of in criminal investigation is that marked differences are found in the red corpuscles of the blood of different animals (Fig. 23). They vary in size, and often in shape, according to the species or group. The corpuscles of most birds and reptiles, for instance, are oval and

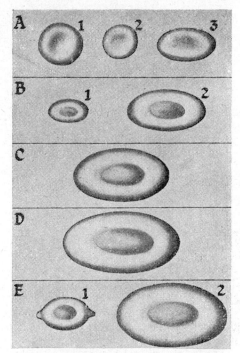

Fig. 23. *Red blood corpuscles of various animals.* (A) *Mammals:* 1, *Man;* 2, *mouse;* 3, *camel.* (B) *Birds:* 1, *Humming-bird;* 2, *ostrich.* (C) *Reptiles: Snake.* (D) *Amphibian: Toad.* (E) *Fish:* 1, *Pike;* 2, *shark. Notice that the various corpuscles have their own characteristic shape and size. Those of most mammals are round and biconcave.*

biconvex, whilst those of most mammals are round and biconcave. The corpuscles of birds, fish and amphibians have a nucleus, those of mammals have none.

The white, or, to speak more accurately, the colourless, corpuscles (Fig. 24) differ from the red corpuscles not only in colour but also in size, structure, and function. They have much in common with the unicellular amœba, since they contain a nucleus, and possess the properties of constantly altering their shape and of moving independently of the blood flow. Like the amœba, the white corpuscles take into themselves particles by pushing out little processes or protrusions at one point of their frame, and by drawing in at another point (Fig. 24). They are able to make their way between the thin lining cells that make up the walls of the capillaries, and so to pass out of the blood stream into the surrounding lymph, and then to make their way back again.

There are several forms of white corpuscle, differing in the character of the nucleus and in the number of granules contained in the cell, as well as in size. The two most important groups are known as leucocytes and lymphocytes, the former being the more numerous. The leucocytes, like the red corpuscles, are manufactured in the bone marrow (Fig. 25), the lymphocytes in the lymphatic glands. The leucocytes, like the amœba, are able to multiply themselves by simple fission; they play an active part in fighting and destroying hostile germs which have effected an entrance into the body.

An interesting and important property of these white corpuscles is their capacity for engulfing and digesting all sorts of germs and other particles which, either in the blood stream or in the lymph spaces outside the capillaries, cause irritation (Fig. 26). Corpuscles able to take in and digest foreign bodies, living or not living, are known by the generic term of phagocytes. They engulf and ingest such things as particles of blood clot and damaged cells, as well as living micro-organisms. The potency of these phagocytes is in large measure dependent on the presence in the blood, in minute quantities, of substances called opsonins (feast preparers) which, in some way, render the foreign body more vulnerable or more attractive.

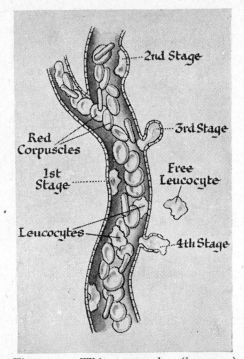

Fig. 24. *White corpuscles (leucocytes) escaping from a capillary. The leucocytes are able to alter their shape and to move independently of the blood flow. They make their way out of the blood stream into the lymph by passing between the lining cells that form the walls of the capillaries.*

Blood Platelets

In addition to the red and white corpuscles, the blood also contains an enormous number of smaller bodies, known as blood platelets. They are about one-quarter of the size of red corpuscles, and vary in shape, some being round, others irregular or ragged in outline. They are not easy to observe, however, as when blood escapes or is removed from a blood vessel, they almost immediately disintegrate. It is thought that they thus liberate a substance which plays an active part in promoting the coagulation or clotting of the blood. We all know that if blood escapes from a wound it forms a clot, and that if the wound be not too grave a one, the clot may actually serve as a plug, stopping the hole in the wounded blood vessel and so ending the hæmorrhage. If blood from any animal is collected in a basin, it quickly becomes thicker and more sticky, and in a short while forms a solid clot occupying the same volume as that of the original blood. A little later, drops of a yellowish fluid begin to escape from the clot, and after a while the clot is found to have shrunk to about half its former size, and to be floating in a quantity of this fluid. This fluid is called blood serum, and is clear and watery in consistency. The corpuscles are retained in the clot, being entangled in a sort of network of fine fibrous material. If, immediately the blood is drawn, it is whipped with some thin twigs, these are soon found to be covered with bunches of fibrous string-like masses. After this has been done, the blood no longer tends to clot. The importance to us of this coagulating quality of the blood is obvious if we reflect on what would happen otherwise. From even a small wound of the smallest artery, blood would continue to drain away until no more remained in the body, or until insufficient were left to stimulate the heart to contract.

Arterial Bleeding

When an artery of any size is wounded, the pressure is too great to bring about spontaneous plugging of the artery by blood clot and artificial means of arresting the hæmorrhage have to be employed. It is, therefore, important to make oneself familiar with the immediate measures to be taken in the event of such an accident. The first thing to be done is by pressure with the thumb or by means of a tourniquet or other constricting band to compress the wounded artery against a bone or other firm structure. There are special points in the course of most of the large arteries at which pressure can be most effectively employed.

Lastly, the blood contains, again in very small quantities, what are called antibodies. These help to neutralize the poisons caused by the activities of organisms responsible for various diseases.

So far, we have spoken of the blood stream and the circulatory system as

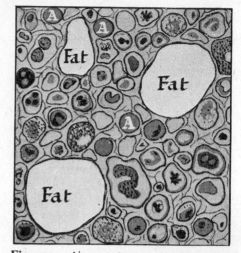

Fig. 25. *Normal bone marrow showing different types of blood cells and distribution of fat. The red corpuscles* (A) *and some of the white corpuscles* (*the leucocytes*) *are manufactured in the bone marrow.*

though they were parts of a clockwork machine which, having been wound up, goes on working for a period without much variation in speed of distribution of force. But the heart and circulatory system generally are much more complicated than this. We all know that the heart does not always beat with the same frequency, and that at one time our skin may be blanched and relatively bloodless, and at another flushed. There is always a reason for these variations, which are generally adaptations to meet variations in circumstance.

When we are engaged in active physical work, for instance, we are conscious that our heart pumps more violently and beats more quickly; so, also, when we are frightened or angry. An infinite number of examples showing modifications in the circulation might be quoted, the extent and frequency of changes in the circulatory flow being far greater than we are consciously aware of. There is something more than mere mechanism, something constantly controlling, regulating and adapting the circulatory system to the conditions and needs of every moment. Of the real nature of this controlling force we still have little satisfying knowledge; but a great deal has been learned about the means employed within the body to bring together purpose and result.

The Heart-beat

Let us first consider the heart-beat. There are, connected with the heart, two important nerves: the vagus and the sympathetic (*see* CHAPTER VIII), which, when stimulated, alter the frequency of its beat. When these nerves have been cut, the heart muscle continues to contract, but the contractions are then incapable of varying

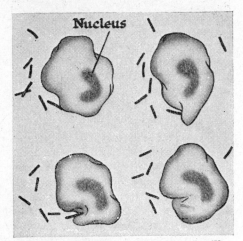

Fig. 26. *Lymphocyte absorbing a bacillus. The lymphocytes have the ability to engulf and digest all sorts of germs which cause irritation in the blood stream or lymph.*

as the need varies. The messages that come through these two nerves are directly opposed, the purpose of those from the vagus being to inhibit or slow down; from the sympathetic to speed up. Ordinarily the mild stimulation passing along these two counterbalancing nerves results in a sort of equilibrium, the contraction of the heart muscle being neither unduly stimulated nor unduly checked. No doubt there are constant minute oscillations on each side of absolute uniformity, but these are, in health, of but small consequence. We find,

indeed, in all examples of bodily equilibrium some measure of instability, but during health, the pendulum never swings far from its central point.

The vagus and sympathetic nerves end in the muscle of the heart in elaborate "receiving" structures, where the messages they bring are "decoded"; probably they effect certain chemical changes which act directly on the heart muscle. At the other end of these nerves are nerve centres situated, one in the hinder region of the brain, the other in the spinal cord. Connected with these centres from which the messages are despatched are other nerve cells which receive messages from various parts of the body. A temporary raising of the blood pressure in the ventricles or in the aorta causes a message to be sent to the nerve centre in the brain from which the vagus starts, with the result that a message is sent down that nerve, and this message slows down the action of the heart. Coincidently, another nerve centre, called the vaso-motor centre (*see* CHAPTER VIII), is rung up, and other messages are sent along nerves leading to the muscles that surround the small blood vessels, causing those muscles to relax and allow the vessels to dilate, which, in turn, help to lower the blood pressure. If the heart-beat becomes too slow the sympathetic nerve centre is rung up by the nerve cells affected, and the heart-beat is then quickened. The reader should understand that these are but the outstanding facts stated in the broadest outline. A great deal is known about the process, but more still remains to be discovered.

Muscles of Blood Vessels

The muscles in the walls of the blood vessels are also to some extent controlled by messages sent to them through special nerves. There are two groups of these nerves, one known as vaso-constrictor, the other as vaso-dilator (*see* CHAPTER VIII). As their names imply, stimulation of one set of nerves causes the muscles to relax, allowing the little arteries to dilate, stimulation of the other having the reverse effect.

None of these variations in the beating of the heart and in the size of the arterioles can be controlled or influenced by the conscious will. We cannot, by taking thought, make our heart beat more quickly or more slowly, nor can we deliberately choose to what part of the body a more generous supply of blood shall flow; but between these phenomena and our emotional states there is a very intimate connexion. When, say through stage fright, the vaso-constrictor nerve centre at the back of the brain is temporarily put out of action the arterioles dilate and, among other phenomena, we are likely to blush and feel faint. An inadequate supply of blood reaches the brain owing to the amount used up in filling the small dilated vessels in the skin and in the abdomen.

Gland Secretions

At the base of the brain is a small gland, called the pituitary body (*see* CHAPTER IX). On the top of each kidney is another small gland, called the adrenal. These glands produce small quantities of specialized chemical substances which pass directly into the blood stream and are distributed to all parts of the body. The amount of the secretions is largely influenced by our emotional states. These secretions either stimulate or co-operate with the sympathetic nervous system and, among other consequences, bring about a contraction of the small blood vessels of the skin and the digestive organs.

The potential capacity of our blood vessels being out of all proportion greater than the total volume of our blood, it would be very wasteful of nature to maintain an equal uniform supply of blood to all parts at all times, remembering how different are the needs of different tissues at different times. When we are eating our dinner, there is not much point in keeping up a full supply of blood to our legs and arms; when we are digging our garden or trying to beat

the hundred yards record, it would be wasteful if a lot of energy fuel were diverted to our digestive organs or to our skin. The only parts which all the while need a fairly uniform supply of oxygen and nutriment are the heart and the brain, and in health the supply of blood to these organs varies but little. When the emotion of fear or of

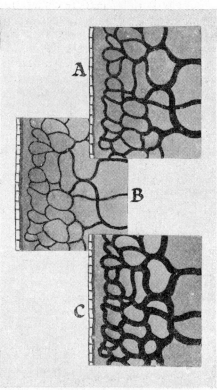

Fig. 27. *Effect of temperature on capillaries. Cold reduces the flow of blood and heat increases it.* (A) *Normal size of capillaries.* (B) *After cold application.* (C) *After hot application.*

anger is provoked, the bodily effects are exactly those which would equip us for reacting efficiently in ways that would prove self preservative amid primitive conditions. The primitive responses to situations giving rise to anger or fear are nearly always the inclination to fight or to run away. Each of these proceedings involves increased muscular activity, and that, in turn, calls for a more generous service of supplies to the muscles. In these circumstances the surface blood vessels contract, producing that paleness of aspect which is proverbially symptomatic both of rage and fear—"white with rage," "pale with fear," as we say. The digestive processes are slowed down, the blood vessels of the muscles and of the heart are dilated, and the heart itself beats more strongly and more quickly. Breathing increases in frequency and depth to furnish the muscles with the extra oxygen needed for the liberation of energy. The liver's stores of sugar are drawn upon for more fuel.

Internal Temperature

One of the most astounding facts of human physiology is the capacity of the body to maintain within itself, amid the most diverse external circumstances, a comparatively uniform environment. We may journey from the tropics to the pole, but all the time, if our health is normal, the internal temperature of our body remains almost constant, though heat is continuously being produced in it. It is said that if the body had not this wonderful capacity for maintaining its equilibrium, the amount of heat produced by half an hour's hard muscular work would raise our temperature to something near boiling point. If that happened all the albumen in our blood and in our cells would be solidified like the white of a boiled egg.

The average temperature of the body in health is 98.4 degrees Fahrenheit, though slight variations from this normal occur. At midnight, and during the few hours that follow, the temperature falls to its lowest point, which may be a degree or a degree and a half below normal. In all inflammatory conditions, such as those set up by the infective fevers, there is a rise of body temperature, danger point being reached at about 105 degrees. When in normal health we may feel hot or cold, the sensation is due, not to variation in the temperature of our blood, but to the amount of blood flowing through the vessels (Fig. 27).

This uniformity is maintained by means of very delicately adjusted living machinery, of the workings of which we are entirely unconscious. Each one of the millions of minute living entities, or cells, of which our bodies are a conglomerate, has an internal life of its own, the subtleties of which are only just beginning to be understood. We speak of ourselves as being land animals. So, in a sense, we are; but the units of which we are composed remain what presumably they always were—water animals. Every one of our living cells is dependent for its continued existence on the fluid medium with which its surface is ever in contact; and so sensitive and delicate are these cellular structures that very small variations in their environment are lethal to them. Hence it is of vital importance to life itself that the blood temperature should remain, within very small ranges, constant. Tireless automatic forces are always operating to preserve a balance which will keep these delicate organisms unharmed. Only to a small extent can we consciously modify our physiological functions. Within limits it makes little difference what we eat or drink. We cannot make our blood more salt by eating salt, or more acid by drinking vinegar. At every stage of digestion, of absorption, and of chemical activity, purposive selection is at work.

Conditions of Life

It was not until the middle of the last century that this idea of an internal environment as distinct from an external one was first clearly defined. A celebrated French physiologist, Claude Bernard, drew the attention of his professional colleagues to the great differences between the conditions to which the outside of our body is exposed — conditions which surround every object, inorganic or living, in a particular country or district—and the conditions with which our living units or cells are brought into contact. He showed that, important as are the external conditions of our life, our internal ones are of far greater importance, and he was impressed by the elaborate arrangements whereby the internal environment is maintained at a constant level, no matter what may be the apparent external circumstances.

Internal Environment

"It is," he wrote, "the fixity of the internal environment which is the condition of free and independent life, and all the vital mechanisms, however varied they may be, have only one object, that of preserving constant the conditions of life in the internal environment."

This important pronouncement, described by the late Dr. J. S. Haldane as "the most pregnant sentence ever framed by a physiologist," is elaborated and in detail exemplified in a book called *The Wisdom of the Body*, by Professor Walter Cannon of Harvard University. In it he shows how stable is the composition of the blood, how little are the variations in the percentages of sugar, of salt, of calcium, and of other elements in the body fluids of a healthy individual. He quotes an experiment performed on themselves by Dr. Haldane and Dr. Priestley. In the course of six hours they drank six quarts of water apiece; at one time, the rate of output through the kidneys rose to over three and a quarter pints per hour. The volume of water borne by the circulating blood from the intestines, where the water was absorbed, to the kidneys, where it was discharged, exceeded by one-third the total estimated volume of the blood. Yet in tests made on the colour of the blood during the period no appreciable dilution could be observed.

Take, again, what is called the acid-alkali balance of the blood, that is, its relative acidity or alkalinity. It is essential to the healthy life of the body cells that the blood shall be ever so slightly alkaline. If, as the sequel to some diseased condition, the tiniest swing of the pendulum over the neutrality line in the acid direction occurs,

coma and death result. If, on the other hand, a minute increase of alkalinity is produced, tetanic convulsions are a possible prelude to an equally fatal conclusion. Professor Cannon shows by what subtle bodily mechanisms this almost neutral reaction of the blood is produced and sustained. The kidneys, the breathing centre in the brain, and the proportion of the so-called buffer salts in the blood itself, all contribute to the maintenance of this uniformity.

Blood Structure

It is only comparatively recently that physiologists have become aware of the complicated structure and composition of the blood. It is far from being a mere dilute solution of salt in water, in which a few million corpuscles float about; nor is the tale more than begun when we say that the blood is also the medium whereby the oxygen we breathe, and the sugar and meat we eat, are distributed to all parts of the body. It is essential to our well-being that due quantities of a variety of mineral substances shall be supplied by the blood stream for the growth and life processes of the many kinds of cell of which our tissues are composed. But there are other, and even more mysterious, ingredients of the blood that are necessary in almost immeasurably small amounts, and of which an absence or an excess quickly leads to disease or even to death. It is by means of the blood stream that the secretions of our endocrine glands are distributed to the organs and structures, the activities of which they regulate. In the absence of sufficient insulin, for instance, we develop the disease called diabetes; and, but for the minute amounts of pituitrin and adrenalin normally kept in circulation, the distribution of blood according to the body's varying needs could not be accomplished.

We must all the time bear in mind that the blood system provides the main transport and communication medium of the body. Thus we find in the fluid part of the

blood many substances in solution or suspension—fats, sugar, and the so-called
amino-acids, which are the products of the
digestion of the protein ingredients of our
food—and these in turn enter into the
composition of nearly all our tissues. Then,
again, and this is very important, there are
certain mineral salts that enter into the
composition of the body cells, the more
important being the chlorides, carbonates
and phosphates of sodium, potassium and
calcium. Among the waste products taken
away by the blood in order to be excreted
from the body by the kidneys and other
organs, are urea, uric acid, and certain
salts of ammonia.

We are apt to think that all communication between different parts of the body is
effected by the telegraphic system of which
our nerves are the wires. But, as in our
social system the postal service is older
established and of more importance than
the telegraph service, so also is the slower
method of communication afforded by the
circulation of the blood as compared with
the rapid transmission of messages by
means of nerves. We have in our bodies
certain specialized groups of cells, or
organs, which produce substances of definite chemical composition the contact of
which with our muscles and other tissues
gives rise to activities quite as marked, and
far more widespread than, the activities
brought about by a nerve message.

Blood Transfusion

When serious hæmorrhage has taken
place, and the blood pressure has fallen
through lack of volume, doctors often in-
troduce into the tissues, or into a vein,
what is called normal saline solution. By
this is meant a sterilized mixture of salt and
water corresponding in proportions and
density with that of the blood itself. Nowadays, in cases of great emergency, direct
transfusion of blood from a healthy person,
called the donor, to a patient suffering
from severe loss of blood or from certain
diseased conditions, is practised. This is

not a novelty, though until recently the
process was not unaccompanied by danger.

In 1901 it was discovered that the serum
of one person's blood if mixed with the
blood of another individual is liable to
cause what is called agglutination, or
clumping, of the red blood corpuscles in
the second person's blood, and this was
shown to be the cause of the collapse which
not infrequently followed the operation of
transfusion. It is now known that people
can be divided into four groups, according
to the mutual compatibility of their blood.
In a blood transfusion, it is the behaviour
of the red corpuscles of the donor's blood,
when brought into contact with the serum
of the recipient's blood, that matters. If
they agglutinate, the donor is unsuitable
for this particular recipient.

Blood Groups

Numbering the Groups 1, 2, 3 and 4, the
known facts may be summarized thus:
Group 1 corpuscles are agglutinated by the
serums of Groups 2, 3 and 4, but Group 1
serum agglutinates the corpuscles of none
of the others. Group 2 corpuscles are
agglutinated by Groups 3 and 4, but not by
1 or 2. Group 3 corpuscles are agglutinated
by Groups 2 and 4 serums. Group 4 serum
agglutinates all the others, but its corpuscles are not agglutinated by any other
serum. For this reason, as sources of blood,
persons belonging to Group 4 are sometimes called universal donors and persons
belonging to Group 1 as universal reci-
pients. Persons whose blood belongs to the
fourth group are, therefore, of exceptional
value in times of emergency. Their blood is
the only one that can safely be introduced
into the blood stream of any one. The compatibility of the blood of one person can be
tested by taking a drop of the proposed
donor's blood and mixing it with very little
of a dilute solution of citrate of soda on a
microscope slide, and then adding to it a
drop of the recipient's serum. If in a few
minutes the red cells are seen to agglutinate, the two bloods are incompatible.

CHAPTER IV

LYMPH AND LYMPHATIC GLANDS

NOURISHMENT OF BODY TISSUES: POSITION AND STRUCTURE OF LYMPH-
ATIC GLANDS: COURSE OF LYMPHATIC VESSELS: THORACIC AND RIGHT
LYMPHATIC DUCTS: NATURE OF LYMPH: LYMPHATIC VESSELS OF LEG
AND ARM: IMPORTANCE OF LYMPHATIC SYSTEM AS DEFENCE MECHANISM

THE BLOOD runs through the body in a system of closed channels. It leaves the heart by the arterial system, from which branches go to every part of the body, breaking up as they go into smaller and smaller subdivisions, until at last the blood is flowing through tiny capillaries lined by a single layer of cells which separates them from the cells of the tissues. In some organs, for example, the lungs and the liver, every cell is in direct contact with the surface of a capillary; in other tissues, such as cartilage, the capillaries do not penetrate into the substance. For the return journey to the heart the capillaries unite to form larger and larger vessels which eventually reach the size of veins.

Nourishment of Tissues

At no point in the circulation, even in the lungs and liver, does the blood come into direct contact with the tissues which it serves. This implies that a separate mechanism is needed for the nourishment of the tissues. This is supplied by the lymph, a tissue fluid which permeates the spaces between the cells so that every tissue in the body is like a sponge soaked in fluid.

The lymph does not ooze about in an uncontrolled manner. Throughout the tissue spaces there is a close network of vessels (Fig. 1) lined with extremely thin cells, and these vessels unite to form definite channels, the lymphatics, which draw off any excess of fluid. All these lymphatics run towards the thorax, and many of them are supplied with valves which prevent the fluid from flowing backwards. At intervals they are interrupted by oval solid swellings known as the lymph glands.

Lymph Glands

These glands are embedded in connective tissue (Fig. 2), and are usually arranged in groups of two or three—though sometimes of as many as fifteen (Fig. 3). In shape they are oval, with a depression at one side known as the hilum. They vary considerably in size, some being smaller than a pea, others as large as a bean. In colour they are greyish pink, though those near the roots of the lungs are blackened by deposits of carbon.

The lymph glands upon the surface of the body are gathered chiefly round the groins and armpits, with a few at the elbow and knee. Inside the abdominal cavity, they are grouped very freely along the course of the aorta and round the pelvis; round the trachea and bronchi they are found lying very thickly.

The lymph leaving a lymph gland contains far more white blood cells (lymphocytes) than the lymph entering it, because lymph glands are factories for lymphocytes, which are also produced in certain lymphatic patches in the spleen, the small intestine and the tonsils.

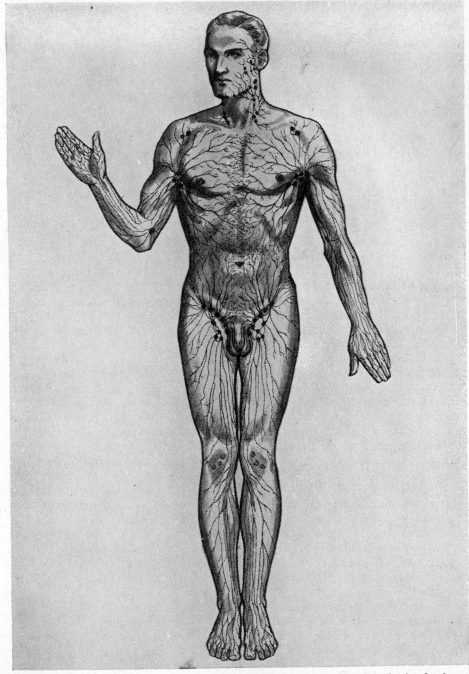

Fig. I. *Grouping of surface lymphatic glands and vessels. The lymphatic glands are found at intervals along the network of lymphatic vessels which run from every part of the body towards the chest. The glands are gathered chiefly round the groins and armpits.*

If a lymph gland is examined under the microscope, it is found to be contained in a capsule from which strands pass into the substance of the gland forming a supporting framework; cross strands of fibrous tissue form a meshwork through which the lymph passes on its way through the gland. In the outer part of the gland near the capsule there are quite large lymph spaces (Fig. 4). The remainder is made up of dense masses of lymphoid cells; these are the lymphocytes in the process of maturing. Numbers of them are constantly leaving the gland with the outflowing lymph and in this way the supply of lymphocytes to the body is kept up.

Course of Lymphatics

The lymphatic vessels (Fig. 5), though interrupted in this way by lymph glands, continue their course towards the thorax, branching freely to make connexions with each other. As they become larger their walls become strengthened by layers of elastic tissue, those of the largest vessels of

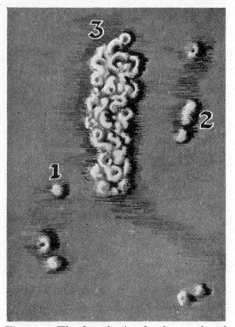

Fig. 3. *The lymphatic glands are found either as isolated nodules (1), groups of two or three together (2), or as larger groups of as many as fifteen together (3).*

all having, like a blood vessel, three layers. The larger the vessel, the more frequent the valves, until the largest vessels show an irregular appearance as the result of the swellings caused by these valves.

Finally all the lymphatic vessels collect up into two terminal channels, one of which empties itself into the left subclavian vein and the other into the right. These two veins spring from the arch of the aorta just after it leaves the heart, and as one of the lymphatic vessels, the thoracic duct (Fig. 6), carries with it all the nutriment derived from fat digestion in the intestines, the blood entering the heart is full of food material which has been carried straight round the body in the course of the circulatory process.

The thoracic duct, which is much the larger of the two terminal lymph vessels, begins in the abdomen as an elongated swelling called the cisterna chyli, at the juncture of several large lymphatic vessels.

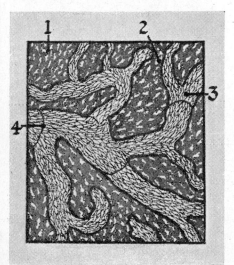

Fig. 2. *Lymphatic vessels and spaces. Between the cells of the body there are: 1, Spaces, filled by connective tissue in which are embedded (2) the lymph vessels; 3, valves along the vessels prevent the lymph fluid from flowing backwards.*

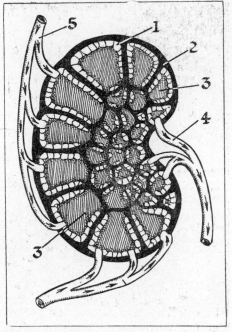

Fig. 4. *Section of lymphatic nodule.* *1,*
Lymph space; 2, containing capsule; 3,
lymphoid tissue; 4 and 5, lymphatic vessels
(arrows show direction of flow).

Here it receives lymph from all the lymphatic vessels leaving the intestine. The fine velvety epithelium lining the intestines consists of closely packed finger-like projections, each one smaller than a hair, the intestinal villi. Running into each villus is a small arterial capillary; leaving it are a venous capillary and a lymphatic vessel. The products of protein and carbohydrate digestion are carried away in the tiny veins leaving the villi, but the products of fat digestion are absorbed by the minute lymphatic vessels, and the creamy appearance of the fat as it travels through these lymphatics has earned for them the name of lacteals.

The lacteals drain into larger vessels which unite with each other and finally enter the cisterna chyli. In addition, lymph from the lower legs (Fig. 7), the abdominal organs and wall and the lower part of the thorax, also drains into the same useful receptacle. At its upper end, the cisterna chyli is continued upwards as the thoracic duct, which runs up the back wall of the thorax on the right side of the aorta until it reaches the level of the fifth dorsal vertebra, where it crosses to the left side and enters the left subclavian vein. All the way up its course it receives branches from the left side of the thorax and heart, the left lung and the left arm. The whole duct measures about eighteen inches long from beginning to end.

The right lymphatic duct is far less impressive than the thoracic duct, though it does nearly as much work. It is only about half an inch long, but it receives lymphatic vessels from the right side of the head and neck (Fig. 8), the right arm, the right half of the thorax, including the right lung and the right side of the heart, the right side of the diaphragm and the upper surface of the liver. All these vessels join together close to the right subclavian vein to form this lymphatic duct, which immediately enters the vein and comes to an end.

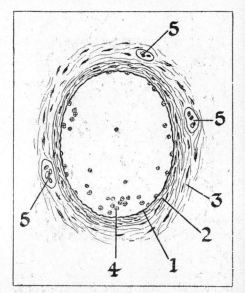

Fig. 5. *Section of lymphatic vessel.* *1,*
Layer of elastic tissue; 2, layer of muscles,
helping to maintain flow of fluid; 3, con-
nective tissue; 4, lymph cells; 5, blood vessels.

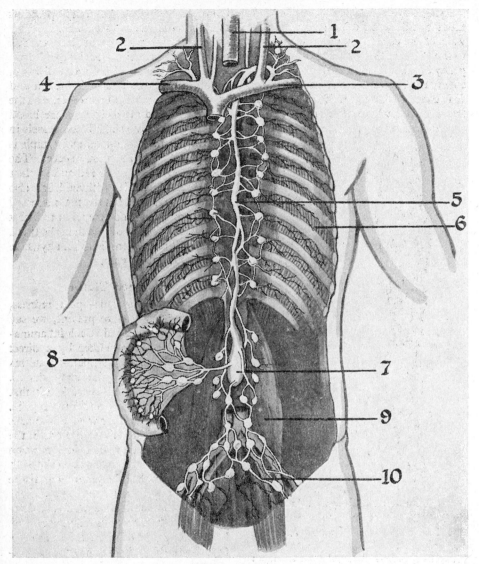

Fig. 6. *Large lymphatic vessel (thoracic duct) showing its position in relation to veins and muscles. 1, Gullet (œsophagus); 2, main veins of neck (jugular veins); 3 and 4, veins of shoulder and upper arm (left and right subclavian veins); 5, large lymphatic vessel running from the abdomen, up the back wall of the chest parallel to the aorta, and entering the left subclavian vein (thoracic duct.) Notice how all the way up its course it receives branches from chest, heart, lung and arm; 6, muscles between ribs (intercostal muscles); 7, elongated swelling in the abdomen at juncture of several large lymphatic vessels, forming beginning of the thoracic duct (cisterna chyli). Into this receptacle flows lymph from all the lymphatic vessels of the intestine, the lower legs, the abdominal organs and wall, and the lower part of the chest; the thoracic duct also carries all the nutriment derived from fat digestion in the intestines; 8, part of the small intestine, showing lymphatic vessels and glands; 9, muscle of the pelvis (psoas muscle); 10, lymph glands of the loin (lumbar lymph glands).*

Lymph is derived from the blood. It filters out between the cells forming the walls of the capillaries, partly in response to the needs of the tissues themselves and partly because it is forced out by the pressure of the blood in the circulatory system. It is a clear yellowish fluid, except in the thoracic duct, where it has a milky appearance owing to the presence of particles of

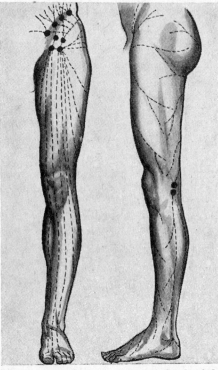

Fig. 7. *Lymphatic vessels and glands of the leg. The chief group of lymphatic glands in the leg is found in the groin, with an additional group at the knee. Lymph from the legs is carried away into the thoracic duct.*

fat. It also contains leucocytes derived from the blood; the number of these is increased in the course of its circulation through the lymphatic glands.

The purpose of the lymph in the tissue spaces is to act as a medium of communication between the blood and the tissues. The muscles take up nourishment and oxygen from the blood by way of the

lymph and pour into it such waste products as carbon dioxide and ammonia.

The lymphatic system has another equally important function: it provides one of the important defence mechanisms of the body. When the skin is broken and tissues are injured, the first response on the part of the body is to bring more blood to the part. All the small blood vessels in the neighbourhood dilate, and lymph is poured out into the tissue spaces. The affected region becomes red and swollen because it is distended with fluid. It is also hot and painful, because the increased blood supply raises the temperature of that part, and the excess of lymph in the tissue spaces causes tension. Tension anywhere in the body causes pain.

Inflamed Tissue

When these four signs—pain, redness, heat and swelling—are present, we say that a tissue is inflamed. Such inflammation may be caused either by a direct injury or by invading micro-organisms which are damaging the body tissues. Lymph is useful on these occasions in that it provides plenty of protein for repairs. It helps also in another way. White cells from the blood are always present in the lymph, and in a region where inflammation is present large numbers of white cells migrate from the blood into the tissue spaces and form a barrier between the healthy tissues and those which are damaged. This barrier is usually successful, because one type of white cell commonly found in the blood has the power of attacking bacteria and engulfing and digesting them just as an amœba digests its food. The cells which have this power are called polymorphonuclear leucocytes, or polymorphs, and they always appear in large numbers at the site of any inflammation.

Usually the polymorphs succeed in destroying the invaders, but sometimes the bacterial organisms are so virulent that they kill many of the polymorphs before they are overcome. Even so they do not

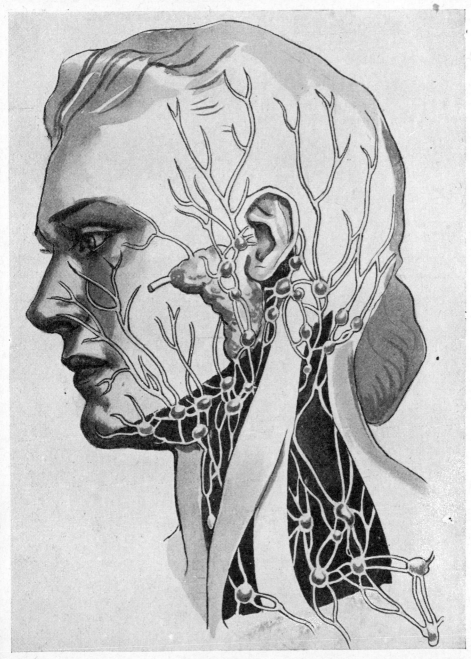

Fig. 8. *Lymphatic vessels and glands of the face and neck. The lymphatic glands of the head are found chiefly around the ear and chin, and another group lies at the base of the neck. The lymphatic vessels of the right side of the head and neck, as also from the right arm, and the right half of the chest, heart and diaphragm, run into the right lymphatic duct, and thence into the left subclavian vein.*

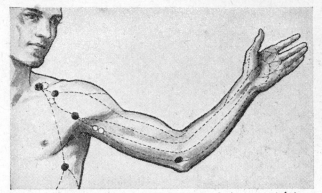

Fig. 9. *Lymphatic vessels and glands of the arm. A large concentration of glands is found at the armpit, and some additional ones at the elbow. The vessels of the left arm run to the thoracic duct, of the right to the right lymphatic.*

break through the barrier of white cells, which keeps the inflammation localized to one spot. The dead polymorphs form a semi-solid clot of the creamy material which we know as pus, and if there is no channel connecting the inflamed area with the surface of the skin, an abscess will form which will need to be opened and drained.

Occasionally the invading bacteria prove too much for the leucocyte barrier and may by breaking through it, carry infection abroad in the body. In that case, they are likely to invade the lymphatic channels first, because the lymphatics are open to the tissue spaces and easy of access whereas the blood capillaries are enclosed in a wall of cells. When the organisms invade the lymphatics we commonly see signs of it in the form of red streaks passing up from the inflamed area to the nearest group of lymphatic glands. Here, however, they commonly meet a check. The lymphatic glands are full of white cells and though these are not polymorphs but lymphocytes, they have the power of checking the invaders and are very often able to rout them. Thus, it is not an uncommon thing for a person to get a scratch on his finger which becomes infected; after a few hours, red streaks may be seen running up his arm to his elbow and an enlarged lymphatic gland may be felt in the elbow region (Fig. 9).

If this gland is unable to conquer the infection, after a few more hours the red streaks will be seen to have proceeded farther up the arm to the armpit (Fig. 10); and again enlarged lymphatic glands will be felt under the skin.

When inflammation proceeds so far up the lymphatic vessels as this it must always be regarded as serious, because it means that the invading organisms are coming perilously near the point at which the lymph vessels enter the blood stream; and organisms in the blood stream are a very serious matter indeed. Science has recently provided certain drugs which seem likely to afford valuable aid to the lymphatics, which are among our most valuable defenders, and would be worth having in that capacity alone, even if they were not essential for nourishment of the tissues and the removal of waste products.

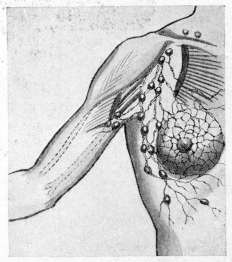

Fig. 10. *Lymphatics of breast and armpit. Above the left breast lies the left subclavian vein, into which enters the thoracic duct.*

CHAPTER V

FOOD, DIGESTION AND NUTRITION

DIGESTIVE TRACT: SALIVARY GLANDS AND SALIVA: TEETH AND MOUTH: MUSCLES OF MASTICATION AND SWALLOWING: THE GULLET: CONSTRUCTION OF STOMACH: SMALL INTESTINE: PANCREAS, LIVER AND GALL-BLADDER: LARGE INTESTINE: PROTEINS, CARBOHYDRATES AND FATS: BALANCING THE DIET: MINERALS, VITAMINS AND INSULIN : DIGESTION OF FATS

FEW PARTS of the human body are more remarkable than the digestive system. Its ability both to break down complicated food substances into simple forms so that they can be absorbed into the blood stream and be built up into living bone, muscle and fat, and also to ignore waste products which would serve no useful purpose if absorbed, is extraordinary.

Digestive Tract

The digestive tract (Fig. 1) begins with the mouth above and ends with the anal canal below, and consists of a long tube into which digestive juices are poured at intervals by various glands. In its fully developed state, the digestive tract is long and winding; it measures about thirty feet from end to end. Food enters the mouth, and passes through the pharynx, or back of the throat, and down the œsophagus, or gullet, into the stomach; thence it travels successively through the small and large intestines. From the last part of the large intestine, the rectum, waste material is evacuated by way of the anal canal.

Food, in whatever form it is taken into the mouth, consists of three main components: protein, usually in the form of meat, cheese, eggs or fish; carbohydrates (sugars and starches); and fats. For each of these components the body has to supply a different chemical in order to dissolve and extract what is valuable. Carbohydrates provide the least serious problem; they are easily broken down into sugars, which are quickly absorbed. Sugar is a useful form of ready-made fuel for the body. Explorers and airmen often take chocolate with them, both because it is so handy and because it acts almost as soon as it is swallowed.

Digestion of starches begins in the mouth, into which three sets of glands, the parotid, the sublingual and the sub-maxillary (Fig. 2), pour their digestive fluid. Each parotid gland lies in the cheek, just in front of the ear, and pours out its secretion by means of a duct which runs through the cheek wall, and opens up on a small raised papilla in the middle of the inner surface of the cheek. This papilla can easily be seen inside the mouth. The parotid glands are affected in mumps, and stones occasionally form in them and may be forced into the duct, blocking it. The condition is painful and the stone usually has to be removed by operation.

Digestive Juices

The sublingual glands lie just below the floor of the mouth, between the tongue and the lower jaw. Each gland has about twelve small ducts which open into the floor of the mouth, just below the tongue, and keep that region always moist. The

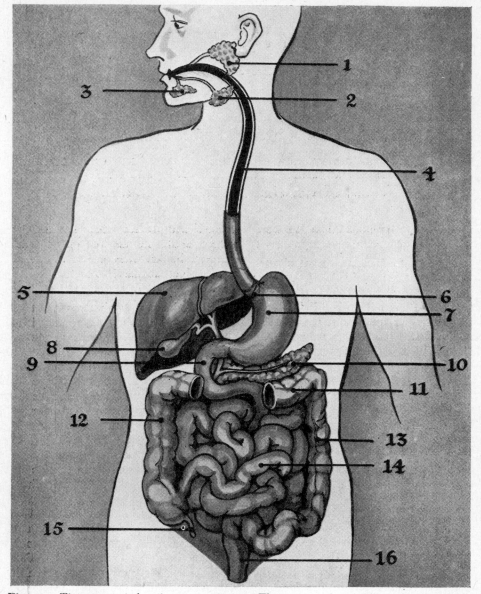

Fig. 1. *The parts of the digestive tract. 1, The largest of the three salivary glands, situated just in front of the ear (parotid gland); 2, gland situated under the lower jaw, with ducts opening upon floor of the mouth (submaxillary gland); 3, gland lying below floor of mouth between tongue and lower jaw (sublingual gland); 4, gullet, the food passage from mouth to stomach (œsophagus); 5, liver; 6, band of muscle at end of stomach nearest heart (cardiac sphincter); 7, stomach; 8, gall-bladder; 9, first portion of small intestine immediately below stomach (duodenum); 10, gland near stomach which discharges a digestive juice into the intestine (pancreas); 11, 12 and 13, parts of the large intestine (transverse, ascending and descending colon; part of the transverse colon has been cut away to show organs behind it); 14, small intestine; 15, appendix; 16, rectum.*

submaxillary glands, as their name suggests, lie under the lower jaw at each side (Fig. 2). Their ducts open upon the floor of the mouth, at either side of the fold of skin beneath the tongue. Like the parotid duct, each submaxillary duct opens at the top of a little papilla, which can be seen clearly with the naked eye. These three glands pour out a digestive juice, the saliva, which contains an active chemical agent capable of digesting starch. Digestive agents of this kind are called enzymes.

Before considering the enzyme contained in saliva, we must examine the cavity in which it acts. The mouth (Fig. 3) is bounded below by a muscular floor and the jawbone, or lower maxilla, and above by the hard palate. The soft muscular walls of the cheeks close it in at the sides. Upon its floor lies the tongue, an active muscular organ, and in the lower and upper jaws the teeth are set. At the back, the soft palate, a curtain of muscular tissue covered by mucous membrane, hangs down, and is prolonged, in the middle, into a tapering muscular tag, the

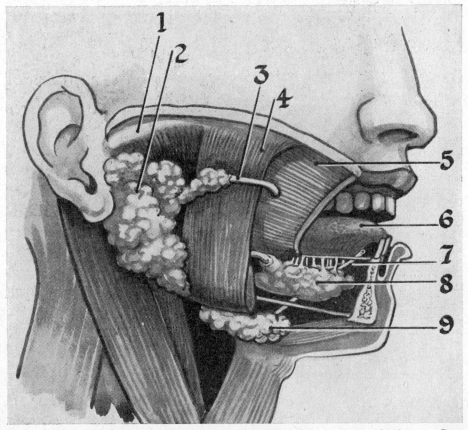

Fig. 2. *Glands and ducts which produce and supply saliva (salivary glands). 1, Bony structure of the cheek (zygomatic arch); 2, largest of the salivary glands, lying in the cheek in front of ear (parotid gland); 3, channel leading through the cheek wall to inner surface of cheek (parotid duct); 4, muscle used in chewing, passing from cheekbone to lower jaw (masseter); 5, flat thin muscle, forming wall of cheek (buccinator); 6, tongue; 7, channel leading from gland lying under tongue into the floor of the mouth (sublingual ducts); 8, gland between tongue and lower jaw (sublingual gland); 9, gland under lower jaw (submaxillary).*

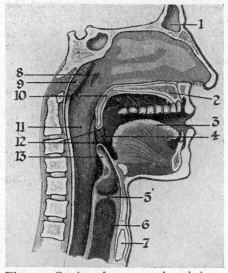

Fig. 3. *Section of nose, mouth and throat. 1, Cavity at top of nose (frontal sinus); 2, hard palate; 3, tongue; 4, tonsil; 5, vocal cord; 6, windpipe (trachea) ; 7, gland lying in the neck (thyroid gland); 8, canal leading from throat to ear drum (Eustachian tube); 9, spongy tissue between back of nose and throat (adenoid); 10, soft palate; 11, cavity communicating with nose, mouth and larynx (pharynx); 12, folds of skin at the sides of the throat (pillars of the fauces); 13, cartilage at back of tongue (epiglottis).*

uvula. At either side of the soft palate are two folds of skin called the pillars of the fauces, and between these pillars, on each side, is the tonsil, a mass of lymphatic tissue exactly like a lymphatic gland without its capsule.

Throat and Gullet

Behind the soft palate the mouth opens into a roomy cavity, the throat or pharynx (Fig. 3), which is continuous above with the cavity of the nose and below with the œsophagus or gullet. Just in front of the œsophagus is the opening of the voice-box, or larynx, and from the front border of this a thin, leaf-like structure, called the epiglottis, projects upwards and rests upon the back of the tongue. The epiglottis is made of cartilage covered with

mucous membrane; its tip can be felt by any one bold enough to push an inquiring finger to the back of his tongue. When we swallow, the larynx is raised and the tip of the epiglottis is pushed backwards over the cavity of the larynx, so that food slips over the epiglottis without getting into the windpipe. Sometimes, we put this mechanism out of order and then the food, as we say, goes the wrong way; it gets into the larynx and makes us cough.

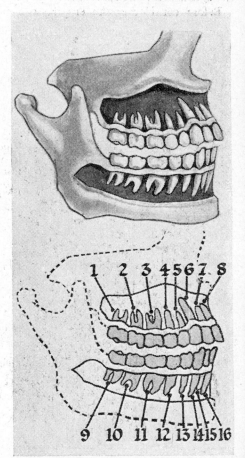

Fig. 4. *Upper and lower teeth, with diagram showing names of the teeth. 1, 2 and 3, Upper molars; 4 and 5, upper premolars; 6, upper canine; 7 and 8, upper incisors; 9, 10 and 11, lower molars; 12 and 13, lower premolars; 14, lower canine; 15 and 16, lower incisors. The two rows are arranged alike.*

The teeth (Fig. 4), in a grown person with a complete set, are arranged alike in the two jaws. If we start in front and work backwards from the mid-line we find, first, two incisors (Fig. 5) on each side; these are flat teeth with a cutting edge, designed for biting. Behind them is the canine or eye-tooth, and behind that again are two bicuspids, or premolars; at the back are three molar teeth, the last being the wisdom tooth. The bicuspids and the molars are chewing teeth; the canines are tearing teeth designed for wrenching meat off bones; as they get very little of this sort of work to do in civilized society, they are small compared with the eye-teeth, say, of an Alsatian dog (Fig. 6).

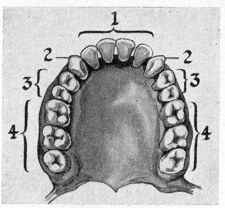

Fig. 6. *Teeth seen from below. 1, Incisors; 2, canines; 3, premolars; 4, molars. The canines are tearing teeth, and are small in humans, as they are little used.*

Organs of Taste

Nature has made sure that we shall not ignore the question of meal-times. She has not only provided us with unpleasant sensations when we do not eat but with pleasant sensations when we do. The satisfaction of hunger is in itself a pleasant sensation, but it is greatly enhanced by the delights of taste. The chief organ of taste is the tongue (Fig. 7), which is studded with specially modified groups of cells called taste-buds. At the back of the tongue are several raised pink nodules called the circumvallate papillæ; taste-buds are found in large numbers round these nodules and also round the sides of the tongue. The taste-buds are made up of

oval, or flask-shaped, nests of cells embedded in the membrane covering the tongue; at the centre of each bud is a small pore through which a group of microscopic hairs protrude.

The nerve of taste supplies fine branches to these hairs and when they are stimulated by some sweet, savoury or bitter substance a message is sent back to the brain and produces the sensations which we associate with an agreeable or disagreeable taste. In the brain, the nerve cells receiving impressions of taste are closely associated with the nerve cells receiving impressions of smell, so that taste is greatly enhanced by a good sense of smell. Any one with a cold in the nose realizes how much of his pleasure in his food is normally derived from the sensations of smell that accompany eating.

The tongue distinguishes four types of taste—sweet, bitter, salt and sour—and endless combinations of these. Not all parts of the tongue are equally sensitive to all four tastes: bitterness is best tasted at the back of the tongue, sweetness and sourness best at the sides. Any one who likes to experiment can prove this for himself with a few crystals of sugar and salt and a bottle of quinine. Besides being an organ of taste, the tongue is a powerful

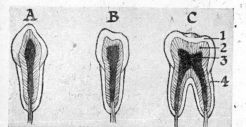

Fig. 5. *Section of teeth. (A) Incisor, a flat tooth with a cutting edge used for biting. (B) Bicuspid, used in chewing. (C) Molar, used in chewing. 1, Enamel coating; 2, hard tissue (dentine); 3, pulp; 4, cement.*

mechanical device for mixing food and moving it round the mouth; in this it is helped by the champing of the jaws which are moved by a special set of muscles.

Five muscles help to move the lower maxilla on its joint with the skull. One of them, the temporal muscle (Fig. 8), is attached to the ramus of the jaw (Fig. 9), which is the upright portion at the back of each end of the lower maxilla. The temporal muscles arise, one at each side of the skull, from the temporal bones and can be felt as thick pads covering each temple. If you place your fingers on the temporal

muscles and move the lower jaw, the contractions of the muscles can be felt.

The second great muscle of mastication is the masseter (Fig. 8), attached above to the cheekbone and below to the outer surface of the ramus of the jaw. When it contracts it pulls the jaw upwards, just as a broad piece of elastic might do; when you clench the jaws you can feel the movement of its fibres by placing your fingers on your cheeks near the angle of the jaw. Two other muscles, the internal and external pterygoids, help to move the jaw. They arise, deep in among the bones of the face, from the under surface of the sphenoid, the palate bone, and the upper maxilla, and they are attached to the inner surface of the ramus of the lower jaw. The last of the muscles of mastication is the buccinator (Fig. 8), which arises from both the upper and lower maxilla and runs forward to blend with the muscles round the mouth. It does not actually help to move the lower jaw at all, so that, in a sense, it is not a muscle of mastication; its task is to flatten the cheeks and bring them into contact with the teeth, so that food does not collect in pouches at either side, a movement essential to successful chewing.

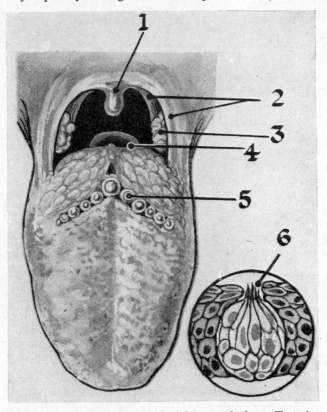

Fig. 7. (Left) The tongue and (right) taste-buds. 1, Tapering tag of muscle forming prolongation at middle of the soft palate (uvula); 2, folds of skin at either side of the throat (pillars of the fauces); 3, mass of lymphatic tissue (tonsil); 4, cartilage at back of tongue which closes the larynx during swallowing to prevent food going wrong way (epiglottis); 5, nodules at back of tongue around which taste-buds are found in large numbers (circumvallate papillæ); 6, hairs of taste-bud, highly magnified.

When food is put into this extremely complex cavity which we call the mouth, it is subjected to two processes: first it is ground up into small fragments by the teeth, and then it is mixed with the saliva. Saliva, as we have seen, comes chiefly from the three pairs of salivary glands, but the mouth is also lined with moist mucous membrane. Under the microscope, mucous membrane is seen to consist of several rows of rather flattened cells, lying one on top of the other to form a layer something like the horny layer of the skin; these cells, however, contain no keratin or horn, and are in fact quite soft; beneath them is a layer of connective tissue, the corium, in which small glands are embedded. The glands produce a slimy fluid called mucin or mucus, and their ducts are scattered freely over the surface of the mucous membrane.

Saliva is a watery fluid containing some mucus derived from the glands in the mucous membrane, a little protein, and an enzyme or digestive ferment called ptyalin. Normal saliva is slightly alkaline, and ptyalin can act only in an alkaline solution. The amount of alkali in saliva is extremely small—we know from experience that saliva is neither caustic or corrosive—but sufficient is present to

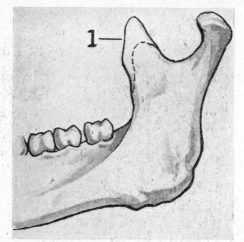

Fig. 9. *The lower jaw. The upright portion at the back of each end of the lower jaw is called the ramus. 1, Attachment to jaw of muscle which covers the temple.*

enable the ptyalin to perform its work.

Between meals, enough saliva is poured out by the salivary glands to keep the mouth pleasantly lubricated, but as soon as food is taken into the mouth the glands become much more active and produce sufficient to soften the food and dissolve some of the particles. If dry food, such as a biscuit, is taken, an extra supply of copious, watery saliva gushes out. Experiments have been performed by the famous Russian scientist, Pavlov, which show that the flow of saliva is governed by the nervous system. When food is taken into the mouth, nerve fibres in the mucous membrane carry a message to the brain, from which fresh messages travel to the salivary glands by way of another set of nerves. So delicate is the nervous mechanism governing salivary secretion that a flow can be produced even by the appearance of food. We all know that the mouth can water at the sight of a favourite dish. This is called a "psychic" flow of saliva, because it is induced not by the presence of food in the mouth, but merely by the thought of that delightful experience.

The salivary glands are diligent little

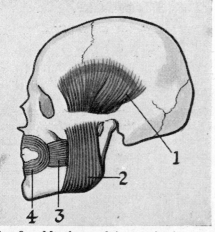

Fig. 8. *Muscles used in mastication. 1, Muscle running from temple to lower jaw (temporal muscle); 2, muscle running from cheekbone to outer surface of jaw (masseter); 3, muscle which flattens the cheeks, running from jaws to muscles of mouth (buccinator); 4, muscle round mouth (orbicularis oris).*

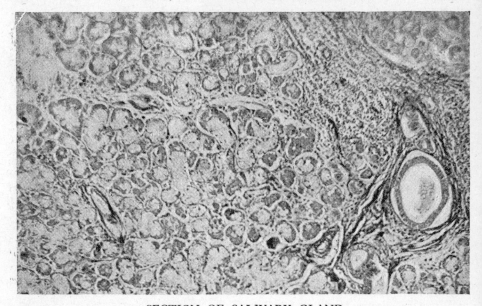

SECTION OF SALIVARY GLAND

The salivary glands are responsible for the first stage in the digestive process. They produce saliva, which keeps the mouth lubricated, softens the food, and dissolves some of its particles.

organs; each of them in the course of a day produces ten or twelve times its own weight in saliva. In man, more than a pint and a half of saliva is poured out in twenty-four hours.

Saliva has no digestive action on proteins and fats, but the enzyme ptyalin begins the digestion of carbohydrates by attacking starch in the food and breaking it down. If you take a solution of starch into your mouth, hold it there for one minute and then transfer it to a test tube, chemical examination shows that all the starch has been converted into sugar. As it is doubtful whether any one spends so long as a whole minute over a single mouthful, it is doubtless rare for the digestion of starch to be completed in the mouth. But when food is swallowed it forms a mass at the upper end of the stomach which the gastric juice does not penetrate completely for about forty minutes. Throughout that time, the ptyalin of the saliva continues the process of breaking up and digesting the starch.

Before the food can reach the stomach, however, it has to be swallowed, and swallowing is quite a complicated feat. As man has adopted the upright position, it might be imagined that swallowing could be left to gravity, that we could use the tongue to push the food into the pharynx and then leave it to drop down the gullet into the stomach by virtue of its own weight. Actually we can swallow equally well when standing on our heads.

The pharynx (Fig. 10) is a muscular chamber opening above into the nasal cavity and below into the œsophagus and larynx. A large number of small muscles come into play during the act of swallowing; most of them are attached to a small horseshoe-shaped bone, the hyoid, which lies in the front of the neck.

The first part of the act of swallowing is voluntary. The food is mixed with saliva until it can be moulded into a smooth oval mass, or bolus, which lies on the back of the tongue; the cheeks are then compressed by the two buccinator muscles, and the mouth is closed; the tongue is raised by the mylohyoid muscle, which runs from the front of the hyoid bone to the lower jaw. The hyoid bone and the larynx are then lifted upwards by means of muscles which attach them to the temporal bone above and this movement forces the food backwards into the pharynx. At the same time, the muscles of the soft palate contract, stretching the soft palate upwards and backwards so that it reaches to the back wall of the pharynx and forms a roof, shutting off the nasal cavity above. This prevents food from being squeezed upwards towards the back of the nasal cavity. Meanwhile the opening of the larynx has been covered over, partly by two triangular cartilages on its

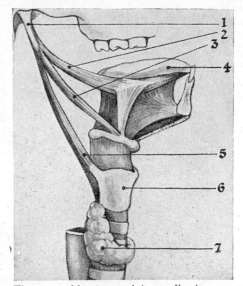

Fig. 11. *Muscles used in swallowing. 1, Projection from base of temporal bone (styloid process); 2, muscle running from temporal bone to tongue (styloglossus); 3, muscle from styloid to hyoid bone; 4, tongue; 5, muscle joining temporal bone to pharynx (stylopharyngeal); 6, thyroid cartilage; its projection forms the Adam's apple; 7, thyroid gland.*

upper surface, and partly by the leaf-like epiglottis, which bends backwards to cover it. The bolus of food slips over the epiglottis and is clasped by the constrictor muscles of the pharynx.

The muscles of the pharynx (Fig. 11) are voluntary muscles, and if examined under the microscope their fibres show the typical ringed or striated appearance. Voluntary muscle tissue forms the wall of the upper part of the œsophagus, but lower down plain (or involuntary) muscle-fibres begin to appear, mingling with the striated fibres, and at its lower end the wall of the œsophagus consists almost entirely of unstriated muscle.

A wave of contraction passes from the muscles of the pharynx down the whole length of the œsophagus, pushing the food before it. The œsophagus relaxes in front of this wave of contraction, allowing the food to slip down easily. At the lower end.

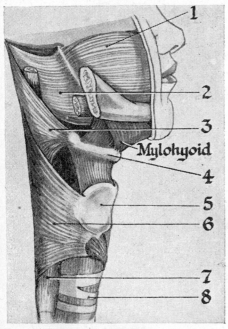

Fig. 10. *Muscles behind the mouth. 1, Muscle used in compressing cheek (buccinator); 2, 3 and 6, muscles of the cavity behind mouth and nose (constrictor muscles of pharynx); 4, bone behind chin to which many muscles are attached (hyoid bone); 5, cartilage helping to cover opening of larynx (thyroid cartilage); 7, gullet; 8, windpipe (trachea). The mylohyoid muscle raises the tongue.*

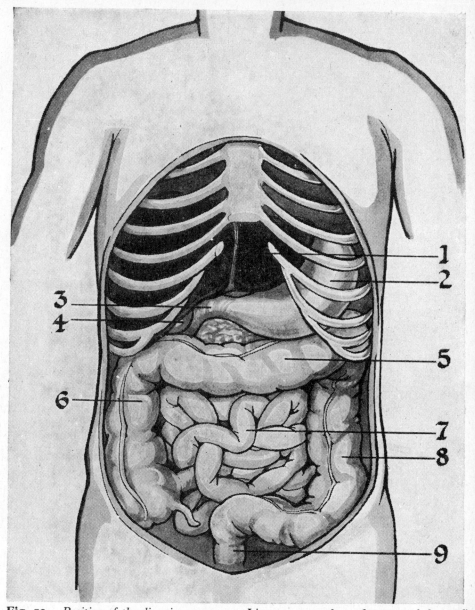

Fig. 12. *Position of the digestive organs. 1, Liver; 2, stomach; 3, first part of the small intestine (duodenum); 4, reservoir for bile produced in the liver (gall-bladder); 5, middle section of large intestine passing below liver to spleen (transverse colon); 6, part of large intestine passing up by right kidney (ascending colon); 7, lower parts of small intestine; 8, part of large intestine passing down by left kidney (descending colon); 9, rectum. After mastication food passes down the gullet across the chest region of the body, without undergoing any further chemical changes. It is when the food enters the series of digestive organs shown here that the real process of digestion is begun by the action of the various juices produced in the stomach, the liver and the pancreas.*

just where the œsophagus enters the stomach, there is a ring or valve of muscle, the cardiac sphincter, which acts like an elastic collar, keeping the entrance to the stomach closed; as the wave of contraction passes down the œsophagus, this valve relaxes and allows the food to pass through. Its name is misleading; it has nothing to do with the heart except that it lies at the end of the stomach nearest that organ. It is the first of a series of four sphincters which lie at different points along the digestive canal.

The whole act of swallowing can be studied by the use of radiography, which shows that food shoots with great speed down the œsophagus, through the thorax, without undergoing any further chemical changes. Having passed through the diaphragm, the œsophagus enters the abdominal cavity (Fig. 12) and expands to form the stomach.

The stomach (Fig. 13) is a J-shaped organ lying close under the ribs on the left-hand side. Its upper end, or fundus, is rounded and usually contains an air-bubble; its lower end curves round and becomes narrower. A ring of muscle, the

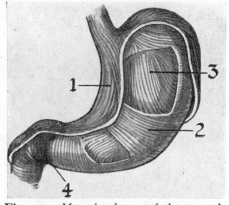

Fig. 14. *Muscular layers of the stomach. 1, Layer of translucent membrane (serous coat); 2, coat of involuntary muscle, in three layers (muscular coat); 3, layer of connective tissue, containing blood vessels (submucous coat); 4, ring of muscle (pylorus).*

pyloric sphincter or pylorus (Fig. 14), similar to that at the lower end of the œsophagus but much stronger and thicker, divides the stomach from the duodenum or upper end of the small intestine. If the stomach is watched for a few moments under the X-rays, waves of contraction are seen to pass down it from the upper end towards the pylorus; these waves follow each other at regular intervals and become more active towards the pyloric end, so that this part of the stomach is sometimes called the pyloric mill. Waves of contraction following each other in this manner are characteristic of movement throughout the digestive canal, and have been given the name of peristaltic waves.

Peristaltic waves are produced by muscular contraction. The stomach wall (Fig. 14) is made up of four layers, the serous coat, the muscular coat and the submucous and mucous layers. The outermost one, the serous coat, consists of shining translucent membrane. The muscular coat consists of involuntary, unstriated fibres, arranged in three distinct layers; those on the outside run longitudinally from end to end of the stomach, those in the next layer are circular and those in the innermost

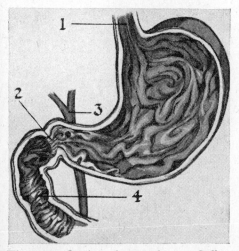

Fig. 13. *Section of stomach. 1, Gullet; 2, ring of muscle, dividing stomach from small intestine (pylorus); 3, bile duct; 4, beginning of small intestine (duodenum).*

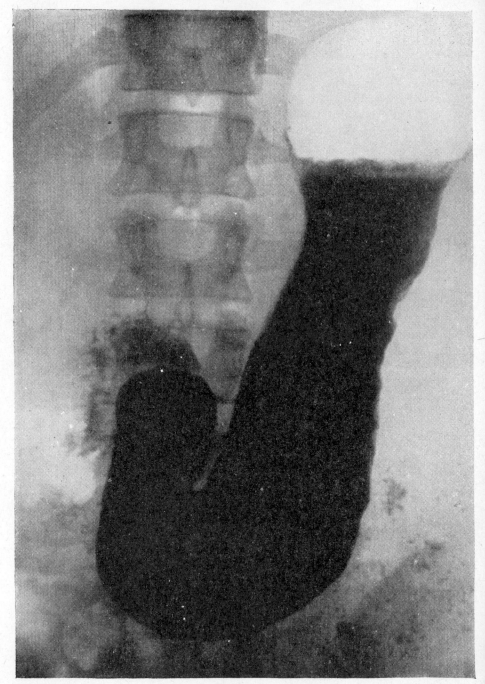

RADIOGRAPH OF STOMACH

This photograph was taken immediately after a meal; the food has passed down the gullet, and fills the stomach in the first stage of the digestive process.

layer are oblique. At the lower end of the stomach the circular fibres become massed to form the pyloric valve. This arrangement of the muscular fibres is beautifully adapted to the needs of the stomach; the circular fibres carry the waves of contraction steadily down towards the duodenum, and the longitudinal and oblique fibres not only reinforce them but make the stomach into such a strong resilient organ that its rupture, except where it has been perforated by an ulcer, is almost unknown.

The mucous membrane of the stomach is attached to the muscular coat by means of loose connective tissue, the submucous layer, which is freely supplied with blood-vessels and lymphatics. When the stomach is empty the mucous membrane is thrown into folds which give the lining a corrugated appearance. The surface is covered with regular oblong cells which produce mucus; each cell produces one drop of mucus at a time, and as each drop forms it almost fills the cell. When the drop is discharged it leaves the cell looking like an empty cup, and for this reason the cells producing mucus are given the name of goblet cells (Fig. 15).

Numerous glands lie in the deeper layers of the mucous membrane and pour gastric juice into the stomach cavity by way of ducts; these ducts are lined with goblet cells like those on the surface. The glands themselves consist of tiny tubules which may be single or branched and are lined with short granular cells which manufacture the

gastric juice. The glands differ slightly according to the region of the stomach in which they are found. In the region of the dome at the top of the stomach, the fundus, the glands are long tubules with short ducts; the cells lining them are square and granular and rest upon a basement membrane. The granules are numerous in the resting stomach and diminish in number after a period of digestion; pepsin, the chief enzyme of gastric juice, is formed from them, and poured into the duct. Cells containing these granules are therefore called peptic cells. Scattered among them are a few cells producing mucus. In addition there are several large round cells, oxyntic cells, lying between the peptic cells and the basement membrane; these produce the hydrochloric acid found in

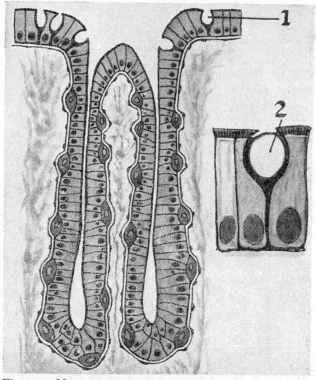

Fig. 15. *Mucous membrane of stomach. 1, Goblet cell; cells covering the surface produce one drop of mucus at a time. When the drop is discharged, it leaves a cup-shaped cavity, hence the name. 2, Goblet cell enlarged.*

gastric juice, and communicate with the central cavity of the gland by means of fine canals running between the peptic cells.

In the body, or central part, of the stomach, glands are comparatively few and are grouped round the opening of the œsophagus. They consist of small single or branched tubules which have a lining of granular cells.

The glands near the pylorus are very long and lined with indistinctly granular cells which may or may not produce pepsin. Although oxyntic cells are most numerous in the glands of the fundus, they are not entirely absent from the glands in the other parts of the stomach except those quite near the pylorus.

A small amount of gastric juice is produced even in the absence of food, but a greater flow begins as soon as food is taken into the mouth. Moreover, as in the case of saliva, the sight, smell or taste of food is sufficient to start the flow, gastric juice produced by one of these being known as "psychic" or "appetite" juice. In the ordinary way digestion in the stomach is begun by the appetite juice; if the meal is unappetizing, however, there may be no appetite juice and for that reason it takes longer to digest an unpleasant meal than a pleasant one. About half an hour after a meal has entered the stomach a second and greater flow of gastric juice occurs and this carries on the work which the appetite juice has begun.

Gastric Juices

The fluid poured out by the gastric glands contains hydrochloric acid and pepsin, as we have seen; it also contains another enzyme called rennin. Pepsin and rennin only begin to act when the hydrochloric acid has neutralized the alkaline saliva and rendered the whole food mass acid. It takes from half an hour to forty minutes for this to occur; the food is mixed with the gastric juice as a result of the rhythmic peristaltic waves passing down the stomach wall. As mixing proceeds the food becomes more fluid and is churned into an acid, semi-solid mass called chyme.

The two enzymes of the stomach have no action on carbohydrates. Pepsin is concerned entirely with proteins, and rennin has only one purpose, to curdle milk. Pepsin breaks down the proteins into simpler substances called peptones. When all the proteins have been reduced to peptones, all the milk curdled and the food converted into acid chyme, the movements of the pyloric end of the stomach become increasingly active and the pylorus relaxes at intervals in order to allow a little of the chyme to squirt through into the duodenum.

The Duodenum

The duodenum is only a small loop of intestine, but it is the region in which digestion is most active. All the foodstuffs are catered for here, and are broken down into forms which the body can use. The duodenum is curved like a horseshoe round the head of one of the chief digestive glands, the pancreas (Fig. 16). The pancreas is shaped rather like an enormous tadpole with a thin tapering tail which stretches behind the stomach as far as the ribs on the left side; the head, which fits into the curve of the duodenum, is a thick solid mass of glandular tissue. A duct runs through the substance of the gland and opens into the duodenum about four inches from the pylorus on the crest of a little eminence called the ampulla of Vater. The bile duct coming from the liver also enters the duodenum at the crest of this ampulla.

Like the stomach, the duodenum and the rest of the small intestine are covered with a serous coat beneath which lies a coat of unstriated muscle, of which the outer fibres are arranged longitudinally and the inner fibres are circular (Fig. 17). But the small intestine has no coat of oblique muscle fibres. Within the muscular coat are the submucous layer and a lining of mucous membrane. The mucous membrane is thickly set with microscopic glands, in the form of small straight tubes lined with oblong cells; these tubes open upon the intestinal canal. Between them are minute finger-like prominences upon the mucous membrane, called the intestinal villi, which project into the canal; these villi are so small and fine that they cannot be seen with the naked eye, but they give a velvety appearance to the lining of the whole of the small intestine. They play an important part in the absorption of food.

The Pancreas

It is chiefly thanks to the pancreas that foodstuffs are reduced to a form in which they can be absorbed. The pancreas (Fig. 16) is a lobulated gland made up of millions of small tubules lined with cells producing digestive fluid; these tubules pour the pancreatic juice into the common duct which carries it to the duodenum. Pancreatic juice contains four enzymes: trypsin which acts on peptones, amylase which acts on starch, lipase which acts on fat and a milk-curdling enzyme which is akin to rennin.

Like ptyalin, pancreatic juice can only act in the presence of alkali, and as the chyme coming through the pylorus is strongly acid it is some time before the pancreatic juice has mixed with it sufficiently to allow duodenal digestion to begin. The pancreatic juice itself is strongly alkaline and easily capable of neutralizing gastric acid. Only a little chyme comes through the pylorus at a time; the valve relaxes to allow a small jet of fluid to squirt into the duodenum and then closes again. As soon as one portion of chyme has been completely mixed with the pancreatic juice, the

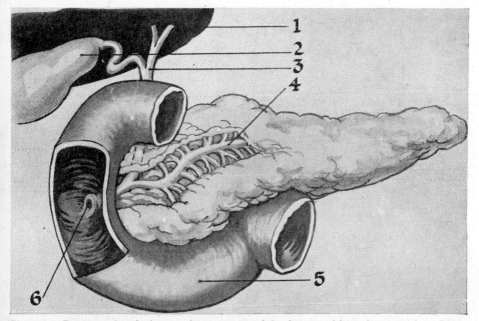

Fig. 16. *Pancreas, in relation to other organs, and duodenum, with section opened. 1, Liver; 2, gall-bladder, which acts as reservoir for bile; 3, channel running from liver and carrying bile to intestine (bile duct); 4, channel carrying juice produced in pancreas (pancreatic duct); 5, first part of small intestine (duodenum); 6, place at which pancreatic duct and bile duct open into the small intestine (ampulla of Vater).*

pylorus opens to allow a fresh instalment through. The action of the pancreatic juice is greatly assisted by juice poured out from the glands of the intestinal mucous membrane; indeed, without the help of this juice, pancreatic juice is completely inactive. Intestinal juice is alkaline, like pancreatic juice, and it helps the trypsin poured out by the pancreas to digest proteins. It also contains an enzyme

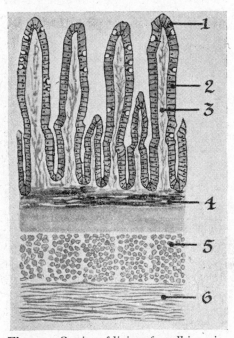

Fig. 17. *Section of lining of small intestine. 1, Cup-shaped cell producing mucus (goblet cell); 2, cells set in mucous membrane (epithelial cells); 3, blood vessels; 4, layer of connective tissue (submucous layer); 5 and 6, inner layer of circular and outer layer of longitudinal muscle fibres.*

which breaks sugar down into the form in which it is most easily absorbed.

Trypsin acts upon the peptones in the chyme by breaking them down into amino-acids. Amylase converts starch into sugar. The action of the fat-splitting enzyme, lipase, is considerably helped by the presence of bile. Bile forms a thin film over the surface of each fat droplet,

and prevents it from coalescing with neighbouring droplets: in short, it changes the fat into an emulsion; this enables lipase to attack the fats much more readily. In the process of digestion fats. are broken down into soaps and fatty acids; the second task of bile is to dissolve soaps and to help lipase to reduce fats to glycerine and fatty acids, in which form they can be absorbed.

Bile is formed in the liver (Fig. 18), the largest gland in the body and the most hard-working. Under the microscope the liver is seen to be made up of hundreds of lobules, each composed of columns of cells which radiate out from a central blood vessel like the spokes of a wheel.

The Liver

Blood is brought to the liver by the great portal vein which collects branches from the whole of the small intestine and enters the liver as a single large vessel; inside the liver it breaks up again into hundreds of small veins which ramify between the lobules (Fig. 19). From these vessels lying between the lobules small capillaries run into the centre of each lobule to join the central vessel. These central vessels unite into one large vein which leaves the liver at its upper border to join the inferior vena cava. Thus the blood coming from the intestine, loaded with the products of protein and carbohydrate digestion, circulates through the substance of the chief factory of the body, an arrangement as simple as it is efficient.

Bile is formed by the liver cells from waste products brought to the liver from other parts of the body by the blood. It is collected up by minute vessels running between the liver cells, and these vessels unite to form tiny bile-ducts running between the liver lobules in company with the branches of the portal vein. These ducts in turn join with each other to form two main vessels (Fig. 20) which unite as soon as they leave the liver; the duct so formed is joined by the duct from

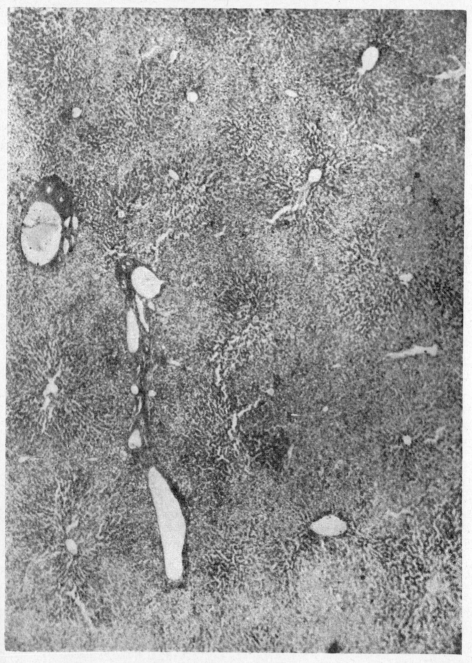

SECTION OF THE LIVER

This highly magnified photograph shows the liver to be made of many hundreds of tiny cells and blood vessels and gives some idea of the continuous activity which goes on in this great chemical factory inside the body. Among its products are bile and glycogen.

M.H.B.—E

the gall-bladder and then runs down to open into the duodenum on the ampulla of Vater. The gall-bladder (Fig. 21) merely serves as a reservoir for bile, which collects in it during the intervals between meals; when food enters the duodenum the gall-bladder contracts and squeezes its contents down the duct into the digestive canal. It is not a very important organ; it is frequently removed from patients suffering from gall-stones, leaving them little the worse; and in some animals the gall-bladder is absent.

Composition of Bile

Bile contains bile salts, bile pigments and cholesterol; it owes its power of emulsifying fats to the presence of bile salts. Like pancreatic juice it is alkaline, and so promotes the activity of pancreatic enzymes; moreover it is a solvent of soaps and fatty acids, so that it takes an important share in normal digestion.

All the while digestion is proceeding, the food is passing down the small intestine, propelled by peristaltic waves, traversing first the jejunum and then the ileum (Fig. 22). Peptones are being broken down into amino-acids, starch into sugars and fats into fatty acids, soaps and glycerine; these substances are absorbed through the walls of the intestinal villi, those minute, finger-like projections of mucous membrane which give a velvety appearance to the lining of the small intestine. The intestinal villi are much more interesting and important than their insignificant appearance would suggest. Each of them contains a small capillary, by which blood enters and leaves the villus, and a minute white vessel called a lacteal, derived from the lymphatic system, into which digested fat is absorbed. Proteins and carbohydrates are absorbed directly into the blood, being taken up by the small capillaries which

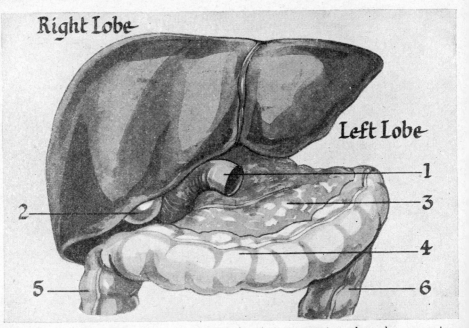

Fig. 18. *Front view of liver: the stomach has been removed to show the organs lying behind it. 1, First part of small intestine (duodenum); 2, gall-bladder; 3, pancreas; 4, middle section of large intestine (transverse colon); 5, first section of large intestine (ascending colon); 6, last section of large intestine (descending colon).*

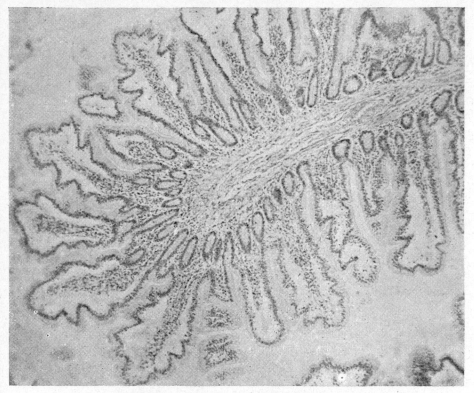

SECTION OF SMALL INTESTINE

This highly magnified photograph shows the finger-like villus, with its blood vessels, and the canals through which the digestive juices, manufactured in the glands, flow into the intestine.

run through the villi. By the time the food reaches the lower end of the ileum, it is a semi-fluid mass, stained dark brown with bile, and made up largely of waste products which have resisted digestion.

At its lower end the small intestine enters the first part of the large intestine, the cæcum (Figs. 23 and 24). In man, the cæcum is a blind pouch from the lower part of which the thin, worm-like appendix dangles. This is a vestige left to us of a much larger cæcum which existed in some of our remote vegetarian ancestors. The appendix, being closed at its lower end, forms a convenient nesting place for any micro-organisms which happen to invade it. If they are organisms capable of causing inflammation, appendicitis develops and an abscess may form

which, if neglected, bursts into the abdominal cavity. In most cases, however, it is possible to diagnose appendicitis before this stage is reached and to remove the inflamed appendix intact.

Another valve of muscular tissue, similar to the pylorus, is found at the point where the small intestine enters the cæcum. Since the lower part of the small intestine is called the ileum, this ring of muscle has been given the name of the ileo-cæcal valve (Fig. 24).

The ileo-cæcal valve normally remains closed until a meal is taken, when it relaxes and allows the end products of the previous meal to pass from the small intestine to the cæcum. For this reason, in training children in regular habits one should see that they evacuate the bowel

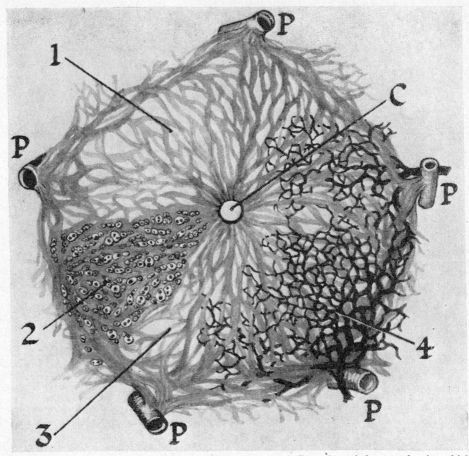

Fig. 19. *Section of liver showing its blood system.* (P) *Branches of the portal vein, which collects blood from the whole of the small intestine, and flows into the liver instead of directly to the heart, like the other veins. 1, Portion showing blood vessels only; 2, portion showing position of cells of liver, with tiny blood vessels running between them; 3, vessels connecting portal vein with central vein (C); this central vein flows back into the main vein of the body (inferior vena cava) and so back to the heart; 4, portion showing blood vessels and bile ducts.*

after a meal, not before it. If they are encouraged to have an evacuation before breakfast, the large bowel will be comparatively empty. After breakfast, however, the ileo-cæcal valve will have allowed the products of the previous day's digestion to pass into the cæcum; if any further attempt to empty the bowel is now postponed until the next morning, it means that waste products accumulate in the large intestine and remain there for twenty-four hours (Fig. 25). Chronic

constipation will be certain to result.

The large intestine consists of the cæcum, the colon, and the rectum (Fig. 26). It is a muscular canal with walls divided into compartments and a wide central cavity. The cæcum lies low down in the right side of the abdomen, and the first part of the colon, called the ascending colon (Fig. 22), stretches up the right side of the abdominal cavity as far as the liver, where it makes a rectangular bend and crosses to the opposite side of the body as the transverse colon (Fig. 22); the third part, the descending colon (Fig. 22), runs down the left side of the abdominal cavity. Waste products enter the cæcum in a semi-fluid condition and are moved along it by peristaltic waves. All along the course of the large intestine water is extracted from the food residues by absorption, so that by the time they reach the lower end of the descending colon they are almost solid and have the appearance of a normal fæcal mass. The lower end of the descending colon is twisted into a loop called the sigmoid flexure (Fig. 26). Here the waste material collects; finally some of it is forced on into the rectum, the last part of the digestive canal. Distension of the rectum gives rise to the desire to defæcate. The lower end of the rectum is closed by another ring of muscular tissue, the anal sphincter (Fig. 26), which is under voluntary control. When the waste products are finally expelled, this sphincter relaxes, and peristaltic waves help to express the contents of the rectum through it; the abdominal muscles also come into play and by contracting bring pressure to bear on the

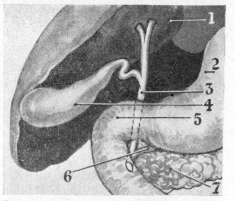

Fig. 21. *Position of gall-bladder. 1, Liver (lifted to show underside); 2, stomach; 3, bile duct, from liver to intestine; 4, gall-bladder; 5, duodenum; 6, pancreatic duct, from pancreas to intestine; 7, pancreas.*

lower end of the large intestine, so helping it to empty itself.

The three main classes of foodstuffs have already been mentioned: they are proteins, carbohydrates and fats.

Classes of Food

Proteins are substances containing nitrogen. Foods containing protein are chiefly derived from animals, common examples being lean meat, such as beef, mutton, pork, chicken and other fowl, fish, cheese, milk and eggs. Small quantities of protein are present in most plants; lentils, peas and beans are rich in it.

Proteins have a complicated chemical structure, the various chemical units which compose any given protein being linked together like a chain. Digestion breaks up the chain so that the separate links can pass into the blood stream. The tissues of the body pick up the various links and build them into their structure to replace those which have been lost by tissue activity. Certain links are essential to life and health.

Carbohydrates include all forms of starch and sugar. Starch is the chief constituent of all cereal foods, including bread, cakes and pastries, porridge, rice,

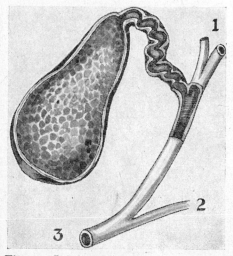

Fig. 20. *Gall-bladder and ducts. 1, Channels running from liver; 2, pancreatic duct; 3, bile duct, running into intestine.*

sago and tapioca, sugar, and of all sweets and preserves, such as jam, treacle and honey. Most fruits and many vegetables contain sugar; potatoes consist largely of starch, and so do bananas. Carbohydrates, which are the most easily absorbed foods, should form two-thirds of our diet. When this proportion is exceeded nutrition suffers with harmful results.

Fats are present in meat, bacon, dripping, butter, lard, suet, margarine and yolk of egg. Fat can be used as fuel by the tissues almost as readily as carbohydrates,

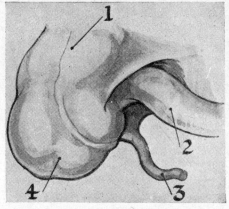

Fig. 23. *First part of large intestine (cæcum). 2, Last part of small intestine (ileum); 3, appendix; 4, cæcum; 1, second part of large intestine (ascending colon).*

but only if carbohydrate is being used at the same time. In the normal diet, fat and protein should each form about one-sixth of the total quantity of food taken.

Besides the three main classes of foodstuffs, the living body requires those accessory food factors known as vitamins, certain mineral salts and water. Apparently we are not particularly good at judging the right proportions for ourselves. It has been estimated in the last few years that over fifty per cent of the population in this country is consuming either not enough or not the right kind of food to suit the body's needs.

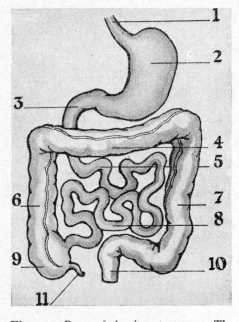

Fig. 22. *Parts of the digestive tract. The gullet (œsophagus) (1) bringing food from the mouth. This expands to form the stomach (2). Food then passes into the duodenum (3) the first part of the small intestine. It then goes through the other parts of the small intestine, the jejunum (5), and the ileum (8), and thence waste products enter the first part of the large intestine, the cæcum (9). The appendix (11) dangles from the cæcum. The large intestine continues as the ascending colon (6), crosses the body as the transverse colon (4) and runs down as the descending colon (7). Finally, the waste material enters the last part of the digestive tract, the rectum (10) and so leaves the body.*

Food as Fuel

The chief purpose of food is to act as fuel for the body. Every living cell is active and needs energy to perform its work; it obtains this energy from food which, with the help of oxygen, it can burn up, or oxidize, in much the same way as a fire burns fuel. As a result of this combustion certain waste products are formed in the tissues which the body must eliminate. One such waste product is carbon dioxide, which is thrown off by the lungs; others are produced by the combustion of protein, and are excreted by the action of the kidneys in the forms of urea and ammonia.

Food has a second purpose, that of replacing outworn tissues. Carbohydrates can be readily employed as fuel, but protein is more useful as a body-building substance. Any excess of protein not needed for the repair of the tissues is used up as fuel. It will be obvious that a growing child or young person will need more protein than an older person, because, in addition to replacing protein which has been lost by the ordinary activities of the cells, he must take in enough to build the fresh tissues demanded by the process of growth. Similarly, a person who lives an active and strenuous life will require more protein than a person who sits at a desk all day and whose activities are less physical than mental.

Measuring Food Values

The amount of energy which a particular class of foodstuff is capable of liberating when burned by the body cells can be estimated. It is usually reckoned in the form of heat and measured in terms of calories. A food calorie is the amount of heat required to raise one kilogramme of water 1 degree centigrade. A few years ago, the Nutrition Committee of the British Medical Association decided that the average man required 3,000 calories a day as food; women and children required less but boys between the ages of fourteen and eighteen were bound to need as much as a full-grown man because they were growing rapidly and, as a rule, taking a great deal of exercise.

Standard Diet

The calorie values of the various foodstuffs have been worked out: 1 gramme of protein is equivalent to 4.1 calories; 1 gramme of fat is equivalent to 9.3 calories; 1 gramme of carbohydrates is equivalent to 4.1 calories.

A standard diet would contain 100 grammes of protein, 100 grammes of fat and 400 grammes of carbohydrates a day, and would have a value of approximately 3,000 calories. Carbohydrate is the cheapest source of calories, since it includes bread and all cereal and starchy foods, potatoes and the commoner vegetables. Protein has the same calorie value as carbohydrates but cannot be used so readily for fuel; moreover, proteins such as meat, eggs, milk and cheese are relatively expensive foods. Fats have a high calorie value but the human digestion is not equipped for dealing with them in excessive amounts.

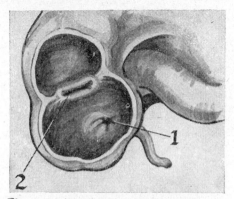

Fig. 24. *Beginning of large intestine. 1, Entrance to appendix; 2, ring of muscle dividing end of small intestine from beginning of large intestine (ileo-cæcal valve).*

On the whole our bodies are designed to take a diet which consists largely of carbohydrate, but we cannot afford to go short of the other two constituents. Unfortunately in many parts of the world people, by reason of their poverty, live on a diet which consists almost entirely of carbohydrate, and malnutrition and ill-health are the result.

Water is present in nearly everything we eat, but in addition we require at least four to five pints daily. This can be taken in the form of various drinks such as tea, coffee or beer, all of which consist mostly of flavoured water. Water helps to dissolve waste products in the tissues and to carry

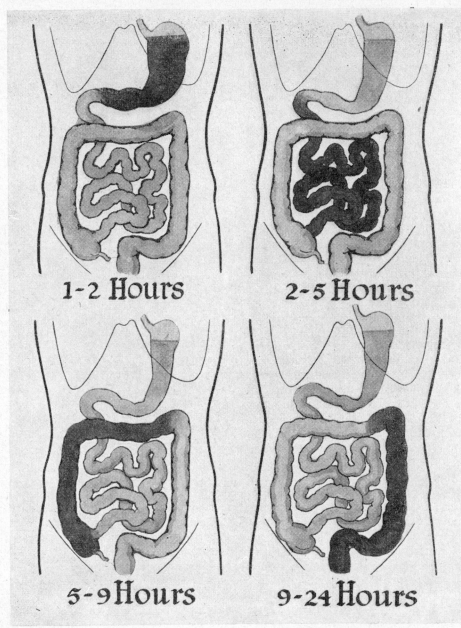

Fig. 25. *Diagram showing approximate position of food during passage through the intestines. In the first two hours, the food passes down the gullet into the stomach. During the next three hours, it passes through the three parts of the small intestine (duodenum, jejunum and ileum). After about five hours, it goes into the first parts of the large intestine (ascending and transverse colon). Finally, it passes into the last parts of the large intestine (descending colon and sigmoid flexure) and so to the rectum. Digestion goes on in the stomach and small intestine, and the waste passes into the large intestine.*

them to the kidneys where they are eliminated in solution and finally expelled from the body. As much as seventy per cent of the body weight is contributed by water alone. It is interesting to reflect that though we contain a number of minerals made up into complicated chemical patterns, we achieve bulk and importance only by means of the kitchen tap.

Minerals

The minerals in our bodies reach us as constituents of meat, milk, cereals and vegetables, in the form of salts of sulphur, phosphorus, sodium, potassium, magnesium, calcium, iron and copper. In the absence of these mineral salts we should die. Iron and copper, for instance, are needed to make blood; calcium and phosphorus are essential to the bones and

teeth; the thyroid gland requires the iodine found in sodium and potassium salts in order to fulfil its function.

Finally, a healthy life is impossible unless the diet contains certain accessory food factors which have been called vitamins. So far, about half a dozen vitamins have been identified.

Vitamin A is found in milk, butter, eggs and animal fats, cod liver oil and halibut liver oil, while carrots and green vegetables contain a substance called carotene which is transformed in the body into vitamin A. Lack of this vitamin interferes with growth, and leads, not to any separate disease, but to mild ill health and poor resistance to infection. It may cause the onset of xerophthalmia, an inflammation of the eyes resulting in severe cases in blindness, and it makes the patient liable

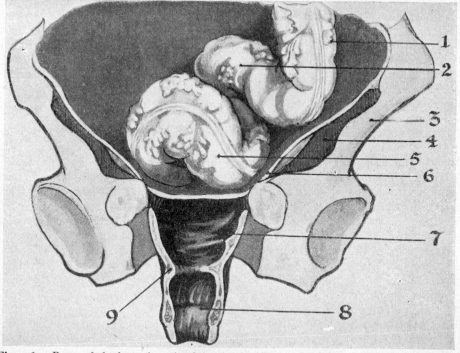

Fig. 26. *Parts of the large intestine lying in the pelvis. 1, Third part of large intestine, which passes near the left kidney (descending colon); 2, loop at end of descending colon (sigmoid flexure); 3, bone of pelvis; 4, section of muscle; 5, pelvic colon; 6, membrane lining abdominal cavity (peritoneum); 7, section of rectum; 8, end of digestive canal (anus); 9, ring of muscle at end of intestine (anal sphincter).*

to fall victim to infections of the skin and mucous membranes, especially to broncho-pneumonia and inflammation of the intestines. Night-blindness, or difficulty in seeing in the twilight, is due to changes in the retina following lack of vitamin A.

Vitamin B, which is really a group of vitamins, is found especially in peas, beans, lentils, the husks of grain (and therefore in wholemeal but not in white bread) and in eggs. The whole vitamin B group is necessary for health and growth. Lack of it may lead in eastern lands to beriberi or pellagra and anywhere to the development of skin eruptions.

Vitamin C is found in fresh foodstuffs, especially the juice of oranges and lemons, and in raw vegetables. Lack of it leads to the development of scurvy.

Vitamin D

Vitamin D is present in fish liver oil, yolk of egg and, to a small extent, in animal fats. It is absent from vegetable oils. Lack of it leads to the development of rickets. Cow's milk contains lime and calcium as well as vitamin D, so that it is a good preventive of rickets.

This vitamin is also essential for the formation of normal teeth. In 1929 Lady Mellanby showed that when a diet is deficient in vitamin D and mineral salts, the jawbones become soft and deformed and the teeth develop poorly. This is especially true if large quantities of cereals are given. Oatmeal, for example, is definitely bad for the teeth. Moreover, teeth which are poorly formed owing to a faulty diet are more liable to decay than those which develop well from the start. If vitamin D is added to the diet and cereals are omitted, the decayed areas tend to harden again and so the progress of the disease is checked.

A fifth vitamin, vitamin E, is present in lettuce, whole wheat, egg-yolk and liver. This is called the reproductive vitamin. It is worth noting, however, that while a child is being breast-fed the mother needs vitamin B to maintain the flow of milk; vitamins A and D are also used in larger quantities at this time than at others, so that reproduction and the rearing of young calls for a diet rich in all the vitamins, not for vitamin E alone.

We have now considered all the constituents of a normal diet and may discuss the various ways in which a balanced diet can be supplied to the body.

Waste Material

Whatever we eat will contain some waste material which cannot be digested and absorbed. In fruits, for example, much of the bulk is made up of a fibrous material called cellulose upon which the digestive juices have no action. Coarse waste material of this kind is called roughage, and serves a useful purpose by stimulating the bowel to contract and push the food-mass onwards. Those who eat a diet deficient in roughage are likely to suffer from constipation; the coarse fibres of cellulose act as a gentle irritant to the walls of the intestine and so behave like a natural aperient.

Aperients other than natural ones should rarely be necessary. If the bowel wall is constantly stimulated by chemical purgatives, it ceases to respond to any other sort of stimulus and it becomes necessary to take a daily dose of some kind of medicine before it will act at all. This is an unhealthy state of affairs; the bowel will respond to quite gentle stimuli provided it is not bullied and dragooned into action by such artificial treatment. Once it has grown used to bullying, however, it seems to understand nothing else. Children, especially, should not be given purgatives except in the last resort; nearly all children can be cured of constipation by increasing the amount of fruit and vegetables in their diet. It has been said that constipation in later life is caused by the first dose of castor oil given to the newly-born infant by the midwife, and though this statement is an exaggeration it contains just sufficient truth to make it worth while remembering.

A balanced diet contains carbohydrates, protein and fat in the proportions 8 : 1 : 1, respectively. Much of the carbohydrate part of the diet consists, nowadays, of white flour and sugar, which are not ideal foods in that they are deficient in vitamins and mineral salts. Some of the protein is derived from plants but most of it is eaten in the form of meat or fish. Cereal foods contain a little protein, but not much. Roughly speaking, about half our protein intake ought to be supplied in the form of meat, fish, cheese, or eggs and the other half as vegetable protein. Fat is usually eaten in the form of butter or margarine, and as the animal fats present in meat.

Proteins

Proteins vary in their nutritive value. Animal protein is first-class protein, as are also cheese and milk. Among fish, the common herring is an excellent source of the best protein available; eggs are also extremely valuable. Cheese has, perhaps, received too little recognition as a source of protein food except among labourers and manual workers. Their "snack" dinner of bread and cheese and an onion constitutes an admirably balanced meal. Among wealthy people there is danger of taking too much protein. Those who begin the day with fish, sausages, or eggs and bacon, lunch off meat or game with cheese at the end of the meal, dine their way through several courses including fish and meat or poultry, and end up in the small hours with lobster mayonnaise or more eggs and bacon, are asking a great deal of their liver and still more of their kidneys. They are eating a grossly unbalanced diet.

Carbohydrates and fat can be used alternatively as fuel by the body, but only up to a certain point; they have to maintain a definite proportion to each other. Carbohydrate is used more readily than fat as a fuel, and it seems that fat is only properly burned up when plenty of carbo-hydrate is being burned at the same time. It is like trying to make a fire with coal and coke: if you get the coal burning well first, you can add the coke and it will take fire, but if you attempt to start the fire with coke you generally fail dismally. The carbohydrate represents the coal, so to speak, which will get the coke going. If, for some reason, sufficient carbohydrate is not available, acid half-burned products of fat appear in the blood stream and give rise to the condition of ketosis, or acidosis, as it used to be called, in which the patient suffers from headache and vomiting, and in severe cases may pass into coma. This state of affairs is sometimes seen in people who are starving and who have been using up the fat reserves of the body as fuel in the absence of carbo-hydrate. It may also occur in a mild form among children who are eating too much fat in proportion to carbohydrate; but it is specially liable to appear in patients suffering from diabetes.

Good Diet

The basic components of a good diet are dairy produce, fresh fruit and vegetables and wholemeal bread. Starting with these as a foundation, meat and fish may be added in moderate quantities. Cereals offer a source of vegetable protein and help to provide roughage, but they have disadvantages which makes it wise to take them in moderation.

We have considered the breakdown of the food in the course of digestion and we know the types of food essential to health. It remains to consider what happens to the food once it has been absorbed into the body through the wall of the small intestine.

In the small intestine (Fig. 22) starch is broken down into sugar, and the sugar is in turn broken down into glucose, the simplest form of sugar obtainable. Glucose is absorbed through the walls of the intestinal villi directly into the blood stream. The blood vessels coming from the intestine unite with each other to form larger and larger vessels until they finally form the portal vein. This enters the liver and there breaks up, distributing its blood throughout the organ by means of small vessels running between the lobules (Fig. 19). Thus the glucose absorbed from the small intestine is carried directly to the cells of the liver.

Metabolism

The process of building up and breaking down of foodstuffs by the body cells is called metabolism, and the liver (Fig. 18) is the headquarters of this process; it is an active factory and its cells are never idle. As soon as glucose reaches them they set to work to turn it into a material called glycogen, in which form it can be stored. If the liver of an animal is examined immediately after a carbohydrate meal it is found to be full of glycogen, but if an animal which has had no meal for some hours is examined the liver is found to contain no glycogen at all. Glycogen is also stored in the muscles: the muscle cells withdraw sugar from the blood stream for this purpose. When the muscles contract, the stored glycogen is converted into sugar and used as fuel. Muscular activity converts glucose into lactic acid which is carried off in the blood stream; the blood delivers the lactic acid to the liver, which builds it up into glycogen again, and stores it for future use.

The tissues remove glucose from the blood stream at a steady rate and the liver, equally steadily, converts its stock of glycogen back to glucose, thus maintaining the supply of glucose in the blood at a constant level. So long as the blood sugar remains at this fixed level, none of it escapes through the kidneys, so that in a normal man the urine contains no sugar.

Importance of Insulin

The liver can make glycogen not only from glucose and lactic acid but from excess of protein absorbed from the intestine; but it cannot make glycogen from fat. The liver could not make and store glycogen without the help of insulin, a material poured into the blood stream from the pancreas (Fig. 16). So far we have considered the pancreas only as a source of the juice poured into the duodenum which plays such an important part in digestion. If the pancreas is examined under the microscope it is found to consist mostly of the cells forming pancreatic juice and the ducts leading from them; but scattered among these cells are little islets of tissue of a different kind. These are the islets of Langerhans (Fig. 27), which

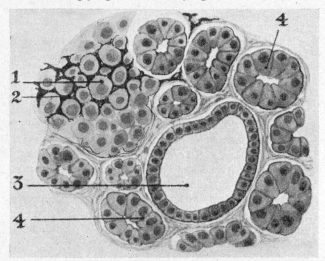

Fig. 27. *Section of pancreas. Most of the cells of the pancreas are engaged in forming pancreatic juice, which flows through the pancreatic ducts into the intestine. But within the pancreas are: 1, Islets of tissue different from the rest of the pancreas, which are engaged in manufacturing insulin which goes directly into the blood stream (islets of Langerhans); 2, blood vessels; 3, main pancreatic duct; 4, small pancreatic ducts.*

manufacture insulin. They are not in communication with the pancreatic duct; their cells pour fluid directly into the blood stream. The pancreas, in fact, is not only a digestive gland but an endocrine gland, that is to say, a gland manufacturing an "internal secretion," as it is called. An internal secretion is an active substance which is poured by a gland directly into the blood stream. Other glands having secretions of this kind are the pituitary, the thyroid, the parathyroid, the supra-renals and the ovaries and testicles. The pancreas, however, is the only one which manufactures insulin.

Insulin has two important tasks to perform: it enables the body cells to use sugar, and it enables the liver to store sugar in the form of glycogen. Patients suffering from diabetes form little or no insulin, and the results which follow the lack of this important substance have thrown considerable light on the metabolism of sugar in the body.

Digesting Fat

Fat is absorbed from the intestine not into the blood stream, but into small lymphatics called the lacteals. These unite to form the thoracic duct, which runs up through the thorax to open into one of the blood vessels near the heart. Nearly all the fat in the food is absorbed, very little being excreted in the faeces unless the bile duct is blocked; in the absence of bile, fat digestion is greatly hindered. The fat from the digestive canal, then, is carried up in the thoracic duct to be poured into the blood in the form of finely divided droplets. The liver and the tissues remove fat from the blood as it circulates round the body. Excess of fat is stored in the fat depots of the body. It is normal to have a layer of fat beneath the skin, which not only provides a protective buffer against the rude shocks of the world, but helps to conserve heat loss from the body surface and to provide those gently rolling contours which are essential to beauty. Other fat depots in the human body are found in the region of the kidneys and in the curtain of fatty material which hangs from the lower border of the stomach and provides a blanket for the abdominal organs.

The fat in these depots is derived partly from fat taken as food, but some of it is also contributed by carbohydrates taken to excess. The body has the power of converting carbohydrates into fat; hibernating animals make use of this capacity to store up large deposits of fat in the autumn upon which they can draw in order to live through the winter.

Fat as Fuel

The liver as usual plays a part in fat metabolism; fats are brought to it from the depots to be broken down into a form in which they can be used as fuel. Fat is not only a reserve form of fuel but takes part in the construction of every cell in the body. This intra-cellular fat is essential to the life of the cell and persists even during starvation. It has been said already that the tissue cells, especially those of muscles, can use fat as a fuel as long as plenty of carbohydrate is being used as well.

The proteins taken in as food are absorbed, after digestion, into the blood vessels in the intestinal villi and are carried thence to the liver. They are then in the form of amino-acids. Some part of them pass directly through the liver in the blood stream and are carried round the body to the various tissues and organs, the cells of which take them up and use them for building and repair. The rest of the amino-acids are subjected to a process in the liver which breaks them down into two kinds of substances, one containing nitrogen and the other free from it. The substance containing nitrogen is then converted into urea by the liver cells and passes into the blood stream to be excreted by the kidneys as a waste product. The remaining nitrogen-free material is converted into glucose by the liver and can then be used as fuel.

CHAPTER VI

WHY AND HOW
WE BREATHE

PURPOSE OF BREATHING: NECESSITY OF OXYGEN FOR LIFE: NOSE, NOSTRILS
AND THROAT: LARYNX AND TRACHEA: COMPOSITION OF LUNGS: AIR
CONTENT OF LUNGS: EFFECTS OF CARBON DIOXIDE: VARIATIONS IN
OXYGEN DEMAND: OXYGEN IN THE BLOOD: SHORTNESS OF BREATH

IT WAS early suspected that one of the purposes of respiration was to get rid of the waste fumes associated with the flame of life within. We now know that such is, indeed, one of the uses of the respiratory act; though we understand by the flame of life a much more subtle affair than the imagination of our ancestors pictured.

Oxygen Supply

We are sustained by a constant series of miniature explosions, or acts of chemical combination, not unlike those which take place in the cylinders of an internal combustion engine. For these explosions a steady supply of oxygen is necessary; and the positive purpose of respiration is to draw into the lungs, where it can be taken up by the blood constantly circulating through them, a continuous fresh supply of air—which is oxygen diluted with four times its volume of nitrogen. Within the body there is a comparatively small reserve of this essential element; we cannot go on living for hours or days at a time without a fresh supply, as we can without fresh supplies of food or water. A pillow over our face, or a blockage in our windpipe, and we are dead from oxygen-want before many minutes have passed. The fire in every one of our cells goes out, effectively smothered.

The atmosphere contains about twenty per cent of oxygen; and all natural waters in which plants or animals live contain a certain amount of it loosely dissolved in them, apart from the oxygen which, in a chemically combined state, makes up by far the greater part of the weight of pure water itself. Very simple microscopic organisms, composed of but a single cell, obtain oxygen direct from the air or water in which they live, without any elaborate specialized breathing apparatus, just as they obtain food and get rid of their waste without any specialized oral or excretory organs. Animals above a very low stage of development are, however, much more complicated. Their bodies are composed of millions of cells, the greater number of which are not in direct contact with the atmosphere or the water in which they live. Yet each of these cells must be constantly supplied with oxygen. In the chapter dealing with blood and its circulation is described the machinery by means of which oxygen, having been taken in through a specialized part of the body, is distributed to each of our body cells. Here we are concerned with the means whereby oxygen is taken into the body from the surrounding air.

Process of Breathing

When we are at rest, certain muscular contractions, which involve visible movements of the chest wall, take place, without any conscious effort of our will, some seventeen times a minute. When we are working or otherwise actively employed, the contractions occur more frequently. Each of these respiratory acts involves two movements, inhalation and exhalation, the first of which causes air to be drawn into the chest, and the second causes it to be expelled.

Man's breathing apparatus consists of the nostrils, the pharynx, the larynx, the trachea, and the bronchial tubes, with the bronchioles and air cells, or alveoli, which make up the essential part of the lungs. Air enters the body through the nostrils (Fig. 1). If these are in any way obstructed, or if there is an exceptional demand for air by the body, the nasal openings are supplemented by the mouth. As a habit, breathing through the mouth is undesirable, because that aperture is not furnished with the protective mechanism which safeguards the nasal entrance. The nostrils join the oral orifice at the back of the mouth, the common chamber being called the pharynx.

Parts of the Nose

The nose may be considered as having an external and an internal part (Fig. 2). The external nose begins above at the slight depression midway between the two eyes. Below, it ends at the top of the upper lip. Its sides and front have a bony structure above, making up what is called the bridge of the nose, and a flexible, elastic part below, known as the *alæ nasi*, or wings of the nose. In the walls of the lower part are small plates of cartilage, or gristle, which can be moved by tiny muscles attached to them. In this way, the nostrils can be expanded and contracted. The skin of the nose is closely adherent to the bony and cartilaginous tissue beneath it. Compared with the rest of the face, there is a poor circulation of blood through this part of it. Wounds of the surface of the nose, consequently, usually take a long time to heal. Thus, also, is partly explained the permanent

dilation of the surface blood vessels of the nose in people who suffer from certain forms of indigestion, or who drink too continuously, or who are more than usually exposed to the weather.

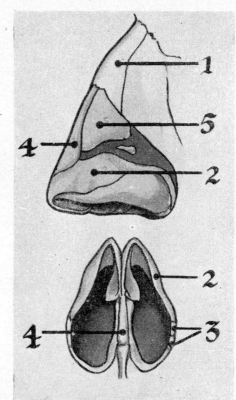

Fig. 1. *Parts of the nose. 1, Bony part of nose, running from between the eyes (nasal bone); 2, flexible, elastic part, movable by muscles (wings of nose, or alæ nasi); 3, piece of cartilage forming part of outer wall of nostril (sesamoid); 4, cartilage dividing cavity of nose into two sides (septum); 5, triangular piece of cartilage.*

The cavity of the nose is divided into two sides by a central cartilaginous septum. These two side chambers—the so-called nasal fossæ—lead from the anterior nares, or outer openings of the nostrils, to the pharynx at the back of the mouth. It may be seen that for a third of an inch the skin of the face is continued to form

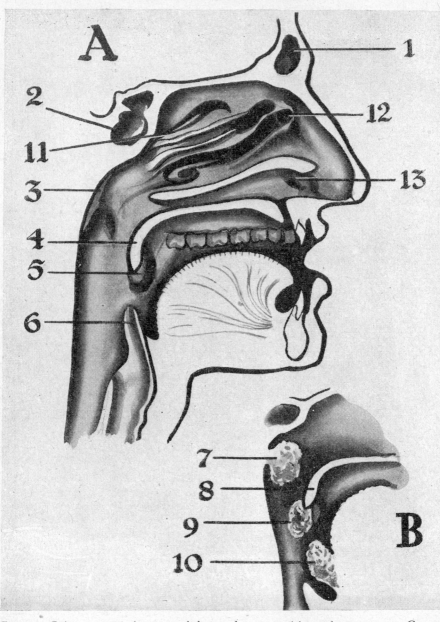

Fig. 2. *Side section of the nose and throat, showing cavities and passages. 1, Cavity at head of nose (frontal sinus); 2, wedge-shaped cavity behind nose (sphenoidal sinus); 3, tonsil lying between nose and throat (naso-pharyngeal tonsil); 4, fleshy part of the soft palate (uvula); 5, tonsil; 6, membrane which closes over windpipe to prevent food going wrong way (epiglottis); 7, mass of spongy tissue between back of nose and throat (adenoid); 8, part of uvula; 9 and 10, tonsils; 11 and 12, cavities situated near the perforated bone through which passes the nerve of smell (posterior ethmoidal sinus and anterior ethmoidal sinus); 13, channel through which tears are carried from the tear glands (lachrymal duct).*

the inner lining of the nostril. This part of the inner coat of the nose is furnished with numerous hairs, called vibrissæ, which serve to hold up dust, insects and other foreign bodies in the air we breathe, and prevent them from reaching the more delicate internal parts. Thus is explained the not infrequent occurrence of inflammation of the little sebaceous glands of the roots of these hairs just within the nostril, as a result of infection. These tiny boils are often very painful and very disfiguring. Further in, the nostrils are lined with a delicate membrane, the cells of which are furnished with microscopic hairs or cilia. These are in constant motion, sweeping outwards the mucus which the cells secrete and any germs that have become caught in the mucus.

Lining of Nose

The nasal lining is equipped with numerous small glands which secrete mucus. This serves not only to trap invading germs but also to moisten the air before it reaches the lungs. There is a fairly good blood supply to the internal parts of the nose, as those who suffer from epistaxis, or nose-bleeding, know. This surface blood supply warms the air passing over it—which is one of the reasons why nose breathing is hygienically to be preferred to mouth breathing. The septum of the nose is almost entirely composed of cartilage; but at the hindermost end it is bony in basic composition (Fig. 1). The nasal septum is nearly always a bit out of the straight, the cartilage generally deviating slightly to the right. This deviation is in some cases so extreme as to constitute a real obstruction to breathing; and an operation may become necessary.

At the higher part of the internal nose is a sensitive surface for the reception of the impressions which stimulate the sense of smell. This is known as the olfactory surface, and in it are the numerous endings of the collecting branches of the olfactory nerve, which takes the messages to the brain, where they are interpreted and appear in our consciousness as the various scents and smells, pleasant and unpleasant, which we experience. Opening into the nostrils are the ends of the lachrymal ducts which carry the tears from the tear-glands in the corners of the eyes. These tears are constantly being produced. They pass across the surface of the eye, cleaning it of fine dust, and empty into the upper end of the lachrymal duct on the inner corner of the orbit.

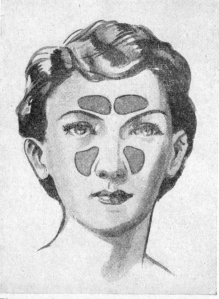

Fig. 3. *Air cavities in the bones of the face. There are cavities in the forehead bones (frontal sinuses) and the upper jawbones (antrums of Highmore).*

Projecting into the side walls of the nostril are three membrane-covered ridges on each side. These are the turbinated bones. Between these ridges, or *conchæ*, are spaces known as meati. Into the lowest of the three meati the lachrymal duct opens. Into the middle meatus open the frontal sinus (Fig. 3), the antrum of Highmore and anterior ethmoidal sinus. Into the highest meatus open the sphenoidal and posterior ethmoidal sinuses.

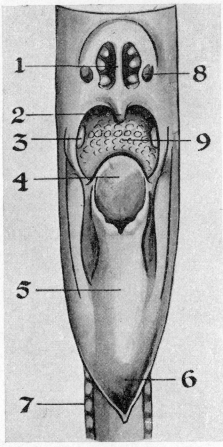

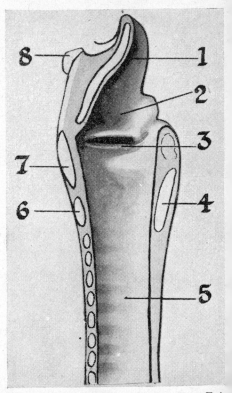

This, also, tends to hinder the escape of discharge. Sinusitis, or inflammation of one of the sinuses, is, therefore, apt to be a very serious and painful condition, which requires expert surgical treatment. At the back, the nasal passages open into the nasal pharynx, the connecting link, as it were, between the air passage and the pharynx proper (Fig. 4), which is common both to the mouth and the nose. In the walls of the nasal pharynx are masses of lymphatic tissue, the chief purpose of which seems to be to collect germs that have succeeded in passing the first lines of defence. Not infrequently, especially in

Fig. 4. *Throat cavity connecting with nose and mouth, seen from behind. 1, Wall of cartilage, dividing nasal cavity into two (nasal septum); 2, uvula; 3, tonsil; 4, epiglottis; 5, lowest cartilage ring of larynx (cricoid cartilage); 6, gullet (œsophagus); 7, windpipe (trachea); 8, channel leading to ear drum (eustachian tube); 9, root of tongue.*

These sinuses, or accessory cavities, of the nose are liable to become infected by germs breathed in, because their lining membrane is continuous with the lining membrane of the nostrils. The orifices of the sinuses at their junction with the nostrils are so small that if they become infected, it is very difficult for the purulent secretion to drain away. Moreover, the lining membrane of the nostrils is particularly liable to swell when inflamed.

Fig. 5. *Side section of larynx. 1, Epiglottis; 2, beginning of larynx (vestibule); 3, vocal cord; 4 and 6, lowest cartilage rings of larynx (cricoid cartilages); 5, lower part of windpipe (trachea); 7, upper cartilage of larynx—the Adam's apple (thyroid cartilage); 8, U-shaped bone to which many throat muscles are attached (hyoid bone).*

children living in unhealthy conditions, these lymphatic masses become poisoned and enlarged, and more or less completely block the nasal airway. These are the so-called adenoid growths (Fig. 2).

The pharynx proper affords common transit for both air breathed in by the nose and food taken by the mouth; thence, these widely differing forms of intake find their way into the body by separate tracks (Fig. 7). At the back of the pharynx are the openings of the gullet, leading to the stomach, and the windpipe, leading to the lungs. The upper part of the windpipe is called the larynx (Figs. 5 and 6), or talking-box, the lower the trachea. The windpipe consists of a series of cartilaginous rings or hoops, continuous in front, but not at the back, where they would press on the gullet which lies immediately behind them (Fig. 6). The rings are covered by an elastic tissue which also

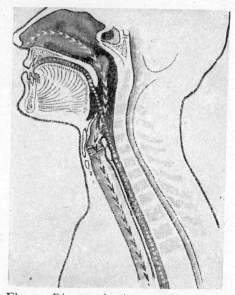

Fig. 7. *Diagram showing passages taken by food and air. The dots show path of food, from the mouth across the throat into the gullet. The arrows show path of air, through the nose, across the throat, into the windpipe.*

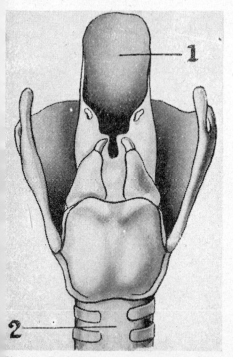

Fig. 6. *Back view of larynx, or talking-box. 1, Epiglottis, which closes over the larynx during eating; 2, windpipe.*

joins their posterior ends, completing the circular tube wall. This arrangement allows for free movement of the neck in every direction.

The cartilaginous framework of the larynx differs widely from that of the rest of the windpipe, and its inner lining is so specialized as to play an important part in our speech. The opening into the laryngeal tube from the pharynx is known as the glottis. Slanting above this is a cartilaginous-framed membrane called the epiglottis (Fig. 2), which acts as a sort of trap-door to the windpipe. When we are eating and are about to swallow food, the laryngeal cartilages are raised towards the epiglottis so that the glottis is temporarily shut. Food is thus prevented from "going down the wrong way." Coincident with this protective act in the process of swallowing, is another reflex act little less important, the raising of the soft palate so as to close the back of the nostrils where they open into the pharynx, thus

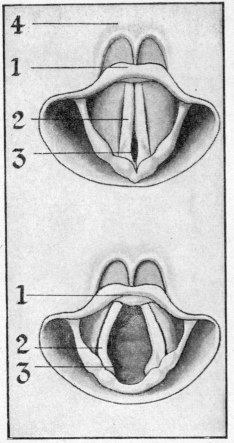

Fig. 8. *Larynx open and shut, seen from above. 1, Epiglottis; 2, vocal cord, movable by muscles to produce sound; 3, opening from throat into larynx (glottis); 4, base of tongue.*

hindering regurgitation of food through the nose (Fig. 8).

Just below the opening from the pharynx, that is, just below the glottis, there are two folds of lining membrane with minute ligaments stretched obliquely across the tube from back to front. These are the vocal cords (Fig. 8). Their attachments at the back are movable by delicate muscles. The vocal cords are taut, and as air passes by them they vibrate so as to produce various sounds. Numerous muscles are connected with the vocal cords and with their points of attachment. By contractions of these muscles the cords can be shortened or lengthened, made thicker or thinner, separated or brought together with the utmost fineness of gradation. The topmost of the cartilages of the larynx is known as the thyroid cartilage (Fig. 5), and is much bigger and more prominent than any of the others. It constitutes the so-called Adam's apple; ligaments and muscles connect it with a queer little U-shaped bone, the hyoid bone. The lowest ring of the larynx, known as the cricoid cartilage (Fig. 5), also differs from the others. It is the only ring in which the cartilage goes completely round. Therefore, it is liable to press somewhat firmly on the gullet, which explains the marked discomfort we sometimes experience at the upper part of the throat when we swallow an insufficiently masticated lump of food.

The Windpipe

The windpipe (Fig. 9) is about four to five inches long, and about an inch wide at its widest part. At its lower end, which is situated on a level with the fourth dorsal vertebra, it divides into two tubes known as bronchi. The right bronchus is shorter and more nearly vertical than the left, which explains the frequency with which foreign bodies that find their way into the windpipe get lodged in the right bronchial tube. The bronchi and the larger of the tubes into which they branch resemble the windpipe in having a framework of incomplete cartilaginous rings, covered and completed by elastic and fibrous tissue. These rings become less and less cartilaginous as the size of the bronchial branches diminishes, until, when the tubes are about one-twentieth of an inch in diameter, they disappear altogether. This secures patency (openness or non-collapsibility) combined with flexibility and some extensibility. Each bronchus (Fig. 10) divides into smaller tubes, and these again into smaller so-called bronchioles. The smallest branch tubes end in an expanded air cell, or alveolus (Fig. 11).

The collection of branches, and sub-branches, with the air cells, together with connective tissue, blood vessels and nerves, make up the substance of the right and left lungs.

The Lungs

The lungs (Fig. 12) occupy the greater part of the thorax, or chest cavity, having the heart, the gullet and the great blood vessels as neighbours. Each lung is roughly cone-shaped, the right being broader and shorter than the left. The lungs are divided by deep depressions into separable parts called lobes, the left lung into two, the right into three. Each lobe is again, less markedly, subdivided into lobules. The crude external appearance of the lungs is that of two spongy elastic conical masses, rather than of bladders filled with air. This is not unnatural when we remember that the diameter of each air cell is about one-hundredth of an inch and that there are about 400,000,000 air cells in the lungs. What is called the root of each lung is made up of the larger bronchial tubes, the big arteries and veins entering and leaving the lung, the nerves, and a mass of connective tissue holding all together. The point of entry of all these tubes is called the hilum. The cavity of the thorax is lined and the surface of the lungs covered by continuous double membrane, the pleural membrane. A lubricating fluid between the two layers helps them to move freely over one another when the chest expands or contracts, that is to say, when the thoracic cavity is increased or diminished in size. By the contraction of certain muscles, we can raise the ribs to a more horizontal position (when we are ourselves erect), and by similar muscular contraction we can lower the dome of the diaphragm and thus make it flatter (Figs. 13 and 14). Each of these movements makes the thoracic cavity larger. That is what we do every time we breathe in.

Between the two layers of the pleura is

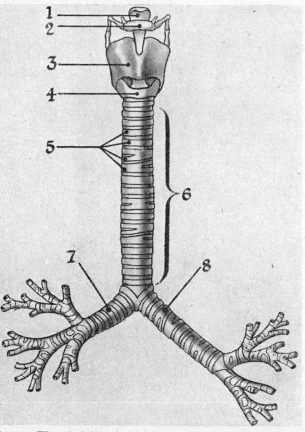

Fig. 9. *The windpipe, showing larynx, trachea and bronchial branches. 1, Epiglottis; 2, hyoid bone; 3 and 4, cartilages of larynx (thyroid cartilage and cricoid cartilage); 5, cartilages of lower part of windpipe (tracheal cartilages); 6, trachea; 7 and 8, branches of windpipe to lungs (bronchi).*

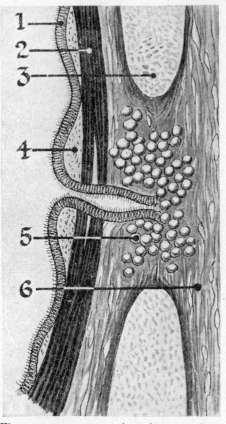

Fig. 10. *Section of branch of windpipe running to lung (bronchus). 1, Outer layer of sensitive tissue (ciliated epithelium); 2, muscular layer; 3, cartilage; 4, mucous membrane; 5, mucous glands; 6, fibrous tissue. The bronchus divides into many smaller tubes.*

a vacuum; the lungs, owing to the diminished pressure around them, expand so as to occupy the enlarged cavity, and air is accordingly drawn in in order to equalize the pressure. Directly the muscles which raised the ribs and lowered the diaphragm cease to contract, the elastic tissue of the lungs causes them to recoil to their former restricted size.

The various methods of performing artificial respiration consist essentially in alternately expelling the air in the lungs by forcible pressure on the lower part of the chest wall, and relaxing the pressure

and so allowing the air again to enter. This double process is carried through about fifteen times a minute.

In violent expiratory movements, as in coughing, there are generally preliminary forced inspirations. These cause the abdominal muscles to come into play. They respond by marked contractions which force the diaphragm upwards as soon as it relaxes, thus bringing about a rather violent expulsion of air from the lungs. Deep inspirations precede both sneezing and yawning as well as coughing. In the first case, the inspiration is followed by a rather violent expiration through the nostrils, and the second by a short expiration mostly through the mouth.

Except at the hilum, each lung is covered by a sort of doubled bag of pleural membrane, known as the pleural sac. Normally, the two layers of this sac lie close together, movement between

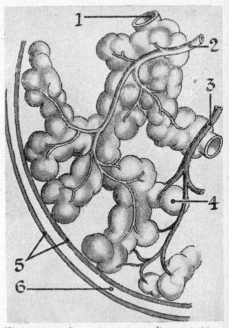

Fig. 11. *Air tubes, air cells and blood vessels making up the lungs. 1, Air tube; 2, artery; 3, vein; 4, air cells (alveoli); 5 and 6, covering of surface of lungs (pleura and pleural cavity).*

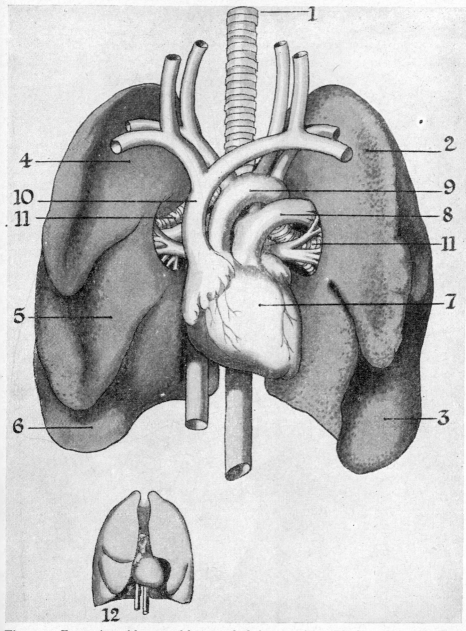

Fig. 12. *Front view of heart and lungs and their connexions. The lungs have been lifted to show the various connexions. 1, Lower part of windpipe (trachea); 2, upper lobe of left lung; 3, lower lobe of left lung; 4, upper lobe of right lung; 5, middle lobe of right lung; 6, lower lobe of right lung; 7, heart; 8, artery carrying blood from heart to lung (pulmonary artery); 9, main artery of the body (aorta); 10, main vein (vena cava); 11, branches of windpipe, running into lungs (bronchi); 12, diagram showing relative positions of heart and lungs. Note that the right lung is broader and shorter than the left.*

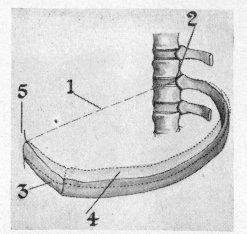

Fig. 13. *Movement of the rib in breathing. The ribs move from the shaded position to the dotted position, thus enlarging the chest cavity. 1, Axis of rotation; 2, joint of rib and spine; 3 and 4, alternate positions of rib during breathing; 5, breast bone.*

them being facilitated by a little lubricating secretion. The outer layer of the pleural sac fits closely to the ribs, the inner to the outer surface of the lung. When, as a result of germ invasion, or other irritant cause, the pleura become inflamed, we have the morbid condition called pleurisy.

The body, especially when actively engaged, needs a large and continuous supply of oxygen. The oxygen of the air has to run a rather elaborate obstacle race in order to become united with the hæmoglobin of the blood, to be again dissociated from the hæmoglobin, to enter into simple solution and pass through two membranes before it can be delivered to its destination. We may well wonder how a sufficient amount can be taken up from the comparatively small cavities of the lungs. In actual fact, the total area of the lining membrane of the millions of air cells which form the terminals of the small branches of the bronchial tubes is enormous. This respiratory surface, as it is called, is nearly a hundred times the surface area of the body; and it is over

this expanse that the blood is spread out to be oxygenated and decarbonized.

The thoracic cavity (Fig. 15) itself is bounded above and at the sides by the ribs and the muscles and tissues associated with them; in front, by the sternum or breast bone; at the back, by the dorsal vertebræ and their attachments; and below, by the diaphragm. The diaphragm is attached behind to the lumbar vertebræ, at the sides to the ribs, and to the bottom end of the sternum in front. When the diaphragm muscle contracts, it tends to become less dome-shaped and flatter, thus increasing the capacity of the thorax and causing the abdomen to bulge. Its muscularity plays an active part in breathing.

In ordinary breathing, we do not at each inspiration fill the lungs to their

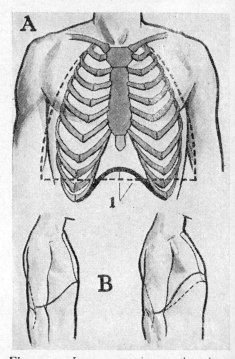

Fig. 14. *Lung expansion in breathing. (A) Front view. (B) Side view. The lungs expand to fill the increased capacity of the chest cavity shown by the dotted line, caused by the movement of the ribs and the flattening of the diaphragm (1).*

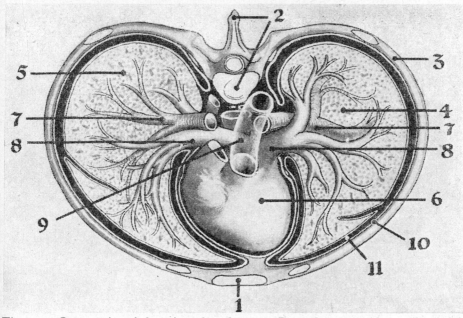

Fig. 15. *Cross-section of chest, just above heart. 1, Breast bone; 2, spine; 3, ribs; 4, left lung; 5, right lung; 6, heart; 7, branches of windpipe (bronchi;) 8, arteries carrying blood to lungs (pulmonary arteries); 9, main artery (aorta); 10, membranes forming outer surface of lungs (pleura); 11, space between pleura (pleural cavity).*

maximum capacity. No more do we at each expiration completely, or even substantially, empty the lungs of air. It is not simply a matter of filling our lungs with a full supply of atmospheric air and clearing out all the carbon dioxide resulting from the activities of our tissues, but of increasing the oxygen content of the contaminated air in our lungs and diminishing its carbon dioxide adulteration. In ordinary quiet breathing, an adult human being inhales and exhales at each breath about 500 cubic centimetres (about 30 cubic inches) of air. This is called the tidal air. If he breathes outward as hard as he can, it is possible for an average adult to exhale another 1,500 cubic centimetres. This is called the supplemental air. By taking a very deep inspiration we can, in health, breathe in a further 1,500 cubic centimetres in addition to the tidal 500 cubic centimetres and the supplemental air. This is called the comple-

mental air. There is, in a normal lung, a residual supply of 100 cubic centimetres that we cannot get rid of by any respiratory effort. This is called the residual air. The total of the tidal air, the complemental air, and the supplemental air, makes up what is called the vital capacity of an individual. The healthy normal in a fully grown adult is about 3,500 cubic centimetres.

Air in Lungs

Breathing is not, then, just a matter of taking in oxygen, and giving out carbon dioxide, but of inhaling and exhaling different mixtures of both of these. Inspired air contains about twenty-one per cent oxygen and about one-twenty-fifth per cent carbon dioxide, whereas expired air on an average contains about sixteen per cent oxygen and over four per cent carbon dioxide. The air in our lungs is never, even after our deepest inspiration, so well charged with oxygen or so free from carbon dioxide as is the air about us. The average composition of the air in our lungs is about eighty per cent nitrogen, fourteen per cent oxygen, and six per cent carbon dioxide. This air is saturated with water vapour at body temperature. The air of an ordinary occupied room contains about 0.04 per cent of carbon dioxide. The proportion of carbon dioxide in the air of the most crowded and window-closed hall can never remotely approximate to the proportion contained in the air which fills the cells of the lung. The air we breathe in has to contain at least a hundred times as much carbon dioxide as the average before we notice any particular inconvenience in our respiration—always provided we are sitting down and taking things easily. When we breathe in air containing as much as three per cent carbon dioxide, the air in our lungs shows a rise of one two-hundredths of its normal content of that gas. Any further rise of carbon dioxide in the inspired air is apt to give rise to unpleasant symptoms and to danger. The first symptoms are headache and mental confusion; if the percentage is markedly increased, the heart slows down, and if continued to excess death will eventually result.

Frequency of Respiration

Here is a table which shows some of the effects produced by a progressively increased percentage of carbon dioxide in the air we breathe.

Percentage of carbon dioxide in inspired air	Average frequency of respiration per minute	Percentage of carbon dioxide in alveolar air
0.04	14	5.6
0.79	14	5.5
2.02	15	5.6
3.07	15	5.5
5.14	19	5.2
6.02	27	6.6

This table shows that by increasing the depth and frequency of respiration, the percentage of carbon dioxide in the alveolar air is kept at a fairly constant level, even when the percentage of that gas in the atmosphere breathed is increased over one hundred times; but that after that point, a limit to the compensatory mechanism is reached, and serious consequences are pretty sure to follow. In contrast with the effect on depth and rate of respiration of relatively small increases in the percentage of carbon dioxide in the air we breathe, is the small effect of even a considerable diminution of the percentage of oxygen in the air inspired. This has been demonstrated by an interesting experiment, in which an individual is made to breathe in and out of a large bag, through a soda-lime mixture, which removes the carbon dioxide from the air passing through it. It is found that the breathing is unaffected until the oxygen in the bag is reduced by one-third, that is, from twenty-one per cent to fourteen per cent. Even then, the increase in the breathing rate is generally too slight to be, as a rule, noticed by the subject of the experiment.

Arterial blood, as it issues from the left ventricle of the heart, contains about eighteen volumes of oxygen in a hundred volumes of blood. The mixed venous blood returning to the heart when we are, comparatively speaking, resting, still contains fourteen or fifteen volumes of oxygen, having given up only about three or three and a half volumes per cent to the tissues. Very marked is the difference in the oxygen content of the mixed venous blood returned to the heart when we are, or just have been, engaged in active muscular exercise. Sometimes the oxygen in this blood is less than five volumes of oxygen in a hundred volumes of blood.

Increased Oxygen Demand

The difference in oxygen demand made by a working muscle as compared with an inactive one is shown by the observed fact that more than double the number of blood capillaries are dilated in the working muscle of one side as compared with the same muscle at rest on the other side. To meet the increased demand for oxygen during active work, there may be as much as a six-fold increase in what is called pulmonary ventilation, that is, in the frequency and depth of breathing (Fig. 16). Also, the heart-beat may be doubled in frequency, so that the oxygenated blood may be circulated more quickly; the blood pressure may be raised; and the number of red corpuscles, or oxygen carriers, may be raised very much above normal, seeming to emerge, fully equipped, from storehouses in connexion with the factories where they are produced.

Oxygenation of Blood

Among the chief purposes of the blood are the carrying of oxygen from the lungs to the cells of the body, and the carrying back to the lungs of the carbon dioxide resulting from the cells' activities. But it must not be supposed that these gases are carried in the blood in a simple state of solution, as sugar might be. A hundred volumes of arterial blood contain on an average twenty volumes of oxygen; but not more than three volumes in a thousand of blood is simply dissolved oxygen. All the rest is conveyed in actual chemical combination with the hæmoglobin contained in the red corpuscles. Just as oxygen in certain circumstances combines with iron to form the iron oxide, or rust, with which we are all familiar, so the oxygen absorbed by the blood from the air which we breathe into our lungs combines with the hæmoglobin to form what is called oxyhæmoglobin. This oxygenation of the blood corpuscles gives blood the bright red colour we find in the arteries. When, in the various tissues, this oxygen is partly given up through the cells, the blood becomes duller or more purple in colour, as in the veins. Blue blood, therefore, indicates not the superior breeding which conventional speech attributes to it, but a deficient supply of

the oxygen required to supply energy.

A second series of chemical processes is involved in the conveyance of the carbon dioxide from the tissues to the lungs. In 100 volumes of venous blood there are forty-eight volumes of carbon dioxide; but only about two and a half of these volumes are in simple solution. The bulk of the carbon dioxide taken from the tissues enters into combination with salts of sodium and potassium to form carbonates

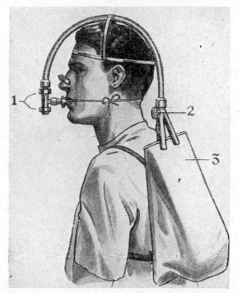

Fig. 16. *Special apparatus for measuring frequency and depth of breathing during exercise. The increased demand for oxygen may result in a six-fold increase in this frequency. 1, Valves; 2, three-way tap; 3, rubbered canvas bag.*

and bicarbonates. When the blood reaches the capillaries in the walls of the air cells of the lungs, some of these carbonates are dissociated, that is, they give up the gas that was combined with them.

Both the blood, and the cells which it feeds, exercise a selective process in their absorption of the various gases brought to them. Thus, although atmospheric air is about four-fifths nitrogen to one-fifth oxygen, both arterial and venous blood contain only one and three-quarter per cent of nitrogen as compared with twenty per cent of oxygen in the case of arterial blood and twelve per cent of oxygen in the case of venous blood. The amount of oxygen absorbed by the body cells is what they need at the time for their activities; and it is found that the same amount of carbon dioxide is given off in an atmosphere of pure oxygen as in one which is only one-fifth oxygen, the output depending entirely on the amount of activity in the tissues.

Oxygen Consumption

When we are engaged in active muscular work, our consumption of oxygen and our production of carbonic acid gas are very greatly increased. A muscle actively engaged in work will consume its own volume of oxygen in about ten minutes. It is fortunate that the blood can convey oxygen to meet such varying needs by means other than simple solution. Otherwise man would need blood vessels of the size and length of an elephant's to meet his body's oxygen needs. As it is, the blood carries at least forty times as much as could be dissolved in it. Blood reaching the lungs can take up about five per cent of its volume of oxygen; but it must be remembered that, in order to reach the blood, the oxygen in the alveolar air has to pass in simple solution in the plasma, or in the lymph seeping to and from the plasma, through two walls, in order to reach the actual blood in the capillaries. It must pass through the membrane lining the air cells, and through the thin wall of the capillary; and it is only when it reaches the blood that it can be taken up into chemical combination with the hæmoglobin in the corpuscles.

Oxygen Distribution

Difficulties of a similar nature are presented at the other end of its journey; for when it has been carried through the arteries to the various tissues needing the supplies which it bears, these supplies, including the oxygen, have again to pass in simple solution both through the walls of the capillaries and through the membrane framing the cells to which they are to be delivered. The carbon dioxide also has to pass in solution through these same two thin walls or membranes, at each end of its journey.

Both the frequency and the depth of respiration, even in a state of health, whether we consciously interfere with them or not, vary according to the body's needs. To some extent we can, for a short time, modify the pace and the depth of breathing. There is, in the back of the brain, a group of nerve cells which constitutes the so-called respiratory centre. This centre responds to messages transmitted to it both by nerves and by chemical substances brought to it by the blood. In other words, it has both a postal and a telegraphic intelligence service. Thus, if there is the slightest excess above normal of carbon dioxide in the blood which passes through it, it accelerates the rate of breathing and increases the depth. This fact is made use of in clinical medicine on certain occasions when breathing shows signs of stopping in the process of administering an anæsthetic, carbon dioxide with oxygen being used to stimulate the respiratory centre to renewed activity.

Acid in Blood

It seems that any increase of the acid in the blood acts much in the same way. For example, lactic acid, which is often found in the blood during very active exercise, markedly stimulates the respiratory centre. Mere lack of oxygen, unless it reaches an extreme degree, does not markedly increase the rate or depth of breathing; one authority says that "the percentage of oxygen may be diminished to about one half of that found in the atmosphere before breathing is markedly affected." It is noteworthy that although a comparatively slight increase in the proportion of carbon dioxide in the blood or n the alveolar air quickly brings about an increased rate of breathing, an increase of carbon dioxide in the air we inhale, even if it amounts to twenty-five times the amount ordinarily found in the atmosphere, produces no appreciable effect.

We must all have experienced the quickening of our breathing which occurs when we are confronted with sudden danger or the expectation of bad news, or, indeed, when we are excited in any way. Almost any form of sensory stimulation causes messages to be sent that affect the respiratory centre. We touch something slimy, or cold, or hot; we are pricked by a thorn or stung by a nettle, and spontaneously the breathing becomes more rapid. Messages from the breathing passages themselves directly influence the respiratory centre, causing us to sneeze, cough, or take a deep breath. Impulses come also from the lungs every time they expand, causing the respiratory mechanism for a fraction of time to go out of action. Again, a rise of blood pressure leads to a partial inhibition of respiration, whilst a fall in blood pressure stimulates it.

Reactions to Danger

For nearly all of these reactions there is a present or evolutionary reason. It is easy to see and understand the protective value of the chemical regulation of breathing. The presence of an excess of carbon dioxide in the blood is a sure enough sign that we need to breathe more frequently and more deeply, and the bringing about of such speeding up is the effect that this excess has on the respiratory centre. But why should fear, or pain, cause the breathing to increase in pace and depth? Fear and anxiety are emotions associated with danger. Throughout the earlier phases of our ancestral life, danger meant for the most part physical danger, the natural self-protective reactions to which were fighting or flight.

These emotions provoke all kinds of bodily reactions appropriate to these two activities. They cause the heart to beat more strongly and quickly so that a good supply of blood may be sent to the muscles. Functions not immediately necessary, such as digestion, are held up. Sugar is despatched from the storehouse of the liver to be conveyed to the muscles, where it is burnt and liberates energy. These are examples of the automatic reactions to emotions associated with danger, emotions calculated to call for a great increase in physical activity.

Artificial Respiration

If, consciously and deliberately, we take a series of deep breaths quickly repeated, we find that these are followed by a short period during which we hardly breathe at all. That is because the blood is charged with as much oxygen as it can do with, and coincidently has reduced its carbon dioxide to such a degree that this no longer stimulates the respiratory centre. The quickened and deepened breathing that spontaneously or automatically takes place when danger is anticipated in like manner so charges the blood with oxygen that, when active muscular exercise immediately follows, there is no panicky call for more air; nor is there any urgent need for getting rid of excess carbon dioxide. Our forces are, indeed, mobilized. Surface stimuli, such as slapping the face, applying cold water to the chest or abdomen, applying an ammonia bottle to the nostrils, or even pricking with a needle, are often employed by anæsthetists and others to provoke an increased rate of breathing in a patient whose respiratory centre has become sluggish.

Blue Blood

Related to dyspnœa (difficult breathing) are certain conditions and symptoms which it may be well here to explain. It is well known that venous blood is, relative to bright red arterial blood, of a bluish or purplish colour. This is due to the presence in its corpuscles of a quantity of hæmoglobin which has given up its oxygen, which has been, as it is called, reduced. There are many morbid conditions in which the blood, even in the smaller arteries, has this bluish colour. This is apt to show itself in certain parts of the surface, especially the extremities, and also in the mucous membrane lining the body's openings to the exterior— mouth, nostrils, and so on. This is the condition called cyanosis, caused by the presence in the blood of an unusual amount of reduced hæmoglobin. Anything which causes a sluggishness of the circulation may bring about this result; the hæmoglobin has given up to the tissues the oxygen which it has collected from the lungs, but has not been hurried on to the veins at a normal pace. Cyanosis indicates that there is a shortage of the oxygen supply to the tissues.

Short Breath

We are now in a position to consider some of the many causes that may give rise to shortness of breath. The two main objects of breathing are to furnish the blood with an adequate supply of oxygen to meet the requirements of the tissues, and to get rid of the excess carbon dioxide resulting from the body's activities. Now, the oxygen needs of individuals vary according to their size and according to the amount of muscular effort they are at the time putting forth.

Using up Oxygen

An average man when not engaged in activity needs an intake of oxygen of about half a pint a minute. When the same man is performing active muscular work, he may use up as much as four gallons a minute. But the respiratory system is not constructed to recharge the blood with oxygen at this pace; a gallon a minute being about the limit. That is why strenuous muscular effort cannot be long continued without breaks. We all know, even the healthiest of us, that state of

affairs when we have been running up a hill or digging against time, that makes us say "I must have a breather." During this period of temporary overwork, waste products accumulate and have to be burnt up or got rid of later. We have run up an oxygen debt, as it has been called, which is paid back during the period of deep inspirations that always follows excessive muscular effort. It was found that in a man who ran 225 yards in 23.4 seconds, normal quiet breathing did not return until twenty-seven minutes after the end of the run. The extra oxygen used during that period, above that used in the quiet state during a similar period, measured the amount of the "debt." The shortness of breath just described is, of course, a perfectly natural and healthy state of things. Without our conscious intervention, it quickly rectifies itself. It is when breathlessness accompanies the ordinary, everyday, less strenuous, human activities that we think of it as morbid, or indicative of some abnormal state of bodily health.

Excess Carbon Dioxide

It has been pointed out that the principal stimulus acting on the respiratory centre, causing the rate and depth of breathing to be increased, is a chemical one, namely, any excess of carbon dioxide in the blood. So small an excess as one five-hundredth of the normal proportion of carbon dioxide in the alveolar air will increase the ventilation of the lung, that is, the rate and depth of breathing, by 100 per cent. Now, we commonly speak of feeling short of breath when the respiration becomes so difficult, or hurried, as to be consciously troublesome. Apart altogether from the exceptional demand temporarily arising from excessive muscular effort, shortness of breath is experienced when the blood is unable to get an adequate supply of oxygen to the tissues, or to get rid of the excess of carbon dioxide which it contains. The fault may be in the composition of the blood itself, may arise from some obstruction in the breathing passages—nose, throat, bronchial tubes or air cells—or in some disorder of the heart or of the blood vessels hindering the adequate circulation of the blood conveying oxygen to the tissues and carbon dioxide away from them. The respiratory centre itself may be injured or diseased, and the results of this injury may be more or less serious.

Although the respiratory centre in the brain is normally stimulated by a slight excess of carbon dioxide in the blood circulating through it, a great excess of carbon dioxide, or an insufficiency of oxygen, is likely to put this important nerve centre out of action altogether. The blood's capacity for carrying oxygen is entirely limited by the number of healthy red corpuscles which it contains. Therefore, all forms of anæmia have as one of their characteristic symptoms shortness of breath. The physical impetus to the circulation of the blood is mainly provided by the contraction of the heart muscle. If this muscle is out of condition, or is in any way diseased, the blood does not circulate as it should, insufficient oxygen reaches the tissues, increased carbon dioxide accumulates in the blood, breathing is quickened, and, in consequence, we feel short of breath.

Colds and Bronchitis

So, again, if the valves of the heart are disorganised, or the walls of the blood vessels have lost their elasticity, or there is any obstruction of the air passages, this inevitably causes dyspnœa. Even a common cold makes us rather short of breath; so does a quinsy; so do bronchitis and pneumonia. In bronchitis the bronchial tubes are more or less blocked with mucus; in pneumonia, the finest tubes and the air cells in which they terminate may be so obstructed as to be put quite out of action. In certain other conditions, such as asthma, the air passages become spasmodically contracted, so that it is only laboriously that air can be forced through.

Percussion of Chest

By percussion of the chest wall, that is, by tapping with one finger on another finger laid close to the chest, a doctor can determine whether the lung beneath his finger is charged with air, or whether it has become solidified or surrounded by fluid. In the latter cases, a dull note results from percussion, as when one lightly taps with a hammer on a solid brick wall; when the condition is good, the note heard is resonant, rather like the pleasant note which one hears when striking lightly on a hollow wall consisting of an air space enclosed by two layers of wood.

When the lungs are healthy a sort of crackling or rustling sound may be heard, through a stethoscope or by applying the ear to the walls of the chest, over most of the area occupied by the lungs during inspiration. This sound is apparently caused by the dilatation or stretching of the smaller air tubes and the air cells at the ends of them. Over the larger branches of the bronchi, a sharper sound may be detected. When the air cells of a part of the lung are put out of action, this "bronchial breathing," as it is called, may be heard over all the affected parts of the lung, including the area occupied by the air cells of the smaller tubes.

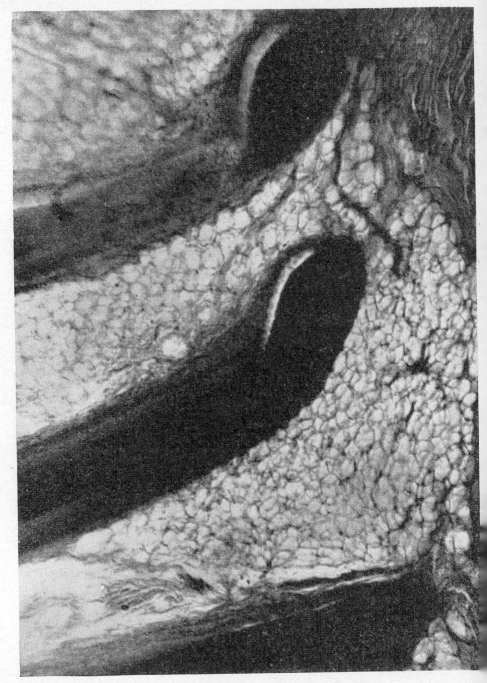

SKIN UNDER THE MICROSCOPE

This highly magnified photograph of a section of the skin of the human body shows its complex structure and the way in which the hair roots are embedded in it.

CHAPTER VII

THE SKIN AND BODY TEMPERATURE

MAINTAINING THE TEMPERATURE OF THE BODY: VARIATIONS IN INTERNAL
BODILY TEMPERATURE: MUSCULAR ACTIONS AND GLANDULAR ACTIVITY:
BRAIN DEVELOPMENT AND TEMPERATURE CONTROL: PRODUCTION OF HEAT:
OUTER SKIN AND TRUE SKIN: SWEAT GLANDS AND SEBACEOUS GLANDS:
SKIN AS PROTECTIVE COVERING: NAILS AND HAIR : HAIR PIGMENTATION

THE SKIN is looked upon by most people as a protective covering for the important tissues that make up the body. It certainly does afford such a covering or containing frame, but it is very much more than this. It is itself one of the most important organs of the body. If the skin were varnished or thickly covered all over with oil paint, the internal organs and tissues of the body would be still further protected—or so it would appear. As a matter of fact, any human being thus treated would quickly die through the prevention of the action of the skin.

Temperature of the Body

The most important function of the skin is to help to maintain the temperature of the blood at a uniform level. Day or night, winter or summer, in Central Africa or in Lapland, whether he is lying on a couch or playing in the Cup Final, the temperature of a healthy man's blood seldom varies by more than a degree above or below $98\frac{1}{2}$ degrees Fahrenheit. Even in acute fevers, the temperature of the body rises but a very few degrees above this normal. Human life is impossible outside a very limited range of variation in internal bodily temperature. The cells of which our bodies are made are tropical or hothouse creatures. We may boast as much as we like about our indifference to cold

and heat, but the living cells of which we are an organized conglomerate have no such power of adaptation.

Every activity of any part of our body involves production of heat. This is perhaps most noticeable in connexion with muscular activity. It is said that three-quarters of the energy of such activity takes the form of heat. This heat must be kept under control. So, just as motor car engines are provided with radiators in order to keep the temperature of the water circulating between the parts of the mechanism at a reasonable level, in our bodies the skin plays the part of radiator, but of a very elaborate kind. Strictly, we cannot altogether separate the functions of the skin from those of the rest of the body, for in ultimate analysis the body is one, though composed of many parts. Yet it simplifies matters, and makes it easier for us to grasp the meaning and relative importance of each part if, for the moment, we consider it separately.

Keeping Warm

We have said that heat is produced by every form of bodily activity. On a cold day, Nature's way of making us warm up is to cause us to perform the series of rapid muscular contractions which we call the shivers, or that other series we call teeth chattering. Almost instinctively we stamp our feet, move quickly up and down, or rub our hands together when we feel chilly. All these are examples of heat-creating muscular movements.

When we are unusually active, or when the air is unusually warm, there is automatically an increased flow of blood to the vessels of our skin. We all know how flushed our skin gets when we are engaged in a strenuous job or taking hard physical exercise. When muscles are actively engaged in work, the blood vessels feeding them are enlarged, more blood runs through them and consequently more blood is warmed. It is the same with blood vessels supplying active glands, which receive a greater supply of blood when called on for additional activity.

Blood Temperature

The more highly developed animals have been divided into two groups, warm blooded and cold blooded. All the mammals, including man, and the birds belong to the warm blooded class, whilst fish and reptiles are cold blooded. This does not mean that the blood of a mammal is always hotter than that of a reptile, but simply that in a cold environment the blood, say, of a fish will be colder than the blood of a man. In tropical conditions the blood of a reptile is likely to be hotter than that of a man. The essential point is that the so-called warm blooded animals are possessed of a mechanism which enables them to keep their blood at an almost uniform temperature, whereas the so-called cold blooded animals have to put up with roughly the same temperature in their blood as exists in the surrounding air or water. That is why many reptiles and fishes are utterly dormant and inactive during the winter time, their internal environment being far too cold for any sort of vital activity to take place. Often they seem dead; but if put in a warm environment, most of them soon begin to show signs of life and movement.

The energy - producing capacity of various foods is estimated in calories. A calorie is really a measure of heat yielded, one calorie being the amount of heat required to raise the temperature of one kilogram of water one degree centigrade. It has been estimated that a man of eleven stone, resting in bed and taking no food for the day, produces about 1,700 calories of heat. Of this amount, 1,200 are produced in the muscles and 500 by the activities of the various glands. In a man leading a fairly active life, taking the normal amount of food, the proportion is very different, ninety per cent of the heat being produced in the muscles as against ten per cent in the glands. In order that the body temperature may be kept uniform, it is obvious that a corresponding amount of heat must be given out into the atmosphere. Some of this heat is lost in the warm air we breathe out of our lungs, and some in our various warm excretions; but the greater part, eighty per cent or more, is lost through the skin.

Both the rate of production of heat and the rate of its loss are determined in large part by external conditions, especially by the temperature and the humidity of the air. A warm, moist atmosphere evokes from us a much smaller loss of temperature than does a dry, cold one; and as we all know by experience, it inclines us to a much reduced muscular activity.

Temperature Control

There is in man a nerve centre which acts as a thermostat, issuing immediate orders when the temperature is rising above or falling below normal. In the latter case, it causes motor impulses to be sent provoking muscular contractions and glandular activity; in the former, messages which cause surface blood vessels to enlarge and, if necessary, the sweat glands to pour out their secretions. Alcohol in large doses is one of those poisons which upset our bodily thermostat. That is why drunken men sometimes die from exposure; they get too cold for the brain cells which regulate their vital activity to keep alive. A case is recorded in which the temperature of a man in a state of alcoholic intoxication fell to 75 degrees Fahrenheit. He recovered, but it was little less than a miracle.

The first thing to do for a drunken man suffering from exposure is to cover him with rugs and put a hot-water bottle near his feet. His physiologically reactive capacity has, in the matter of heat regulation, been reduced to that of the prematurely born baby in whom the heat-regulating centre has not been fully developed. Such an infant has to be kept swathed in cotton wool, or placed in an incubator until the regulating machinery has developed.

It seems that this incapacity to survive internal cold which characterizes most birds and mammals is consequent on the special development of their brains; for it is the temperature-regulating centre in the brain cells which cannot continue stagnant and yet live. Fish may be frozen, and yet recover if the water is very cautiously warmed. Even hibernating mammals can on occasion be frozen and yet come to life with the first rays of spring sunshine. Evidently, their heat-regulating centre can be kept alive in cold storage.

Hibernation

A hibernating mammal is really a warm blooded animal in summer and a cold blooded one in winter. It is interesting, from an evolutionary point of view, to find that the egg-laying marsupials of Australia, which are in our conventional hierarchy placed immediately below the lowest layer of the mammalian strata, creatures such as the ornithorhynchus (the duck-billed platypus) and the echidna (the spiny ant-eater), possess the power of internal temperature regulation, but in a much inferior degree to that of the mammalia proper. When they are placed in a cold atmosphere their temperature is much above that of the surrounding air,

but it is very far from constant. For instance, when the external temperature is 40 degrees Fahrenheit the body temperature of the spiny ant-eater is found to be about 75 degrees. When the external temperature is 67 degrees, the body temperature is about 85 degrees; and when the external temperature is 95 degrees, the body temperature is almost identical with it. A newly born mouse or rabbit is practically naked, and its power of temperature adaptation is almost nil; whereas the newly hatched chick is well covered with feathers, and its temperature-regulating mechanism is almost next door to perfect. The guinea pig, also, is born covered with hair, and, consequently, has much more power of resistance to cold than has the newly born rabbit.

Skin and Nerves

The nervous mechanism of heat regulation responds to messages sent from the skin conveying information as to changes of temperature; for it is in the skin that the nerve endings sensitive to variations in heat and cold almost entirely exist. When we feel cold it does not necessarily mean that the internal parts of our body are any colder than usual. It merely means that the surface of our skin is cold. This sensation promptly increases the tone and activity of the muscles, often so pronouncedly as to cause shivering. Our mind and inclinations are also affected, and we voluntarily increase our muscular activity by stamping our feet or walking about, swinging our arms or rubbing our hands, to increase our surface temperature.

Producing Heat

When we feel cold, the blood vessels of the skin are contracted, when we feel hot, they are distended; and it is the less or more blood circulating in the neighbourhood of the sensitive nerve endings that determines the sensation. When we are out of condition, and our muscular tone and activity are very low, little heat is produced; we may complain of feeling chilly on quite a warm day simply because our controlling temperature regulator does not think it advisable to order a dilatation of the surface blood vessels and so induce a loss of the comparatively small amount of heat that is being produced. On the other hand, on the coldest day in winter, near the surface, so that more blood may be exposed to the cool air and, by radiation, conduction and convection, give off heat to the air without. Without knowing the reason, it was in order to facilitate this process of cooling the over-heated blood that the man threw off his outer garments.

In this cooling process, the services of

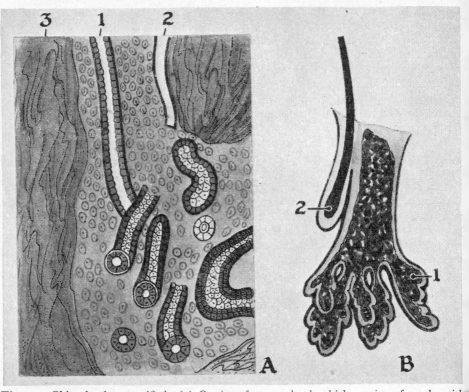

Fig. 1. *Skin glands, magnified.* (A) *Section of sweat gland, which consists of a tube with many turns and twists:* 1, *Channel by which sweat leaves the gland and reaches surface of skin (lumen or excretory duct);* 2, *blood vessel;* 3, *connective tissue.* (B) *Oil gland (sebaceous gland) made up of a number of microscopic pouches, and producing oil to lubricate hair and surface of skin. They are most abundant in the hairy parts of the body:* 1, *Contents of oil gland, composed of fat cells;* 2, *root of hair, enclosed in sheath.*

a man vigorously trenching his garden patch may feel so hot that he throws off his jacket and waistcoat for comfort. He is producing heat at a great pace, and his internal thermostat, in order to prevent the temperature of the blood from rising above the normal, sends messages ordering the immediate dilatation of the arteries the sweat glands are also requisitioned. They are stirred into increased activity, and pour out fluid in the form of slightly salted water, on to the surface of the skin; by the evaporation of this fluid, the skin is still further cooled. By the wearing of almost impervious garments, we stupidly hinder this physiological protective measure. Our sweat evaporates readily only when the outside air is but partly saturated with moisture. That is why we feel so limp and inactive in muggy weather. But if the air is cold and dry and we are not actively moving, we may unduly tax our heat-regulating mechanism. It is only thanks to the external aids which clothing and fires and houses afford us, that we have succeeded in living healthily in lands so far away from those sub-tropical regions which probably were our primal habitat.

Structure of Skin

The skin (Fig. 1) is composed of two very distinct layers, which, like all other parts of the body, are made up of microscopic cells. The outer or more superficial part is called the cuticle or epidermis, the underneath part or true skin the corium. The epidermis is made up of a number of layers of flattened cells which, unlike most of the cells of the body, are not furnished with blood vessels or with nerves. The innermost epidermal cells are kept moist and are nourished by lymph which oozes from the small blood vessels in the corium, the moisture and the nourishment diminishing as we approach the surface. The outermost cells can hardly be said to be alive. They become dry and firm and almost transparent. They constitute the horny flakes that are constantly being brushed or rubbed off in the course of our work or ablutions. When they are gently scraped off, the process gives rise to no sensation of pain. The epidermal cells generally contain particles of pigment, the number and intensive colouring of which varies in relation with race and climate.

The under or inner surface of the epidermis is attached to the outermost layer of the corium, or true skin, by a number of projections, or papillæ, in the latter, which fit into minute depressions in the cuticle. There are also microscopic tubes proceeding from the cuticle to join with the ducts of the sweat glands, enabling the

secretion of these glands to reach the surface and evaporate into the outer air. The corium itself is well furnished with both nerves and blood vessels (Figs. 2 and 3), and, because of the former, it is highly sensitive. But for the epidermal covering we should be constantly experiencing excruciating pain. It is only when a thorn or a needle has pierced through our cuticle and come into contact with the sensitive true skin beneath it that we feel anything worthy of the name of pain; up

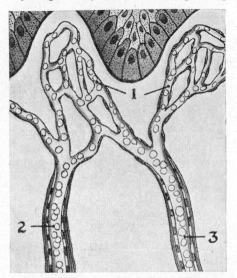

Fig. 2. *Blood supply of skin. The outer skin (epidermis) has no blood vessels, but the underneath skin (corium) is well supplied with them. 1, Capillaries; 2, smallest branches of arteries (arterioles); 3, smallest branches of veins (venules)*

to that point the sensation is one merely of slight pressure, and the sharper the needle the less that sensation is likely to be felt.

The corium varies in thickness from about one-fiftieth of an inch to one-eighth of an inch, being generally thicker on the back of the head and trunk than on the front. It is much thicker, as is also the cuticle, on the soles of the feet and the palms of the hands. The more superficial of the layers of the corium contain the sensitive endings of the nerves (Fig. 3) and the terminal expansions of the small blood vessels (Fig. 2). The follicles or roots of the hair are embedded in the corium, as also are the sebaceous or oil glands. At the deepest part of the true skin and often extending into the so-called subcutaneous tissues, which lie directly beneath it, are the sweat glands. The size, frequency and importance of these may be judged by the fact that there are between two and three million of them distributed in the human skin. They are not, however, distributed evenly, being most abundant in the armpits, the groin, the palms and the soles. The amount of sweat secreted by these glands in a day varies enormously. On a hot day, or in a hot enclosed space, men engaged in strenuous work may pour out quarts of sweat. Even in sedentary and cool conditions, a certain amount of invisible

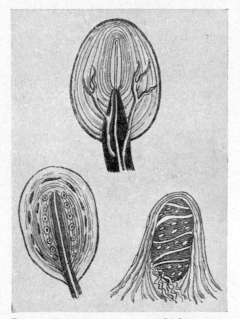

perspiration is constantly being exuded. Sweat consists mainly of water, but contains in solution a small amount of salt and a trifling quantity of organic matter.

Glands of Skin

Examined under a microscope, the sweat glands (Fig. 1) are found to consist of a tube turned and twisted upon itself so as to form a kind of wall, from which the end of the tube issues in a somewhat curved or corkscrew fashion through the skin towards the surface of the body. The sebaceous or oil glands (Fig. 1) for the most part surround the hair follicles into which their tubes lead. They are most abundant in the hairy parts of the body, and their purpose seems to be to lubricate the hair and the surface layers of the skin. The oily secretion is known as sebum or sebaceous secretion. Sometimes the openings of sebaceous ducts become blocked, giving rise to the condition called acne. The retained material may then become infected by germs and give rise to tiny pustules or miniature abscesses. The sebaceous glands are made up of a varying number of microscopic saccules or pouches, from which proceed tubes opening into a duct leading to the hair follicle. These glands have been compared in appearance to a bunch of grapes on a stem.

Whilst the most important function of the skin is to help to maintain the uniform temperature of the body, it serves other purposes almost as important. We all know the dangers that accompany the smallest break in the skin; even the tiniest prick can offer an opening through which dangerous germs may effect an entry into the sensitive tissues beneath. It is only thanks to the discoveries of such men as Pasteur and Lister that many of the operations now performed at our hospitals daily can be carried out without serious risk of infection. The skin is, in fact, our first natural line of protection against the hostile unicellular world. It serves also as

Fig. 3. *End organs of nerves, highly magnified. The sensitive endings of the nerves lie in the second layer of the skin (the corium or true skin). The outer skin (epidermis) has to be pierced before the nerve ending is affected and as a result the sensation of pain is felt*

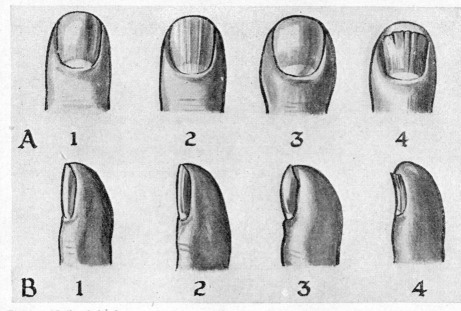

Fig. 4. *Nails of the fingers, showing modifications due to diseases.* (A) *Front view.* (B) *Side view.* 1, Normal nails; 2, grooved nails; 3, clubbed nails; 4, spoon-shaped nails. The nails are like the outer skin (the epidermis), in that they have no blood vessels and no nerves, and are hardly living tissue. That is why they can be cut without either pain or bleeding. The nail bed (matrix) is part of the true skin, has blood vessels and nerves, and is very sensitive.

a sort of buffer against minor impacts with external forces. We have first of all the outside horny insensitive layer and behind it an appreciable deposit of fatty tissue, both of which in different ways prevent minor assaults from disturbing the sensitive tissues within. Then again the particles of pigment in the epidermal cells help to neutralize the harmful effects which the sun's rays might produce if in their entirety they penetrated to the deeper parts. Only the deeply pigmented races have succeeded in establishing a permanent habitation in tropical countries; and we know how continuous exposure to sunlight induces in any of us that protective freckling or tanning which we show, on returning from a short summer holiday by the sea or in the open air.

The nails (Fig. 4) which lie at the ends of the dorsal surfaces of the fingers and toes are modified growths of the epidermis. They have no blood vessels and no nerves, at any rate so far as the visible part of the nail is concerned. This visible or uncovered part is known as the body of the nail and is almost lifeless. The back of the nail, its root, is normally covered by a fold of skin into a groove of which it fits. The nails are four sided, slightly curved bodies closely adherent to the nail beds on which they rest. The nail beds are parts of the corium or true skin; they are well supplied with blood and very sensitive. The innermost layer of the nail, as also the root, is much softer and less horny than is the superficially exposed nail.

The Nail Bed

The nail bed is called the matrix, and it is from the matrix and from the root that the nail itself is generated. As fresh cells are produced beneath and behind it, the nail is urged forward, so that it extends beyond the ends of the fleshy parts of the finger or toe. The projecting claws of

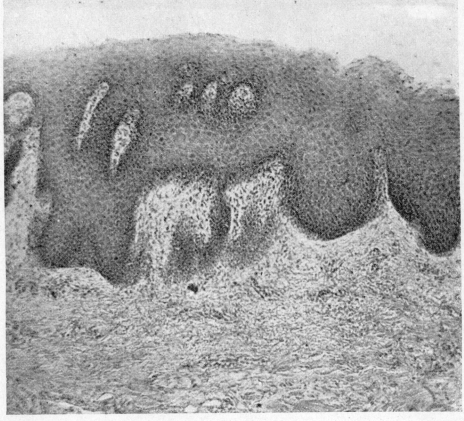

SKIN OF THE LIPS

The microscope shows clearly how the outer layer of surface skin cells protect the living tissue beneath. As the outer skin has no nerves or blood vessels, we do not feel pain or bleed unless it is penetrated, and contact is made with the true skin.

wild animals are helpful in the hunt for food. Civilized man finds it necessary to cut these projecting portions. The matrix is thickly covered with small projections or papillæ. These are mostly arranged in long rows, forming ridges which are clearly manifest through the almost transparent nails. The cuticle of the front of the fingers and of the bottom of the toes becomes continuous with the under surface of the nail just short of its extremity or free edge. When a nail is removed, either by suppuration or by physical violence, a new nail is formed so long as the matrix is not removed or diseased. A finger-nail takes about three or four months to re-grow, whilst a toe-nail may take as much as a year.

Hairs (Fig. 5), like nails, are outgrowths of the skin, of the outer layer of which they are modifications. The principal purpose which animal hair serves is the conservation of bodily warmth. The hair on the average human body can, of course, do very little in this respect, and is probably to be regarded as a mere survival from earlier stages in the history of our evolutionary progress.

A hair consists of a stem of varying length, and of a root. The root is a sort of bulbous enlargement of the end of the stem, and lies at the bottom of a sort of pocket formed by the inturning of the cuticle, which thus forms the lining of the depression, or hair socket. At the lowest part of the socket, or follicle, as it is sometimes called, the cavity dilates to correspond with the enlargement of the root of the hair, which it surrounds. The root of the hair is intimately connected with the follicle at its base and, as this is generously furnished with blood vessels, it serves as the means whereby the hair is nourished and enabled to grow. The stem of the hair, however, contains no blood vessels and, except possibly for a short distance from the root, can hardly be said to be nourished at all. It is insensitive, and can be cut without causing pain.

The hair stem is composed principally of a tough, fibrous substance sometimes covered with a coating of finely imbricated scales. In some animals, these scales are very prominent and serve important protective purposes. The colour of hair is due to the presence of patches of granules of pigment distributed in the fibrous substance of the stem. This pigment is identical with that in the skin itself; and, apparently, differs only in amount and disposition in the skin of the negro and in that of the Northern European. Attached to the sides of the hair follicle are small muscles which pass down obliquely from the outer part of the true skin. When these muscles contract, the hair becomes more or less erect, and the effect called goose skin is produced. It is well known that cold often causes these muscles to contract, the more or less

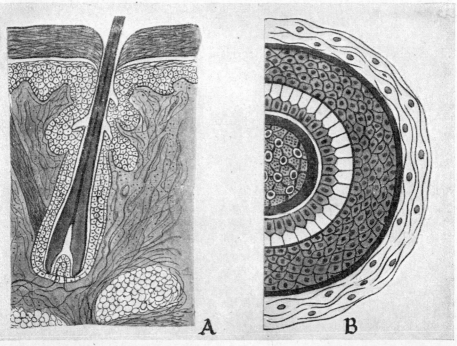

Fig. 5. *Hair.* (A) *Section through the skin, showing hair and its roots. The root lies in a pocket formed by an inturning of the outer skin (hair socket or follicle). At the base of the socket, the cavity is enlarged to accommodate the root of the hair.* (B) *Cross section of one-half of a human hair. The stem is composed principally of a tough fibrous substance, with an outer coating. The hair's colouring is derived from patches of pigment in the stem*

erect hair helping to conserve the heat of the body. This is particularly obvious in the feathers of birds in winter time. Opening into the hair follicles are the ducts of tiny glands to which reference has already been made—the sebaceous or oil glands. The secretion of these glands serves to keep the hair from becoming too dry, and also slightly oils the surface of the skin thus keeping it in a healthy condition.

As people get older, the power to produce pigment at the roots of the hairs is often lost, and consequently the hair becomes increasingly grey. The further change of the hair from grey to white is due to little air lacunæ in the fibrous substance of the hair shafts. Seen by transmitted light, white hair may appear dark, but it becomes brilliantly white when viewed by reflected light.

Seeing that the only vital part of the hair is at its root, deeply embedded in the skin, it is obvious that external applications can make but little difference to its healthy growth. Only in so far as by friction or other means can an improved circulation be promoted in the skin itself, and much good likely to be effected.

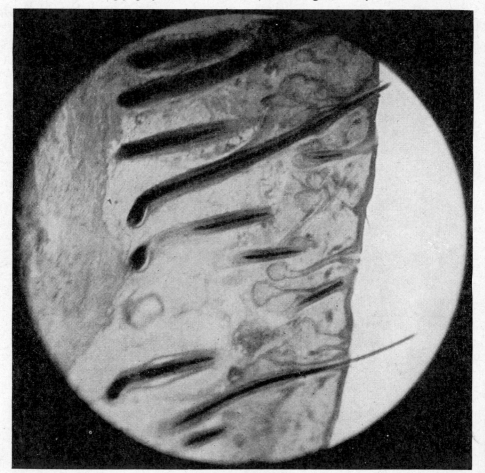

SKIN AND HAIR

Notice the hair lying in the socket or follicle, and the enlargement at the root. The connexion of the root with the follicle provides the hair's nourishment.

CHAPTER VIII

THE NERVOUS SYSTEM

FUNCTION OF NERVOUS SYSTEM: PRIMITIVE NERVOUS MECHANISMS:
DEVELOPMENT OF BRAIN: CONSTRUCTION OF NERVE CELLS: PARTS OF
BRAIN: NERVES OF HEAD: MEMBRANES ENCLOSING BRAIN AND SPINAL
CORD: COMPOSITION OF SPINAL CORD: REFLEX ACTION: SENSORY AND
MOTOR NERVES: END ORGANS OF NERVES: SPINAL NERVES AND THEIR
PLEXUSES: SYMPATHETIC AND PARASYMPATHETIC SYSTEMS

IF WE are to understand even the elementary principles of the workings of the human body, we must have a clear idea of the interrelations between the mind of man and the organs with which its functioning is most closely associated, and also between these and other phenomena of bodily life.

Function of Nerves

Though nerves are found in all the higher animals, they are not essential to life, not even to that of fairly elaborately organized living things. Plants have no nerves, and apparently no corresponding structures. Yet between root and stem, leaf and flower and fruit, there is a constant harmonious interplay, the breakdown of which spells disaster, and may lead to death.

If we are to think of life and mind as identical, or even as essentially coincident, we shall have to interpret "mind" in a much wider and vaguer way than is customary. We have no knowledge nor experience of mind that is not related to the existence and functioning of some sort of brain and nervous organization.

Most of us find it virtually impossible to picture any real connexion between a material structure like a nerve cell or a brain and a conscious thought or sensation. It is this phenomenon of consciousness which refuses to fit in with a purely mechanistic view of man. Even of the mechanical organization whereby the mind operates on and communicates with our bodily environment, comparatively little is known.

The crude anatomical facts are these. The nervous system, like the rest of the body, is composed of microscopic units called cells. They are highly specialized cells, distinct from all others in appearance and function. Proceeding from them are fibres, some of which run to a length of several feet. Bundles of these fibres make up the white cords which we know as nerves. The sciatic nerve, which is the largest in the body, is as big as a little finger; it consists of millions of microscopic fibres, each connected with the particular nerve cell from which it sprang. These nerve fibres extend from the cells collected in the brain and spinal cord—together spoken of as the central nervous system—to practically every tissue in the whole of the body.

Nerve Fibres

One set of fibres, known as sensory nerves, is used for conveying messages inward to the centre; others, called motor nerves, convey messages from the centre to the muscles and glands, causing these to function. The fibres themselves are all of a kind; like telegraph wires, they carry one message as well as another, so that,

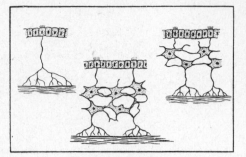

Fig. 1. *Primitive type of nervous system. The sensory cells on the surface have fine branches on their inner side, which form a network containing nerve cells.*

for example, the fibres of the optic nerve, if it were possible to change their terminal connexions, would just as readily convey the stimulus which we interpret as sound as now they transmit the stimulus we interpret as light.

It is the terminal connexions that are differentiated. The receptive terminus in the retina of the eye, for instance, is not stirred into activity by the vibrations which give rise to sound, whilst the central terminus of the optic nerve interprets as light every stimulus of that nerve, whether it be caused by vibrations in the ether, or by a blow with a fist.

Some animals are too simply constructed to need a nervous system. The amoeba, being composed of a single cell, responds to a stimulus unreservedly with its whole being. The protoplasm of which it con-

sists is irritable: it has the power of reacting to a stimulus. It also has the power of conducting an impulse so that the whole animal is affected by a stimulus which may be applied to only a minute part of its surface.

The properties of irritability and conductivity are common to all living tissue, but are more highly developed in nervous tissue than in any other kind. As we move higher in the animal scale we find increasingly that cells take on special tasks, and consequently become differentiated from each other. In the sea anemone, for example, some of the cells have formed a layer of cuticle which protects the underlying tissues, while others have become capable of contracting and withdrawing the animal out of danger, thus behaving as if they were primitive muscle fibres. The sea anemone has no true nervous system but its bodily mechanism foreshadows one.

A little higher in the evolutionary scale we find animals in which the sensory cells on the surface have developed fine branches on their inner side, and these branches form a network beneath the cuticle; nerve cells appear in this network and contribute additional branches to it (Fig. 1). This arrangement is present in the jelly fish. It shows all the essential components of a nervous system, including sensory nerve cells to receive impressions from outside, motor nerve

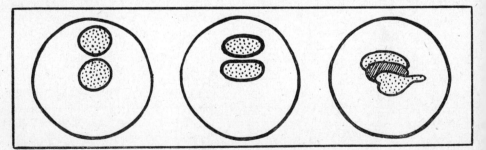

Fig. 2. *Beginning of development of human embryo. When the ovum divides after fertilization, it forms two hollow spheres of cells, which are in contact with each other. Where they touch is a small disc-shaped area, called the embryonic plate, from which the child develops.*

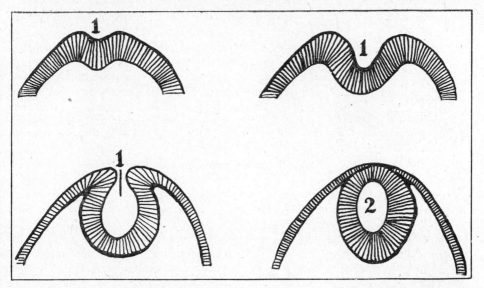

Fig. 3. *Diagram showing development of nervous system in the embryo. 1, A small groove appears on the upper surface of the developing embryo. This rapidly becomes deeper, and the skin cells multiply until they roof over the groove converting it into (2) the neural tube.*

cells to transmit the messages to muscles in other parts of the animal, and muscle cells themselves which, though they cannot be regarded as part of the nervous system, are the final link in the chain of nerve action without which the rest would be pointless.

In the higher animals the body is so large and complex that long lines of communications are needed, not only to bring the animal into harmonious relationship with the outside world but to keep each part of the body in touch with the other parts. These long lines of communication are centralized in the nerves, spinal cord and brain.

In vertebrate animals the front end of the nerve cord becomes enlarged to form a brain. The motor cells lie within the brain and spinal cord, and the sensory cells outside it. The latter, however, no longer lie on the surface of the animal, but have migrated inwards to a position of greater safety. They maintain communication with the outside world by sending one nerve fibre to the skin and a

second into the central nerve cord. In man, the sensory cells have migrated so far from the surface of the body that they lie just outside the spinal cord in groups or clusters situated on the spinal nerves; these clusters of cells are called the dorsal root ganglia.

When the human ovum begins to divide, after fertilization, it quickly forms two hollow spheres of cells which are in contact with each other; where they touch is a small flat area of cells shaped like a disc. This disc is called the embryonic plate (Fig. 2), and the whole child develops from it. At an early stage in the process, a groove forms upon the upper surface of the developing embryo and rapidly becomes deeper; the skin cells at either side of the groove multiply until they roof it over, thus converting it into a tube, called the neural tube (Fig. 3). From this tube the brain and nervous system develop.

The front part of the tube, which is to form the brain, grows particularly quickly, and soon enlarges into three bulbous

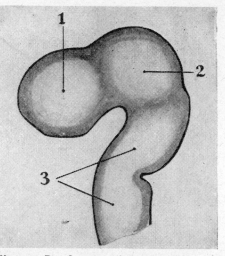

Fig. 4. *Development of the brain from the neural tube. The brain is an enlargement of the front end of the neural tube, which rapidly grows into three bulb-shaped swellings: 1, Forebrain; 2, midbrain; 3, hindbrain.*

swellings, the forebrain, the midbrain and the hindbrain (Fig. 4). These three swellings go on increasing in size until the growing brain becomes bent upon itself in a number of folds.

At the front of the forebrain, on either side, a stalked club-shaped swelling now appears. Soon the club becomes folded in upon itself to form a cup. The optic cup (Fig. 5), as it is called, develops into the retina of the eye, and the stalk joining it to the brain becomes the optic nerve. At the same time an indentation appears in the skin of the embryo at either side of the head and soon becomes deeper, forming a hollow depression; surrounding cells grow over it and roof it in, just as the neighbouring cells roofed in the neural tube. From the little cluster of skin cells thus cut off from the surface, the lens of the eye develops and finds its way into the optic cup which has budded out from the developing brain.

Meanwhile the brain has been growing more complex (Fig. 6). Swellings appear at either side of the forebrain, and these rapidly enlarge to form the main part of the human brain, the cerebral hemispheres (Fig. 6). The original neural tube was a hollow structure, and the brain and spinal cord are also hollow; the cavity of the old neural tube persists in the cerebral hemispheres as two cavities, the lateral ventricles, which are continuous below with a third ventricle. The third ventricle lies between two large and important masses of nerve cells which develop at the base of the forebrain, called the thalami.

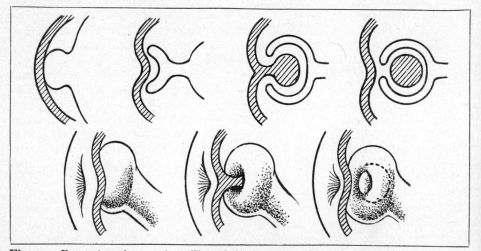

Fig. 5. *Formation of eye. A swelling of the forebrain folds in on itself to form the optic cup (which becomes the retina) and a deepening indentation of skin becomes the lens.*

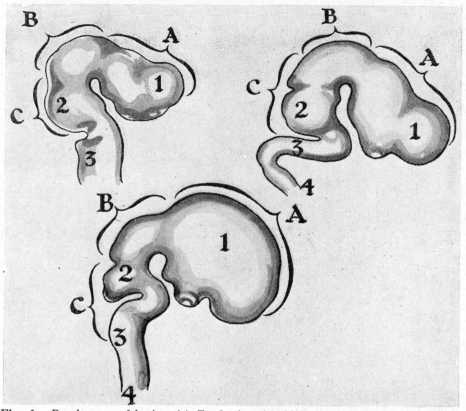

Fig. 6. *Development of brain.* (A) *Forebrain.* (B) *Midbrain.* (C) *Hindbrain. In the forebrain develops: 1, The main part of the human brain, the cerebral hemispheres. In the hindbrain develops: 2, the cerebellum and 3, the medulla oblongata, which connects the brain with 4, the spinal cord. The midbrain remains fairly small.*

The midbrain remains fairly small; it consists mainly of a large stalk of nerve tissue, branching into two above, and connecting the two cerebral hemispheres with the hindbrain. A passage runs through the midbrain, a tiny canal which is called the aqueduct of Sylvius, and connects the third ventricle, which lies in the forebrain, with the fourth ventricle lying in the hindbrain.

From the hindbrain a number of important structures have developed. Its upper part forms the pons (Fig. 7), a broad bridge of nerve fibres running transversely to connect the two hemispheres of the cerebellum which have budded out above. The lower part of the hindbrain constitutes the medulla oblongata, which is continuous below with the spinal cord.

The medulla oblongata is much more important than its small size might suggest; in it lie the nervous centres governing such vital functions as the heart beat and the automatic process of breathing. Injury to it causes instant death. It rests on the occipital bone (*see* CHAPTER I) and projects through into the first part of the spinal canal. The odontoid process of the second vertebra (the axis) lies in close relationship to it. Humane killers, used by butchers and veterinary surgeons, are designed to project a bolt or bullet straight into the medulla oblongata, so that the animal is slaughtered instantly and without pain.

Below the medulla oblongata the original neural tube develops into the spinal cord, lying in the spinal canal formed by the vertebræ. The cavity of the original neural tube persists as a small central canal running through the middle of the cord.

The brain and spinal cord is composed of neurons embedded in a supporting bodies (Fig. 9). These bodies are more numerous in resting nerve cells; they disappear or become much reduced in number after prolonged physical exertion. Mental exertion appears to have no effect on them one way or the other.

Each nerve cell gives off protoplasmic branches, one of which, called the axon (Fig. 9), is long and, for the greater part of its length, unbranched, while the others, called dendrites, are short and

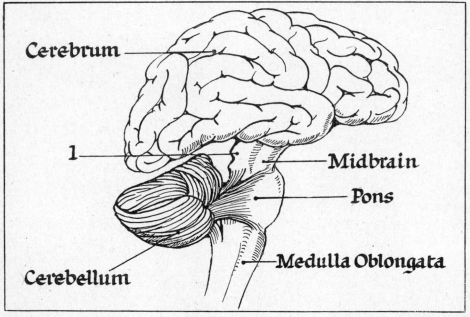

Fig. 7.　*Parts of brain. The main part of the brain is the cerebrum, in the forebrain, consisting of two hemispheres. The midbrain remains small; it includes: 1, A system of nerves connected with the ear. The hindbrain develops into a bridge of nerves (pons) connecting the two hemispheres of the cerebellum, and the medulla oblongata, which connects the brain with the spinal cord, and contains nerve centres controlling vital functions.*

tissue called neuroglia. Each neuron consists of a nerve cell together with the fibre to which it gives rise. Impulses travel through the nervous system from neuron to neuron, and in this way long lines of communication are laid down. Like every other cell, the nerve cell consists of protoplasm and has a central mass, the nucleus (Fig. 8). Other bodies exist in the nerve cell; fine granules usually packed together in dense clumps, known as Nissl branch freely. The axons of the nerve cells are identical with the nerve fibres mentioned already; the terms axon and nerve fibre are interchangeable.

The nerve fibres develop special sheaths which give them a white and glistening appearance. Each axon becomes coated by a relatively thick layer of fatty material called myelin; enclosing this again is a thin membrane, the neurilemma. The neurilemma is constricted at intervals, so

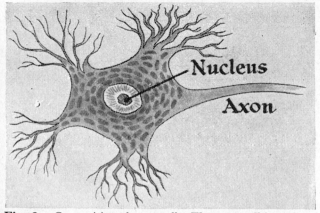

Fig. 8. *Composition of nerve cell. The nerve cell is made up of protoplasm, and has a central mass, the nucleus. The cell communicates with other cells by means of the nerve fibre (axon).*

ling through the nervous system enter by way of the dendrites and pass through the cell body and down the axon or fibre. The axon ends in a brush of tiny fibrils which seem to be interlaced with the dendrites of the next neuron in the chain. Although the end of the axon is in such close contact with the dendrites of the next cell it does not join; every neuron in the nervous system is separate from every other.

that the nerve fibre in its sheath looks something like a string of sausages. Each sausage, that is to say, each portion of a fibre between two constrictions, has a flattened nucleus, derived from the neurilemma, lying just outside the myelin sheath. The fatty myelin is responsible for the white glistening appearance of the fibre, and all the "white matter" of the brain and spinal cord is made up of fibres (axons) encased in this way. The "grey matter" is made up of clusters of nerve cells.

Some axons measure as much as three feet; nerve fibres running from the spinal cord to the sole of the foot, for example, may reach this length. Others are short, acting as connexions between nerve cells lying near each other in the central nervous system. Messages travel-

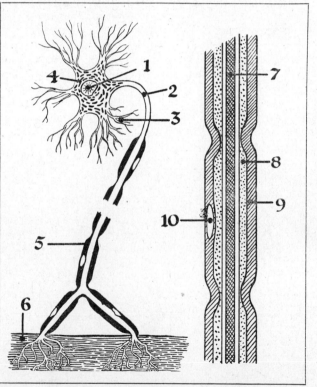

Fig. 9. *(Left) Nerve cell and branches (neuron): 1, Nucleus 2, axon: 3, smaller branches (dendrites); 4, fine granules (Nissl bodies); 5, fatty sheath (myelin); 6, muscle. (Right) Axon, magnified: 7, Nerve fibre; 8, myelin; 9, thick membrane coating (neurilemma); 10, nucleus of neurilemma.*

The place where the axon of one cell comes into contact with the dendrites of another is called a synapse (Fig. 10). We do not know exactly how a message is transmitted across a synapse, but we are certain that it can pass in one direction only; the synapse will not allow a message to travel backwards from the dendrites of one cell to the axon of another. This peculiarity of nerve conduction in vertebrate animals is sometimes called the law of forward direction, and is a far cry from the diffuse conduction in the nervous system of the jelly fish, where a message spreads in all directions almost like ink on blotting paper.

Before leaving the study of nerve cells a word must be said about the neuroglia, the tissue which supports the cells and fibres of the central nervous system. Neuroglia cells (Fig. 11) are unlike ordinary nerve cells in that they have no axon but innumerable fine hairy branches which give them the look of a spider; these branches thrust thickly in all directions between the neurons and form a thick, felt-like supporting network in which the nerve cells and their fibres are securely embedded.

The brain of man differs from that of other animals chiefly in the greater development of the cerebral hemispheres. These are fused together below and consist essentially of a surface layer of grey matter, called the cerebral cortex (Fig. 12), and a central core of white matter, composed of fibres running upwards to the cortex from the spinal cord, fibres running downward to the spinal cord from the cortex, fibres connecting different parts of the cortex with each other (association fibres), and fibres connecting the two hemispheres with each other across the middle line (commissural fibres). The cerebral cortex is the great controlling exchange in the telephone system connected by millions of wires (fibres) with all the other exchanges (local groups of nerve cells or ganglia) in the system, and through them with every part of the body; it is the region of consciousness. All the work of conscious feeling and thinking is carried on, we believe, by the mass of grey cells covering the surface of the cerebral hemispheres. In man the cortex is so abundant that it is thrown into folds, called convolutions, which are divided from each other by deep grooves

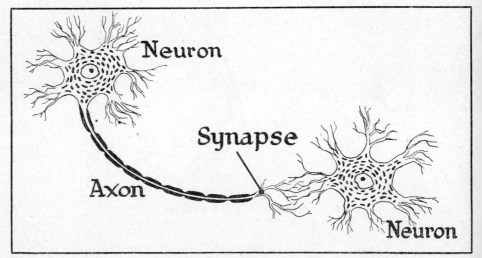

Fig. 10.   *Communication between nerves.   The point where the main branch (axon) of one neuron joins the smaller branches (dendrites) of the next is the synapse.*

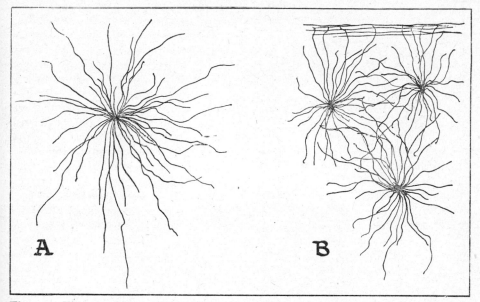

Fig. 11. *Tissue supporting cells and fibres of the nervous system (neuroglia cells).* (A) *Single cell.* (B) *Combined cells. The neuroglia cells have no axon, but form a thick supporting network in which the nerve cells and fibres are securely embedded.*

or fissures. Some of these are sufficiently distinct to have received separate names and to serve as landmarks by which the cortex can be mapped out into lobes. One such is the fissure of Sylvius (Fig. 12), a deep horizontal cleft at the side of each hemisphere. The portion of the brain below this fissure is called the temporal lobe, and is concerned with the senses of hearing, smell and taste; messages from the ear, nose and tongue are carried into the brain by special nerves and are relayed on to the temporal cortex where they enter consciousness (Fig. 13).

The fissure of Rolando (Fig. 12) divides the frontal lobe from the parie-

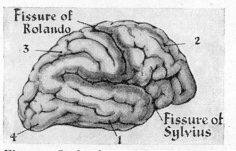

Fig. 12. *Surface layer of the cerebral hemisphere (cerebral cortex), the great controlling centre of the nervous system. 1, Section near the temple (temporal lobe); 2, section near forehead (frontal lobe); 3, section near top of skull (parietal lobe); 4, section near back of head (occipital lobe).*

tal lobe. At either side of this fissure is an important convolution or fold of grey matter. The convolution lying behind the fissure contains the cells to which messages from the sensory nerves of the body are finally brought, and is known as the sensory cortex; in front of the fissure is the motor cortex, made up of large nerve cells which send out messages to the muscles of the body. These two convolutions are connected with each other by association fibres, so that a message reaching the sensory area from, say, the great toe, is relayed to the motor area, whence a message is then sent out to the appropriate group of muscles.

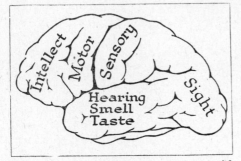

Fig. 13. *Cerebral cortex, showing areas with which the nerves running to the brain from the special sense organs are connected.*

The muscles thrown into action will vary with the nature of the stimulus to the toe. The owner of the foot may withdraw it, or kick out, or bend down to scratch it, or merely frown if the sensation was unpleasant or smile if it was pleasant. Which of these actions he performs will depend upon conscious deliberation, and it may be that such deliberation, as well as other forms of mental and emotional activity, is carried on by the cells in the frontal lobes of the brain. Recent work suggests that intelligence probably depends on the cortex as a whole, and that the frontal lobes, being rich in association fibres, contribute to general intelligence by connecting up the messages which are continually travelling from one part of the cortex to another.

The parietal lobe (Fig 12), lying behind the frontal lobe, forms a wedge-shaped segment in each hemisphere and is

Fig. 14. *Interior section of the cerebral cortex (island of Reil). This section of the brain is completely overlapped by the frontal and temporal lobes.*

divided from the occipital lobe at the back by the parieto-occipital fissure. The occipital lobe receives the messages carried into the brain by the optic nerve and is concerned with sight: the grey matter in this region is called the visual cortex.

In addition to these four lobes there is a fifth, so hidden away as to be invisible on the surface of the brain. This is called the island of Reil (Fig. 14); it lies at the bottom of the fissure of Sylvius and is completely overlapped by the frontal and temporal lobes.

The hemispheres are separated from each other by a deep cleft, at the bottom of which a thick band of fibres, the corpus

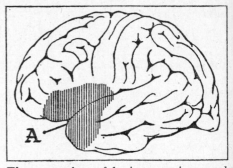

Fig. 15. *Area of brain governing speech and writing (Broca's area). This usually lies on the left side of the brain and is the only part of the brain which is unpaired.*

callosum (Fig. 16), connects the two halves. Messages reaching one hemisphere are quickly communicated to the other side of the brain by means of this connecting band of fibres, and thus our actions are governed by the brain as a whole. All the structures in the left hemisphere are repeated in the right hemisphere, with one exception: the centre governing speech and writing appears only on the left side of the brain. It occupies an area of cortex at the tip of the temporal lobe and the lower part of the frontal lobe, known as Broca's area (Fig. 15).

It is interesting to find that this latest acquirement of the mammalian brain, this piece of cortex responsible for the gifts of speech and writing which is peculiar to man alone, should be unpaired, while every other structure is present on both sides. It seems to be associated with right handedness, for in left-handed people Broca's area is found in the right side of the brain instead of the left. For this reason, a child who is naturally left handed

So far we have considered only the surface of the brain, the layer of grey cells making up the cerebral cortex, which can be regarded as the central exchange in the body's telephone system. Scattered through the brain and spinal cord are other clusters of cells which act as relay stations similar to the smallest exchanges

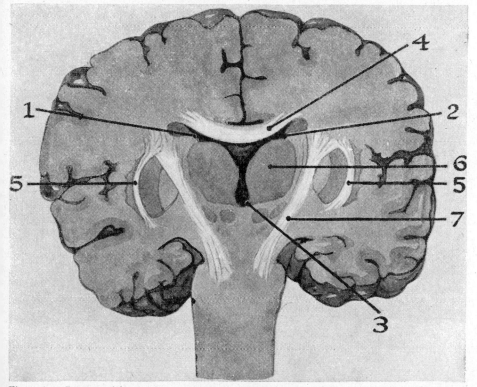

Fig. 16. *Section of brain showing groups of nerve cells at base of brain (basal ganglia). 1 and 2, Cavities in cerebral hemispheres (lateral ventricles); 3, slit between hemispheres (third ventricle); 4, nerve fibres connecting hemispheres (corpus callosum); 5, nerve fibres responsible for maintaining muscular tone (corpus striatum); 6, nerve fibres concerned with sensations of pain, heat, cold and touch (thalamus); 7, channel through which pass fibres between cortex and spinal cord (internal capsule).*

should not be forced to use his right hand, even for writing; the centre governing his speech and writing is the right side of his brain, and has more natural control over his left hand than his right. Children who are forced to use their right hands against their natural bent may experience such confusion in the speech centre that they often develop a pronounced stammer.

in a telephone service. Each of these groups or clusters of cells is called a ganglion. Two important ganglia are to be found embedded in each hemisphere near its base; they are appropriately called the basal ganglia (Fig. 16).

Neither of the cerebral hemispheres is completely solid; each of them contains a cavity, the remains of the cavity

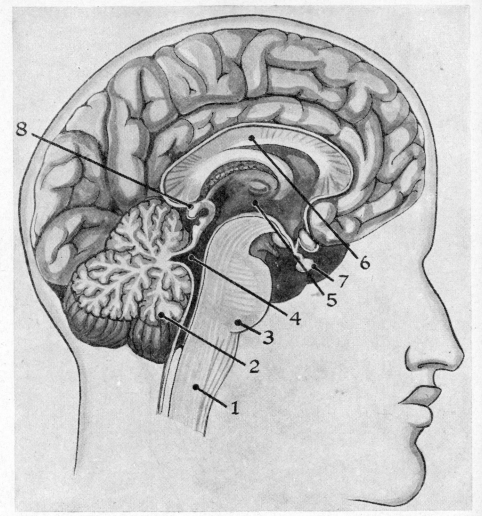

Fig. 17. *Section of the brain. 1, Lower portion of hindbrain, forming connexion with spinal cord (medulla oblongata); 2, part of hindbrain (cerebellum); 3, nerves forming bridge between parts of cerebellum (pons); 4 and 5, cavities (fourth and third ventricles); 6, nerves connected with muscular tone (corpus callosum); 7, gland concerned with growth (pituitary); 8, remains of what, in some of our prehistoric ancestors, was a third eye (pineal body).*

of the original neural tube, called the lateral ventricle. The two lateral ventricles open below into a third ventricle, a mere slit lying between the bases of the two hemispheres; the walls of this slit are formed by the two most important basal ganglia, the thalami (Fig. 16).

The thalami are paired masses of grey matter lying one on each side of the mid-line near the base of the hemispheres, and divided from each other by the cavity of the third ventricle. A second mass of grey matter, the corpus striatum (Fig. 16), lies to the outer side of each thalamus, separated from it by a band of white matter called the internal capsule. All the fibres running up to the cortex from the spinal cord, and all the fibres down to the spinal cord from the cortex have to pass through the internal capsule, which is thus like a bottleneck through which two lines of traffic must pass.

The second of the basal ganglia, the corpus striatum (Fig. 16), is a tadpole-shaped mass of grey matter lying on the outer side of the thalamus at the base of each cerebral hemisphere. It is connected by fibres with the cortex, the thalamus, the cerebellum and the spinal cord; its business is to maintain a slight state of tension in the muscles which is known as muscle tone. A healthy muscle is not lax and flabby but firm and springy; when it contracts it does not have to take up any slack, but is ready to contract at once.

The thalamus, like the corpus striatum,

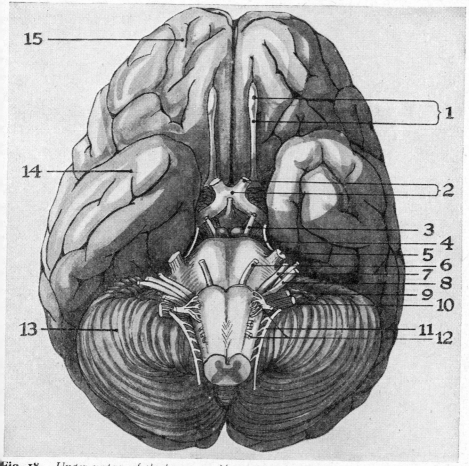

Fig. 18. *Under surface of the brain.* 1, *Nerve of smell ending in bulb (olfactory nerve);* 2, *nerves of sight and their junction (optic nerve and optic chiasma); 3, 4 and 6, nerves concerned with movement of muscles of eyeballs (oculomotor, trochlear, and abducent nerves); 5, nerves supplying skin of eyelids and nose, cheeks, temples, teeth and tongue (trigeminal nerves); 7, nerve supplying muscles of expression (facial nerve); 8, nerves concerned with hearing and balance (auditory); 9, nerves of throat and tongue (glossopharyngeal nerves); 10, nerve sending branches to windpipe, throat, heart, lungs, stomach and intestines (vagus nerve); 11, nerve of neck muscles (accessory); 12, nerve of tongue muscles (hypoglossal), 13, cerebellum: 14, temporal lobe of cortex; 15, frontal lobe of cortex.*

is connected with other parts of the brain and spinal cord, but it is interesting chiefly because all fibres carrying messages to do with pain, heat, cold and touch enter it on their way to the cortex, and some of them end there. This means that the messages they carry actually enter consciousness at that level: we *feel* with our thalami. In some of the lower animals the thalamus is the chief region of sensation; in such creatures the cortex is insufficiently developed to make it possible for them to receive more delicate sensory impressions.

Feeling Pain

Through the thalamus we experience crude sensations of pain, sensations of extreme heat or cold and sensations of rough touch. Finer sensations of moderate degrees of temperature and light touch are relayed on to the cortex and experienced there. The thalamus may thus be regarded as a sort of subsidiary exchange for the sensory cortex; relatively unimportant messages are handled by it, but messages requiring special attention are forwarded to the higher exchange.

Before leaving the region of the third ventricle we may as well note an odd structure projecting from its posterior end. It will be recalled that the third ventricle is a narrow slit lying near the base of the cerebral hemispheres and separating the two thalami from each other. At the posterior end of this slit a small nodule of grey matter projects backwards and overhangs the corpora quadrigemina of the midbrain. This is the pineal body (Fig. 17); it represents all that remains to us of a third eye which used to adorn the forehead of some of our lizard ancestors in far-off times. So far as is known it serves no useful purpose now.

Brain's Under-surface

The basal ganglia, as their name implies, lie near the floor of the brain, but there is room beneath them for a few more little masses of grey matter which recent investigation has shown to be important. Let us now examine the under surface of the brain (Fig. 18) which lies in contact with the bony floor of the skull.

First, we shall see the under surface of most of the structures which we have seen already, the frontal lobes of the cerebral hemispheres, the two temporal lobes, and the cerebral peduncles. We cannot see the under surface of the occipital lobes because they are concealed by the hindbrain, that is, by the pons, the medulla oblongata and the cerebellum.

Twelve pairs of nerves (Figs. 18 and 19) spring from the under surface of the brain. These are the cranial nerves. Some are motor, some sensory and some mixed, that is, composed of both motor and sensory fibres. For the most part they supply the head and neck, but some leave the skull and travel far afield to supply distant organs. They are named:—

1. Olfactory, or nerve of smell.
2. Optic, or nerve of sight.
3. Oculomotor.
4. Trochlear.
5. Trigeminal.
6. Abducent.
7. Facial.
8. Auditory, or nerve of hearing.
9. Glossopharyngeal.
10. Vagus.
11. Spinal Accessory.
12. Hypoglossal, or nerve of tongue.

Cranial Nerves

The olfactory nerves are purely sensory. They lie on the under surface of the frontal lobes as two long bands, the olfactory tracts, each ending in a club-shaped swelling, the bulb. Sensory fibres leave the lining of the nose and make their way into the skull through the tiny holes in the cribriform plate of the ethmoid bone (*see* CHAPTER I), enter the olfactory bulbs, and run by way of the tracts into the brain, where they finally travel to the cortex of the temporal lobe. Thus the sense of smell is experienced in the part of the temporal lobe of the brain concerned with smell.

The two optic nerves run towards the brain but fuse with each other before they get there; immediately after fusing they divide again to form the optic tracts, which enter the brain substance and finally end in the visual cortex of the occipital lobes. The X-shaped junction formed by the two optic nerves is called the optic chiasma.

The third, fourth and sixth nerves (the oculomotor, trochlear and abducent) are all motor nerves supplying the little muscles which are used in moving the eyeballs to and fro.

The fifth (trigeminal) nerves are mixed and have a great deal of work to do; their sensory fibres supply the skin of the eyelids, and the sides of the nose, cheeks and temples, as well as the teeth; they also send taste branches to the tongue. To say they send branches is, of course, only a convenient way of putting it; we must always bear in mind that sensory fibres run inwards to the brain and motor fibres outwards to muscles and glands. The motor fibres of the trigeminal nerves supply the muscles of mastication.

The muscles of expression, which are constantly active during waking hours, are supplied by the seventh or facial nerves. If one of these nerves is paralysed the whole side of the face droops, the eyelids cannot close properly, and when the patient tries to smile, his mouth is pulled over in a one-sided grimace.

The eighth or auditory nerves are purely sensory; they carry not only messages of hearing but messages concerned with bal-

ance inwards to the brain. The ninth, the glossopharyngeal, nerves, are mixed; they supply the muscles of the pharynx and some of the muscles of the tongue, and also carry taste fibres from the tongue, being especially useful in conveying the taste of bitter things.

The tenth nerves, the vagi or wanderers, are intensely interesting; they are mixed nerves which send branches to the larynx, pharynx, heart, lungs, stomach and intestines, and help to regulate the actions of all these organs.

The eleventh or spinal accessory nerves are motor nerves to some of the neck

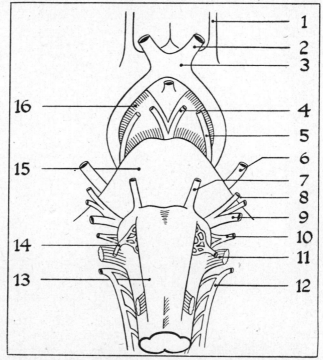

Fig. 19. *The twelve pairs of nerves of the head (crania nerves.) 1, Nerves of smell (olfactory); 2, nerves of sight (optic); 3, junction of sight nerves (optic chiasma); 4, 5 and 7, nerves of eyeball muscles (oculomotor, trochlear and abducent); 6, nerves of eyelids, nose, cheeks, teeth (trigeminal); 8, nerve of face (facial); 9, nerve of ear (auditory); 10, nerve of tongue and throat (glossopharyngeal); 11, nerve of throat, heart, lungs, stomach (vagus); 12, nerve of neck muscles (accessory); 13, 15 and 16, parts of brain (pons, medulla oblongata and cerebral peduncle); 14, nerve of tongue muscles (hypoglossal).*

muscles; the twelfth or hypoglossal supplies the muscles under the tongue, which help to raise the larynx in the process of swallowing, and also sends branches to the muscular tissue of the tongue itself.

One more important structure must be noted before we leave the base of the brain. Just behind the optic chiasma is a stalk which has been cut off short. Attached to it is a small round body which looks insignificant enough but which is really extremely important. This mere trifle, no bigger than a pea, is the pituitary gland (*see* CHAPTER IX). It is enclosed in a small bony box, the Turkish saddle, which lies in the floor of the skull. The gland remains attached to the base of the brain by the stalk mentioned, and joins the under surface of the hemispheres just below the basal ganglia (Fig. 17).

Of all the structures developing from the three original swellings at the front of the neural tube, the midbrain shows the least change. It consists essentially of two thick stalks of white matter, the cerebral

peduncles, uniting below, and connecting the cerebral hemispheres with the hind-brain; these stalks are made up of bundles of sensory fibres running up from the cord and motor fibres running down from the hemispheres. A tiny canal, the aqueduct of Sylvius (Fig. 20), pierces the midbrain, and connects the third ventricle above with the fourth ventricle below. Small clusters of nerve cells lie round and above this canal, those above it forming four little grey swellings, the corpora quadri-gemina. These swellings are relay stations, or local exchanges, for messages travelling up from the ear to the cortex of the temporal lobe. Messages from the ear are carried into the brain by way of the auditory cranial nerve.

The grey matter lying below the aqueduct of Sylvius acts as a small local exchange for the nerves supplying the little muscles which move the eyeball. These muscles lie inside the eye socket itself. Movements of the eyeballs are governed by the motor cortex. Lines, that is, nerve fibres, go out from this central

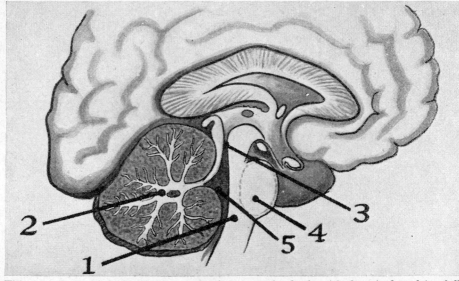

Fig. 20. *Parts of the hindbrain. 1, Section connecting brain with the spinal cord (medulla oblongata); 2, cerebellum; 3, passage through midbrain connecting cavity in forebrain (third ventricle) with cavity in hindbrain (fourth ventricle) (aqueduct of Sylvius); 4, nerves forming bridge between parts of cerebellum (pons); 5, cavity (fourth ventricle).*

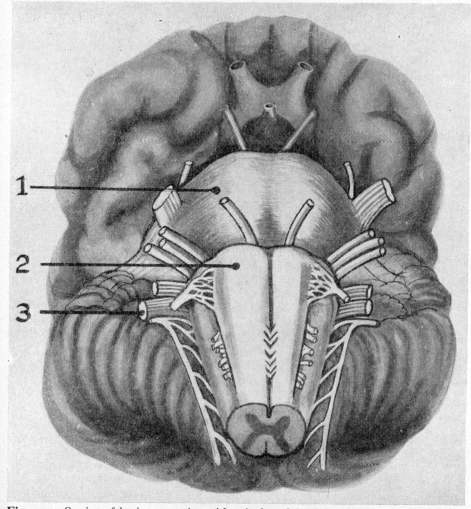

Fig. 21. *Section of brain connecting with spinal cord (medulla oblongata). This section governs the vital activities of the body, such as breathing and the heart beat. 1, Thick band of fibres forming bridge between parts of cerebellum; 2, medulla oblongata; 3, vagus, or wandering, nerve with branches to heart, lungs, stomach and intestines.*

switchboard. When they reach the mid-brain they end, and a fresh relay is sent out by the cells beneath the aqueduct. These run to the muscles of the eyeball by way of the three cranial nerves (Figs. 18 and 19). Sometimes the cells in the midbrain act without a message from the cortex. For example, when we hear a sudden noise we turn our eyes, and often our heads as well, in the direction of the sound; and we do it automatically without conscious thought. This is an example of a reflex action, and it occurs when one of the local exchanges in the telephone system acts on its own responsibility, without getting into touch with the central controlling office.

It is easier to understand the structure of the fully developed hindbrain if we approach it from below upwards instead of from above down. If we follow the spinal cord upwards we find that it broadens out above to form the medulla oblongata (Fig. 21). This small but important structure contains the so-called vital centres, which govern the vital activities of the body such as breathing and the beat of the heart, and which are to be found in the grey matter forming the floor of the fourth ventricle. The nerve fibres which carry the messages from these centres to the organs which they control leave the medulla in the great vagus, or wanderer, nerves. In addition to the vagus nerves the medulla gives rise to several other pairs of nerves; in fact, of the twelve pairs leaving the brain no less than eight take origin from it.

The Cerebellum

At the upper part of the medulla, on its under surface, a thick band of fibres crosses it transversely, forming the pons, or bridge; this actually is a bridge, connecting the two lobes of the cerebellum, or little brain, which lies above the medulla oblongata.

The cerebellum (Fig. 22) is a curious looking structure consisting of closely

packed folds of nervous tissue arranged in two fairly well defined lobes. When it is cut across it is found to have an outer layer of grey matter (cells) and an inner core of white matter (fibres) just like the cerebral hemispheres. The white matter in the centre of the cerebellum has a strange arrangement of its own; it radiates outwards from a central stem like the branches of a tree to which the much infolded grey matter appears to form leaves. To this appearance the name of the Tree of Life has been given.

Sense of Balance

The cerebellum is chiefly concerned with balance. Innumerable small adjustments have to be made in order to enable us to maintain our balance, even in taking a single step. Special sensory nerves carry messages from the muscles and joints, conveying information to the brain about the position of the limbs and trunk. Some of these messages travel right to the sensory cortex and give us conscious information, so that we can say at any moment what position our limbs are in without looking; but some messages never reach consciousness at all. After all, we do not maintain balance by a conscious effort; by far the greater part of the minute muscular adjustments which we make from moment to moment are achieved without having to think. The cerebellum has the task of looking after just these movements, so it receives all the messages from muscles and joints which do not enter consciousness; it sends out messages too, which travel out from it, down the stem of the Tree of Life and the spinal cord, to the muscles by way of the spinal nerves.

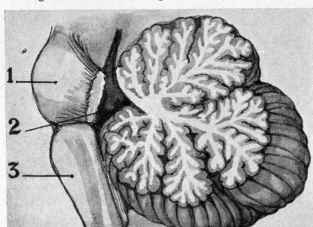

Fig. 22.   *The " little brain," or cerebellum.   This consists of closely packed folds of nervous tissue.   It is chiefly concerned with balance.   1, Bridge connecting halves of cerebellum (pons); 2, cavity (fourth ventricle); 3, medulla oblongata.*

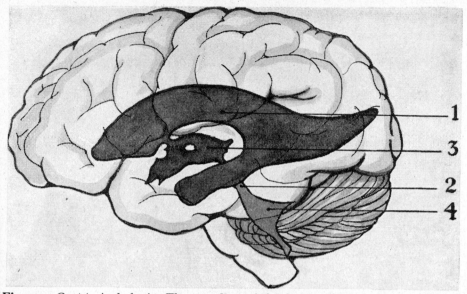

Fig. 23. *Cavities in the brain. These are the persisting feature of the cavity of the embryonic neural tube. 1, Cavities in the cerebral hemispheres, to which hang blood vessels serving brain (lateral ventricles); 2, channel between third and fourth ventricle; 3, slit between the cerebral hemispheres (third ventricle); 4, cavity in hindbrain (fourth ventricle).*

A strange and interesting mechanism exists in the ear to keep us informed about movements of the head; it consists of a device akin to that found in the jelly fish, which so successfully prevents that creature from swimming upside down. Messages from the ear reach the brain through the eighth or auditory pair of cranial nerves; the fibres which come from the organs of balance enter the medulla and are distributed not only to the cerebellum but to the corpora quadrigemina in the midbrain and finally to the cerebral cortex itself. In this way we get news about the position of the head both consciously and unconsciously. These unconscious centres are every bit as important as the great conscious exchange, the cerebral cortex; for though we are apt to rate consciousness rather highly we must not forget that the unconscious, not the conscious, processes are those which mainly keep us going.

In the fully formed nervous system, the cavity of the neural tube of the embryo persists as the series of cavities, called ventricles (Fig. 23), which are found embedded in the solid structure of the brain and play an important, and indeed fundamental, part in its activity.

The lateral ventricles, lying one in each hemisphere, are strangely shaped, rather like two curving horns which penetrate far into the substance of the hemispheres, one prong stretching into the frontal lobe, one into the occipital lobe, and one curling outwards and downwards into the temporal lobe. They serve an important purpose; hanging into them are closely knit wreaths of tiny blood vessels. Throughout life fluid steadily oozes out of these blood vessels into the ventricles of the brain, nourishing the delicate nerve cells and fibres, and carrying off waste products formed by their activity. The cerebrospinal fluid, as it is called, flows from the lateral ventricles into the third ventricle, and thence through the aqueduct of Sylvius into the fourth ventricle; here it makes its escape from the brain by way

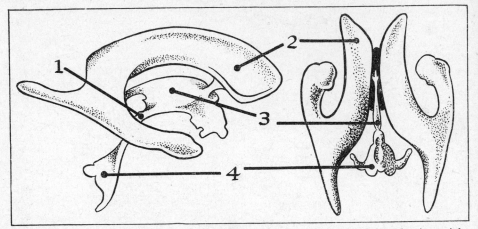

Fig. 24. *Diagram showing relative position of cavities in the brain (left, side view; right, front view): 1, Channel connecting third and fourth ventricles (aqueduct of Sylvius); 2, lateral ventricle; 3, third ventricle; 4, fourth ventricle.*

of an opening in the roof, and flows over the surface of the brain and spinal cord, percolating between the membranes which enclose them (Fig. 24).

There are three such membranes: the dura mater, the arachnoid and the pia mater (Figs. 25 and 26). The dura mater or "hard mother," lies on the outside, and is a stout closely woven membrane, lining the skull

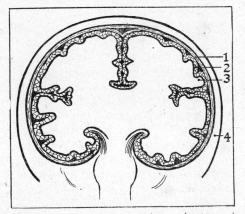

Fig. 25. *Membranes enclosing brain and spinal cord (meninges). 1, Closely woven outer membrane, lining skull and spinal canal (dura mater); 2, delicate, web-like membrane (arachnoid); 3, fine membrane closely adhering to surface of brain and spinal cord and containing blood vessels (pia mater); 4, bone.*

and vertebral canal, and forming an extra protection to the valuable structure which lies within. The arachnoid, so called because it consists of fine delicate strands resembling a spider's web, lies inside the dura mater, and forms a loose network between it and the innermost membrane, the pia mater or "devoted mother." The pia mater is a very fine transparent membrane so closely applied to the surface of the brain that it dips down into all the fissures and can only be stripped away with difficulty. It carries numbers of blood vessels into the brain to nourish and maintain the cortex. The pia mater, like the dura and arachnoid, is carried down over the surface of the spinal cord, and supplies it with blood vessels just as it does the brain.

When the cerebrospinal fluid from the inside of the brain escapes from the fourth ventricle, it makes its way through a gap in the pia mater into the subarachnoid space between the arachnoid and the pia mater; here it is absorbed again into the blood stream, and in this way a constant flow of cerebrospinal fluid is maintained.

The three membranes enclosing the brain are sometimes called the meninges; the disease of meningitis, or cerebrospinal fever, is an inflammation of these membranes of the brain or spine.

The remainder of the original neural tube forms the spinal cord (Fig. 27). The cord is enclosed in the bony canal made by the vertebræ which encircles it rather in the manner of beads threaded on a string. It is only eighteen inches long and terminates at the level of the first or second lumbar vertebra, that is, in the small of the back. Though a tiny structure, no greater in diameter than an ordinary lead pencil, it carries more messages in an instant than an Atlantic cable does in a year. When it is cut across (Fig. 28), we find that it consists of a central core of nerve cells enclosed in a thick layer of fibres. These fibres, owing to their myelin sheaths, are dazzling white, but the nerve cells, which are simply naked specks of protoplasm, have a greyish colour when seen in the mass. The spinal cord, then, consists of a central core of grey matter completely surrounded by an outer layer of white matter. In the very centre of the cord is the tiny canal which is all that remains of the cavity of the original neural tube from which this whole complicated structure developed.

If we cut the spinal cord across we see

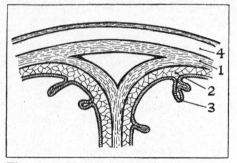

Fig. 26. *Membranes enclosing brain and spinal cord (meninges). 1, Outer membrane (dura mater); 2, second membrane (arachnoid); 3, inner membrane (pia mater); 4, bone.*

that the grey matter in the centre forms a definite shape. Some people like to describe it as resembling two crescents joined back to back by a bridge, but a simpler symbol for it is the letter H. One upright bar of the H lies in each half of the cord and the transverse bar connects them across the middle line. Whereas the two horns or prongs of grey matter projecting towards the front of the cord (the anterior horns) are rounded and completely ensheathed in white matter, the two horns at the back (the posterior horns) are much narrower and reach to the surface of the cord. At the front of the

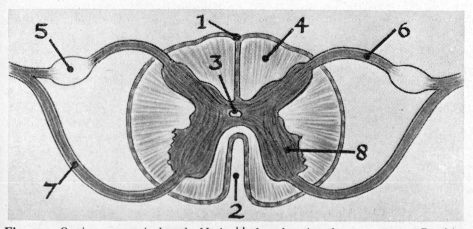

Fig. 27. *Section across spinal cord. Notice H-shaped section of grey matter. 1, Partition between halves (posterior fissure); 2, deep cleft (anterior fissure); 3, central canal; 4, white matter; 5, nerve cluster (ganglion); 6 and 7, posterior and anterior roots; 8, anterior horn.*

cord there is a deep groove or cleft called the anterior fissure; at the back there is no such groove, but only a thin partition between the two halves.

If we imagine the cord divided into halves by a line running from front to back, we see that the white matter is roughly split up by the horns of grey matter so that we can say that there are three columns of white matter in each half of the cord—one in front, one at the side and one at the back. These three columns are named the anterior, the lateral and the posterior columns of the cord (Fig. 28).

Reflex Action

The grey matter in the centre of the cord consists almost entirely of nerve cells, the white matter forming the three columns on each side consists of fibres. We must now consider where these various fibres are running and what is the purpose of the grey matter in the centre of the cord. Some of the fibres merely connect cells at one level of the cord with cells at a higher or lower level, so that an incoming message is distributed quickly

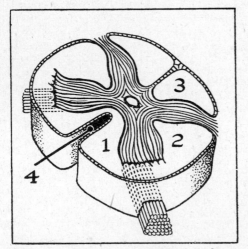

Fig. 28. *White matter of spinal cord.* I, *Front section (anterior column);* 2, *side section (lateral column);* 3, *back section (posterior column);* 4, *anterior fissure.*

to several segments of the cord and not merely confined to the point of entry. These fibres are important in connexion with reflex action.

A reflex action is a motor response to a sensory stimulus and is performed automatically without our having to think about it. A message travels up by way of a sensory nerve to the cord and a second message travels down a motor nerve to a muscle, causing it to contract. The message never goes up to the brain at all. It takes a short cut through the cord, and the final muscular contraction is performed without conscious control.

Quite a number of useful actions are performed in this unconscious manner; for example, a man stepping out of doors on a cold day shivers involuntarily; a housewife who touches a hot stove pulls her hand away long before she has had time to think the matter over and decide that that is the proper course to follow. These are both examples of reflex action; they are as brisk and unconscious as the withdrawal of the jelly fish when it is prodded, and they are performed by an exactly similar simple mechanism. Let us follow the course the message takes.

The Reflex Arc

A sensory nerve fibre runs under the skin—a nerve fibre sensitive to pain, let us say. When the skin over this fibre is pricked with a pin, the nerve fibre receives a message which travels up along it to the spinal cord, entering it near the posterior horn of grey matter. The fibre carrying the message runs forward through the posterior horn to the anterior horn and there forms a synapse with a motor cell; the message is transferred to the motor cell and travels down its axon (nerve fibre) to end in a muscle. As soon as the message reaches it, the muscle contracts.

This, the simplest form of nerve mechanism in the body, is known as the reflex arc (Fig. 29). There are one or two points about it which deserve notice, the

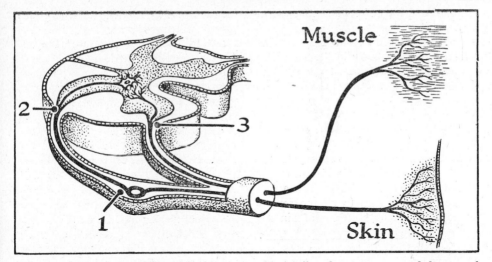

Fig. 29. *Reflex action. If a nerve fibre in the skin is affected, a message travels by way of the nerve cluster at the back of the spinal cord (1), (posterior root ganglion) to the posterior nerve root (2), and thence through the anterior nerve root to a muscle (3).*

first being the position of the motor nerve cell; all the motor nerve cells of the spinal cord lie in the anterior horns of grey matter and are known as the anterior horn cells. They are extremely important, because any message to the body muscles must finally be delivered through them; there is no alternative route. Sensory messages, as we know, may be carried into the central nervous system from all directions: we receive information from eyes, ears, tongue, nose or skin, or from inside the body itself. But when we want to do something about it, we use the anterior horn cells of the spinal cord.

The anterior horn cells have been called the final common path for all motor impulses. They remind us again that the nervous system is like a telephone service; a man with a telephone can receive messages from all over the world, and the messages may be of all kinds—agreeable, disagreeable, exciting, depressing, soothing or painful. Millions of wires are needed to give him this remarkable service, but wherever the message comes from, and however many wires are involved, in the end it has to reach him by a final common

path—the particular wire which runs to the telephone he uses. If that wire is out of action the rest of the system is useless to him. No matter how well the other wires are working, they cannot give him the least hint of a message unless his own line is in order.

Now the man in this simile represents the muscle fibre, and his private telephone line represents the motor neuron—the anterior horn cell and its axon. Just as the man is powerless to receive messages without his telephone, so the muscle fibre is cut off from information if anything happens to its anterior horn cell. It becomes paralysed; lacking its nervous messages, it cannot contract.

In the arc described, only three elements took part—the sensory neuron, the motor neuron and the muscle fibre. If, however, we consider any reflex action, it will be obvious that large numbers of muscle fibres are called into play, and yet the area stimulated may be extremely small; it may be supplied by one or two nerve endings.

The explanation is simple; when a sensory nerve fibre enters the spinal cord, it branches. Some of the branches run up the cord to higher levels and some down to lower levels, while some very long ones travel right up to the brain. The branches which run up or down in the cord form synapses with anterior horn cells at different levels; so that in addition to exciting the anterior horn cells at its own level the sensory fibre excites those above and below as well. Moreover, by way of its long ascending branch it sends information about the whole incident to the brain. The anterior horn cells do their work long before the brain can take action by sending messages to all the muscle fibres which can usefully contract in this

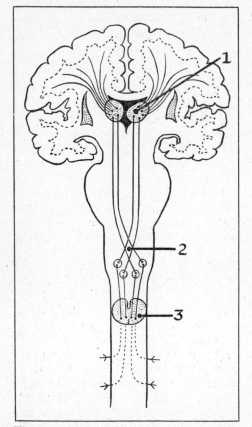

Fig. 30. *Path of nerves carrying sensations to the brain (sensory tracts). 1, Nerve centre at base of brain (thalamus); 2, special point in medulla oblongata (sensory decussation); 3, posterior column of spinal cord.*

emergency. The result is an appropriate gesture. The brain is notified a fraction of a second later; and then we take any further appropriate action.

Many of the fibres carrying sensory messages to the brain run in the posterior columns of the cord, that is, in the two thick columns of white matter which lie at the back of the cord between the two posterior horns of grey matter (Fig. 30). These columns run up the whole length of the cord and grow thicker as they approach the brain, because increasing numbers of fibres are entering them from the spinal nerve roots. Some of the sensory fibres, however, do not enter the posterior columns but cross over as soon as they enter the cord and travel up in the lateral columns of the opposite side. Fibres carrying sensations from the muscles and joints and sensations of light touch are those which enter the posterior columns; they travel up to the medulla, where they encounter clusters of nerve cells which receive the messages and relay them on.

Receiving Information

The new fibres cross the middle line and run up towards the cerebral hemisphere of the opposite side. The point in the medulla where the fibres from the two sides cross is called the sensory decussation (Fig. 30). Before the fibres reach the cerebral cortex they encounter the thalamus, the big basal ganglion embedded in the white matter of each hemisphere near its base. The thalamic cells relay the message on to the cerebral cortex. In this way we receive conscious information about the positions of the limbs and their movements, as well as sensations of light touch.

Now let us turn to the other set of sensory fibres, those which crossed over as soon as they entered the cord. These are the fibres carrying sensations of pain, pressure, rough touch, heat and cold. They enter the cord in the ordinary way and form synapses with the cells of the posterior horn of grey matter on the same side. The new fibres cross to the opposite side of the cord and run straight up in the lateral column, through the medulla, pons and midbrain, until they come in their turn to the thalamus. There some of them end and their messages actually enter consciousness. Thalamic feeling includes sensations of crude pain and of extremes of temperature, that is, of heat above 45 degrees centigrade and of cold below 25 degrees centigrade. The rest of the sensations travelling by this route are relayed on to the cortex by the cells of the thalamus.

Most of our movements are not reflex: they are deliberate and voluntary. We perform them because we want to perform them. Such deliberate movements have their origin in the brain. We decide to move one hand, say, and the brain sends a message down the spinal cord to the exact group of anterior horn cells supplying the muscles we intend to use.

Sending Messages

These messages start in the cells of the motor cortex, the fibres of which form two great tracts (Fig. 31), one from each hemisphere. These are the pyramidal tracts, which run down through the hemispheres and midbrain to the medulla where they divide into two. One half of each tract runs down in the anterior column of its own side of the cord, and the other half crosses over and runs down in the lateral column of the opposite side. The point of crossing is called the motor decussation (Fig. 32).

In the cord, fibres from the *crossed* tracts form synapses with the anterior horn cells of their own side, whereas fibres from the *direct* tracts form synapses with the anterior horn cells of the opposite side of the cord. The net result is exactly the same in both cases; messages which start in the left side of the brain finally take effect on muscles on the right side of the

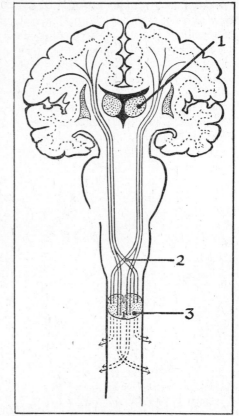

Fig. 31. *Path of nerves carrying messages from brain to muscles (motor tracts). 1, Nerve centre in brain (thalamus); 2, point in medulla oblongata (motor decussation); 3, anterior column of spinal cord.*

body, and vice versa, whether they travel by way of the direct or by the crossed pyramidal tracts.

The significance of the motor and sensory decussations will now be clear; all messages from the left side of the body finally reach consciousness in the right side of the brain, and all motor messages starting from the right side of the brain finally take effect on the left side of the body, and vice versa. Thus each half of the body is controlled by the opposite half of the brain. No satisfactory reason is known why this should be so.

We now examine the nerves leaving

the cord and running to all the out-lying parts of the body. Thirty-one pairs of spinal nerves (Fig. 33) spring from the cord and leave the spinal canal by means of passages, called foramina, between the vertebræ. During early development the spinal cord occupies the whole of the spinal canal, and the spinal nerves pass out horizontally through the foramina; but as the embryo grows, the vertebral column

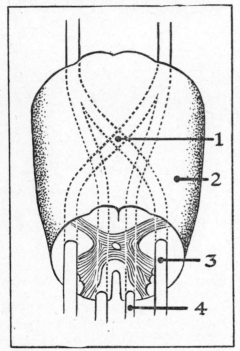

Fig. 32. *Passage of motor nerves. 1, Motor decussation; 2, medulla oblongata; 3 and 4, tracts by which nerves pass. Note that nerves from left side of brain affect right side of body and vice versa.*

becomes far longer than the spinal cord, and the nerves have to lengthen considerably in order to reach their point of exit from the spinal canal. At the lower end of the cord, indeed, the nerves have to run so far before they can escape from the canal that they form a thick bundle, sufficiently like a horse's tail to have been called the cauda equina (Fig. 33).

The spinal nerves are named according to the level at which they leave the spinal canal, as follows: eight cervical, twelve dorsal or thoracic, five lumbar, five sacral and one coccygeal. The presence of eight spinal nerves in the cervical region, where there are only seven vertebræ, is explained by the fact that the first pair of spinal nerves leave the canal between the atlas and the skull.

The spinal nerves are mixed nerves; they contain both motor and sensory fibres; but these fibres do not enter the cord together. Each spinal nerve arises from the cord by two roots, a motor root and a sensory root, and these two roots then fuse together. Thus if we were to cut the spinal cord across at the level of a pair of spinal nerves we should see four bundles of fibres sprouting from it—two motor roots near the front and two sensory roots near the back. Just outside the cord we should find the motor root from each half of the cord uniting with the sensory root of the same side to form a spinal nerve. It is convenient to talk of nerves leaving the cord because this is what they appear to do; actually the motor fibres are running outwards to the muscles and the sensory fibres are running inwards to the cord.

Nerve Centres

On each sensory root, just before it plunges into the cord, there is a small swelling. This is the dorsal root ganglion (Fig. 33); it is made up of a cluster of sensory nerve cells.

The sensory nerve cells which lie in the dorsal root ganglia have axons rather different from those of other nerve cells. Sensations reach the spinal cord and brain from all over the body, from every part of the skin, from the muscles, joints, intestines, glands and other organs. The sensory fibres have to be long enough to reach from the dorsal root ganglia to each of these structures. In addition to this the messages received have to be conveyed on from the cells in the dorsal root ganglion into the spinal cord. In some of the simpler animals this need is met by a sensory cell with two axons: one axon bringing in the messages from the outlying parts, and another, leaving the cell at the opposite side, carrying messages into the spinal cord. Such a cell is called a bipolar nerve cell (Fig. 35). But this rather primitive arrangement has been abandoned by the vertebrates, in which each of the sensory cells in the dorsal root ganglia has only one axon, like any other nerve cell. Instead of proceeding as a

cluding pain, touch, pressure, heat and cold. These various feelings are transmitted to the nerve fibre by special groups or clusters of cells which can be compared with the taste buds in the tongue: they are specially designed to pick up one kind of sensation and one kind only. They are sometimes called end organs because the nerve fibre ends in them.

The end organs conveying sensations of touch have a thin capsule; a sensory nerve axon enters this capsule, makes several spiral turns and breaks up into a

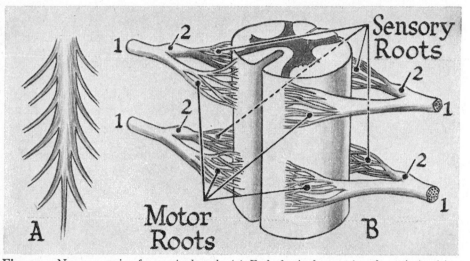

Fig. 33. *Nerves running from spinal cord.* (A) *End of spinal nerve (cauda equina).* (B) *1, spinal nerves; 2, nerve clusters (dorsal root ganglia).*

single fibre, however, this axon divides into two shortly after leaving the cell, one, the incoming fibre, arriving from the skin or some other part of the body, and the other, the central fibre, plunging straight into the spinal cord (Fig. 35). It is difficult to see any particular advantage in this arrangement over the more primitive one, but it certainly seems to be confined to the higher animals.

The nerve fibres which carry messages from the skin and other parts of the body are just like any other nerve fibres, but the sensations which they convey are very different. In the skin alone we can distinguish several different sensations, in-

network of tiny nodular fibres. These touch end organs are found in large numbers in the skin of the fingers and palm, as well as scattered elsewhere over the skin of the body. Touch is also transmitted by the hair follicles; nerve fibres enter the walls of the follicles, and give off branches which encircle the follicle or run vertically in its walls, finally ending in tiny nodules or flat plates.

Sensations of cold are thought to be conveyed by structures called the end bulbs of Krause (Fig. 36), which consist of a round capsule in which the axon loses its myelin sheath and forms a network, rather like that found in a touch nerve

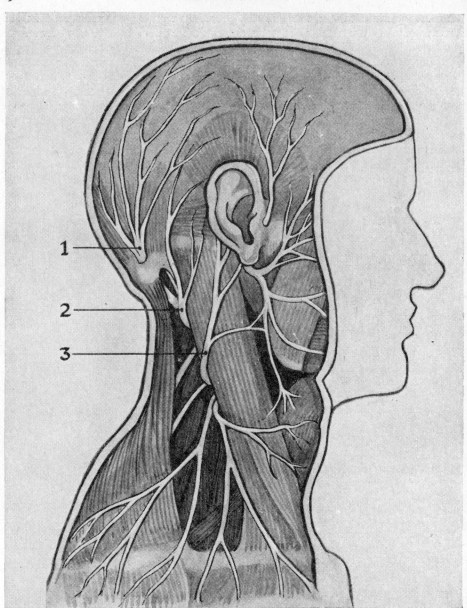

Fig. 34. *Nerves of the head and neck. The head is chiefly supplied by the cranial nerves which spring directly from the brain itself, and which include the nerves and the muscles of the face and the front of the neck, as well as the great nerves of special sense—the nerves of smell (olfactory), of sight (optic); and of hearing (auditory). The sense of taste is also served by fibres from cranial nerves. In addition to the cranial nerves, some nerves which serve the head are branches of the nerves of the neck, deriving ultimately from the spinal cord. 1, Nerve running up back of head to supply scalp (great occipital); 2, smaller nerve of back of head (lesser occipital); 3, branch running from neck to serve the ear (great auricular).*

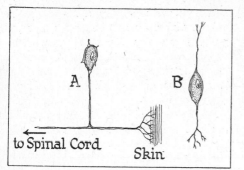

Fig. 35. *Nerve cells connected with spine. (A) Unipolar cell, possessing single axon which divides into two branches. (B) Bipolar cell, possessing two axons.*

ending. Warmth is probably transmitted by another type of end organ, cylindrical in shape; one or two axons pierce the cylinder somewhere along its length and, after branching once or twice, end in flattened expansions.

Pain is conveyed by naked axons which have lost their sheaths and which branch freely among the cells of the epidermis; teeth, to our grave disadvantage, are supplied only with naked nerve endings of this kind, though fortunately they are buried deep in the pulp of the tooth.

In the deeper parts of the skin of the hands and feet and also in the tendons, the muscles, the joints and the periosteum of bones, in the peritoneum, pleura and pericardium, end organs of another type are to be found in large numbers. They are called Pacinian bodies (Fig. 36) and are relatively large oval structures, large, that is to say, by comparison with the other end organs, though actually microscopic. They are made up of concentric layers of cells which make them look under the microscope rather like an onion. Several axons enter each of these bodies, and one of them runs to the end of the Pacinian body, where it forms a flattened expansion. End organs of this type are thought to convey sensations of pressure. Those in the neighbourhood of muscles, joints and tendons tell us something of the

positions of these joints. If we shut our eyes, for example, we can still state accurately exactly what position our hands, feet, fingers or any other parts of our body are occupying. Lacking this sense of position we should have to look to see what had become of an arm or a leg before making a statement about it, and walking would be impossible, for without the detailed information constantly reaching the cerebellum from the muscles and joints, we should be quite unable to make the countless adjustments entailed in maintaining our balance. The Pacinian bodies, therefore, convey one of the most important forms of sensation. Yet it is a purely domestic sensation, so to speak; it is a message whose origin lies inside, not outside, the body.

We must now trace the course of the motor nerves when they leave the spinal cord. The fibres run out of the cord by way of the anterior (motor) nerve root and join with the sensory fibres of the posterior nerve root to form the spinal nerve. After the spinal nerves have left the vertebral

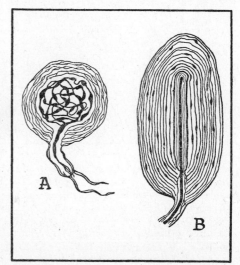

Fig. 36. *End organs of nerves. (A) Nerve ending conveying sensations of cold (end bulb of Krause). (B) Nerve ending conveying sensations of touch, pressure and position of parts of the body (Pacinian bodies).*

canal, they begin to branch and distribute fibres to the various organs of the body, including the muscles and the glands. Motor fibres which end up in muscles branch freely towards the end and finally form thick, irregular terminal branches, which have no sheath, but which rest in

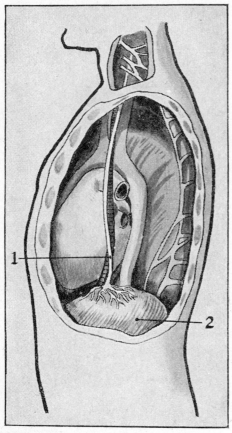

Fig. 37. *Nerves concerned in breathing. 1, Branch running from network of nerves in the neck through the chest and down to the diaphragm (phrenic nerve); 2, diaphragm.*

a special bed of protoplasm in the body of the muscle fibre. We do not know how messages are transmitted from one neuron to another and we are equally ignorant about the way in which a nerve fibre causes a muscle fibre to contract. The point at which the motor fibre comes into contact with the muscle fibre is called the motor

end plate, and it is by some change, probably chemical, in this end plate that the nervous message is passed on to the muscle, which translates it into terms of muscular action.

The spinal nerves between them supply the body and limbs. The head is chiefly supplied by the cranial nerves, which spring from the brain itself. The cranial nerves include nerves to the muscles of the face and the front of the neck, as well as the three great nerves of special sense—smell, sight, and hearing. The sense of taste is also served by fibres from these cranial nerves.

Spinal Nerves

Thirty-one pairs of spinal nerves serve all the rest of the body. Each nerve of a pair serves its own side of the body and does precisely the same work as its fellow of the opposite side. It will be as well to bear this in mind when reading the following description, which otherwise might be rather misleading; when the sciatic nerve is mentioned, for example, it must be remembered that there are two sciatic nerves—one in each leg; in the same way there are two phrenic nerves, two brachial nerves and so on.

The spinal nerves, after leaving the vertebral canal, branch and make connexions with each other, and the networks formed by their communicating strands are called plexuses. The plexuses formed have been named according to their position as follows:—

The cervical plexus, formed by the upper four cervical, or neck, nerves.

The brachial plexus, formed by the lower four cervical and the first thoracic, or chest, nerves.

The lumbar plexus, formed by the upper four lumbar nerves.

The sacral plexus, formed by the fifth lumbar and the upper three sacral nerves.

The coccygeal plexus, formed by the lower two sacral and the coccygeal nerves.

A large branch from the second cervical

nerve forms the great occipital nerve (Fig. 34), which runs up the back of the head to supply the scalp.

The cervical plexus, formed from the upper four cervical nerves, supplies branches to the muscles at the front and sides of the neck, and a small ascending branch, the great auricular, to the ear. By far the most important nerve derived

The lower four cervical nerves and the first thoracic nerve form the brachial plexus (Fig. 38) which sends nerves to the arm and shoulder. The first nerve to be given off is the long thoracic (Fig. 39), which runs down the side of the chest wall to supply the anterior serratus muscle; but most of the branches of the plexus are given off in the armpit. Here

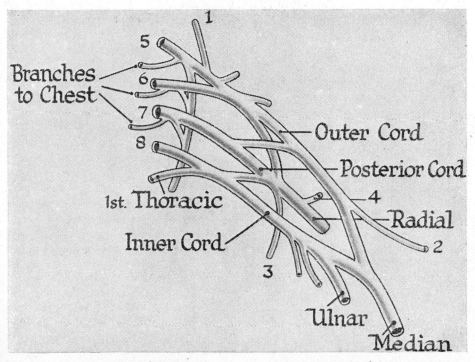

Fig. 38. *Nerve centre supplying branches to arm and shoulder (brachial plexus). 5, 6, 7 and 8, Lower four nerves of the neck (cervical nerves); 1, fourth cervical nerve; 2, nerve supplying muscles on front of upper arm, and the skin over them (musculocutaneous nerve); 3, branches to muscles of back; 4, branches to muscles of shoulder joint.*

from this plexus, however, is the phrenic nerve (Fig. 37), which runs down through the neck and thorax until it reaches the diaphragm. The phrenic nerves are the motor nerves to the diaphragm, and therefore of great importance in respiration. When we get the hiccup it is due to irregular spontaneous motor impulses travelling down the phrenic nerves, and causing contractions of the diaphragm.

M.H.B.—G*

the network of nerves sorts itself into three large cords, called from their position the outer, inner and posterior cords.

The outer cord sends a branch to the muscles of the chest and then divides into two branches. One of these joins with a branch from the inner cord to form an important nerve, the median; the other, the musculocutaneous nerve, supplies the muscles on the front of the upper arm and

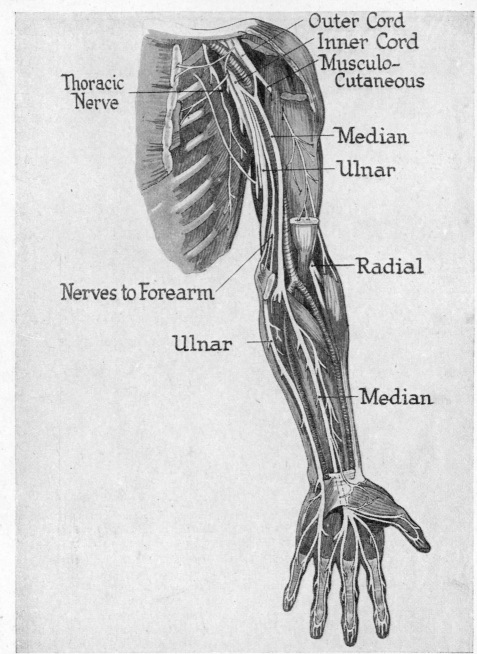

Fig. 39. *Nerves of the arm. From the network of nerves in the armpit, branches go to the muscles of the chest and to the front of the upper arm. Other branches join to form the median nerve, running into the forearm and supplying the skin of the palm. The ulnar and radial nerves run down the upper arm to the muscles of the forearm and also have branches in the skin of the hand and the fingers. The median nerve runs along the arm to the thumb.*

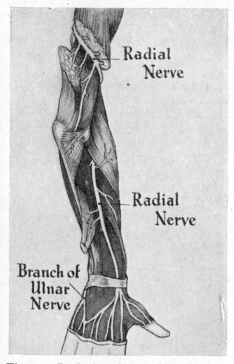

Fig. 40. *Back view of nerves of the forearm. Notice how the radial nerve supplies muscles of back of forearm and almost all the muscles of the back of the hand.*

the skin over them. The inner cord sends one branch to the median nerve and also gives rise to the ulnar nerve. The posterior cord sends branches to the muscles round the shoulder joint, and then, after winding round to supply the muscles on the back of the upper arm, passes behind the elbow to enter the forearm as a third important nerve, the radial (Fig. 40).

The median (Fig. 39) runs down the upper arm, lying close beneath the border of the biceps muscle, and passes into the forearm where it supplies the muscles lying towards the outer side and some of the small muscles of the thumb. It also gives off a sensory branch which supplies the skin of most of the palm (Fig. 41).

The ulnar nerve (Fig. 39), which springs from the inner cord, runs down behind the inner side of the elbow and supplies the muscles on the inner side of the forearm and some of the small muscles of the little finger. It also sends sensory branches to the skin covering the little finger and half the ring finger; this accounts for the fact that a blow on the elbow often produces tingling and pins and needles in the outer part of the hand. We remark on such occasions that we have bumped our funnybone, but actually the sensation is caused not by an injury to the humerus but by pressure on the ulnar nerve where it passes round the elbow.

The third great nerve, the radial (Fig. 40), supplies all the muscles lying at the back of the forearm and sends a long sensory branch down to supply the skin over the back of the hand except that covering the little finger and the inner side of the ring finger, which is supplied by the ulnar.

The twelve thoracic, or chest, nerves are intercostal nerves, running round the chest wall in grooves beneath the ribs. They supply the intercostal muscles and the skin of the chest wall.

The upper four lumbar nerves form the lumbar plexus (Fig. 42), which lies inside the abdominal cavity embedded in the great psoas muscle on either side. This plexus sends branches to the muscles of the abdominal wall and the skin over them, and one important branch, the femoral (Fig. 43), which crosses the brim of the

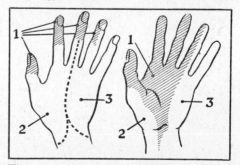

Fig. 41. *Nerve supply of the hand. 1, Median nerve, supplying most of palm; 2, radial nerve, supplying most of back of hand; 3, ulnar nerve, supplying rest of hand.*

pelvis, supplies the muscles on the front of the thigh. The femoral nerve gives off a sensory branch, the long saphenous, which travels all the way down to the foot, supplying the skin on the inner side of the leg and sole.

The fifth lumbar nerve joins the upper three sacral nerves to form the sacral plexus. The nerves springing from this plexus supply the muscles round the pelvis, the muscles on the back of the thigh and all the muscles of the leg and foot. The word leg is used by anatomists to refer to everything below the knee, the region above the knee being termed the thigh; the thigh therefore corresponds to the upper arm and the leg to the forearm. After supplying the muscles round the pelvis, the nerves from the sacral plexus form one thick cord, the great sciatic nerve (Fig. 43), the largest nerve in the body. This runs down among the muscles at the back of the thigh and supplies them; it also sends a branch down to the calf muscles before emerging into the space behind the knee-joint. Finally it divides into two branches; one of these, the tibial, runs down the leg, buried under the calf muscles, some of which it supplies before passing into the foot to supply the muscles

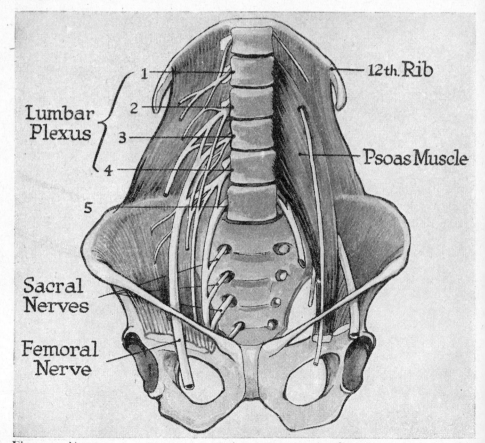

Fig. 42. *Network of nerves of loin and their connexions (lumbar plexus): 1, 2, 3 and 4, Upper four nerves of loin; 5, fifth nerve of loin, joining with upper nerves of the base of the spine to form the sacral plexus, which supplies nerves to the pelvis, back of thigh, leg and foot. The femoral nerve crosses the pelvis and supplies the muscles on the front of the thigh*

of the great toe and the little toe. The other branch of the sciatic, the common peroneal, winds round to the front of the leg and supplies all the remaining muscles of the leg and foot. The sciatic nerve is thus a very important one.

The coccygeal plexus is formed from the last two sacral nerves and the coccygeal nerve. This little plexus is more important than it looks: it supplies the organs lying in the pelvic cavity.

So far we have been studying the nerves which carry conscious sensation and those which send messages to voluntary muscles. But a large number of messages go out from the brain which are not under conscious control—to the sweat glands of the skin, the heart and blood vessels, the intestines and other abdominal organs, the lungs and bronchi.

Effects of Anger

We can recognize changes produced in this way, though we have no conscious part in producing them. When we are angry or frightened, for example, several startling things happen to us: we breathe more deeply and our hearts beat faster; our blood pressure rises and at the same time the surface of the body feels hot. The phrase "keep cool" springs from this sense of heat felt by angry or excited people. Our sweat glands begin to pour out moisture, and it is a common observation that a man may sweat with fear. If his alarm is great the pupils of his eyes will dilate, his upper eyelids be drawn back, and a small muscle at the back of the eyeball may contract, causing the eye to protrude. The little muscles round the hair follicles contract, producing goose-flesh, and the man may begin to shiver with fear, or tremble with rage, as the case may be. The muscles round the hair follicles may contract so forcibly that the hair actually stands on end. We are accustomed to seeing the hair rise on an angry dog, and speak of his hackles being up. Secretion from the salivary glands may

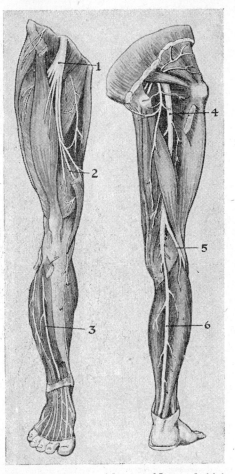

Fig. 43. *Nerves of leg. 1, Nerve of thigh (femoral); 2, branch of thigh nerve running to sole (long saphenous); 3 and 6, nerves of skin (anterior and posterior tibial); 4, nerve of back of thigh and calf (sciatic); 5, branch of sciatic nerve, the largest nerve in the body, running to front of leg (peroneal).*

be free, and it is this which causes a man to foam at the mouth.

In addition to all these outward signs of fear and anger there are changes in the internal economy of the body. Digestion ceases; the peristaltic waves which normally pass continuously down the intestine come to a stop, the bowel remains relaxed and the sphincters closed. The body requires energy and blood for other and

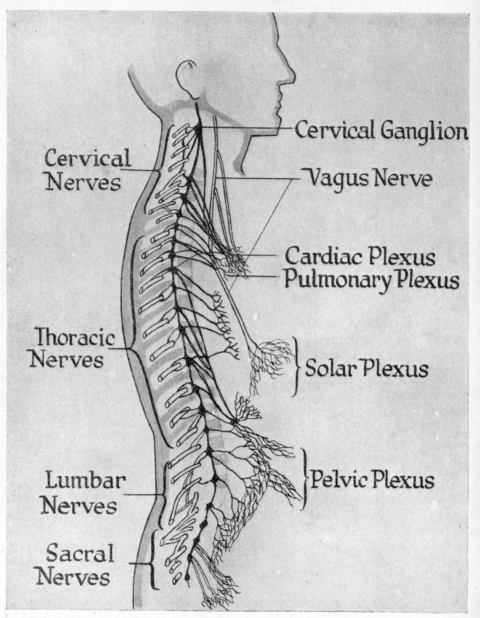

Fig. 44. *The sympathetic system. The sympathetic nerves branch out from the spinal cord, and carry messages to the many organs of the body which are not under conscious control, such as heart and blood vessels, lungs, intestines and other abdominal organs. The branches from the spine form networks concerned with special areas. The cardiac plexus acts on the lungs. The solar plexus is the chief network affecting the blood vessels and muscles of the abdomen and the digestive system. The vagus nerve is the chief member of the parasympathetic group, and branches to the heart, liver, intestines, etc., have the effect of offsetting the actions of the sympathetic system, such as increasing the heart-beat and blood pressure.*

more warlike purposes than digestion. The bulk of the blood is circulating through the voluntary muscles.

The body, then, undergoes a definite set of changes in face of danger, changes which for convenience we may call the body's preparations for war. The opposite picture is seen when no danger threatens, and the body assumes the duties of peace. At such times the heart-beat is slow and calm and the blood pressure normal; the pupil is small and the eyelids may droop lazily. The skin is cool and dry, digestion proceeds actively and the hair remains lying down.

Autonomic System

All these changes are governed by two sets of nerves, antagonistic to each other, the sympathetic nerves (Fig. 44) and the parasympathetic nerves. These two sets together constitute the autonomic system. The sympathetic system, despite its name, is the one which prepares the body for warfare, and the parasympathetic takes charge in times of peace.

The sympathetic nerves leave the spinal cord with the motor nerve roots of all the thoracic and the upper two or three lumbar nerves. The parasympathetic nerves are less easy to follow, because some of them take origin from the brain and travel in cranial nerves, and the rest leave the spinal cord with the nerves of the sacral region. Classifying the autonomic system from above downwards, we get:—

1. Cranial parasympathetic nerves (travelling in the third, seventh, ninth and tenth cranial nerves).
2. Sympathetic nerves (travelling in all the thoracic, and the upper two or three lumbar nerves).
3. Sacral parasympathetic nerves (travelling in the second and third sacral nerves).

Sympathetic Nerves

The nerve cells of the sympathetic system lie midway between the anterior and the posterior horns of grey matter of the spinal cord. The fibres travel out from the cord with the anterior (motor) root, but they soon leave the spinal nerve as a fine strand of white fibres which ends in a sympathetic ganglion (Fig. 45). A chain of sympathetic ganglia lies on each side of the vertebral column, each ganglion being attached to a spinal nerve by a fine strand of sympathetic fibres. The strand is known as the white ramus communicans (Fig. 45). From the ganglion a fresh relay of fibres carries the sympathetic message forward; the new fibres, however, have no myelin sheaths and are therefore grey, not white. These grey fibres leave the ganglion and return to one or other of the spinal nerves as a second slim strand, the grey ramus communicans (Fig. 45); so that each sympathetic ganglion is attached to one or more spinal nerves by white and grey rami. In addition, each ganglion in the chain is attached to the ganglia above and below. The lower ganglia send rami to the coccygeal and sacral nerves, so that sympathetic fibres travel with the spinal nerves and are able to serve all the outlying parts of the body.

Head and Neck

Sympathetic fibres to the head and neck follow a special course. They pass from the motor nerve roots in the neck to the three top ganglia, the cervical, in the sympathetic chain which lie at either side of the neck close to the spine. Fresh relays of grey fibres leave these ganglia and form a network round the internal carotid artery; they travel up with it to supply the little muscle which dilates the pupil and the muscles which draw back the upper lid and force the eyeball forward.

Other fibres from the cervical ganglia form a network round the external carotid artery, and send branches to supply the skin of the face; they also send fibres to the salivary and lachrymal glands, causing them to pour out their respective secretions. An angry person may cry with rage as well as foam at the mouth.

The cervical ganglia also send branches to the organs in the chest. Several important branches pass to the heart, forming the network of the cardiac plexus (Fig. 44). They cause the heart to beat rapidly and forcibly so that the body muscles receive a rich supply of blood. Other fibres pass to the bron-

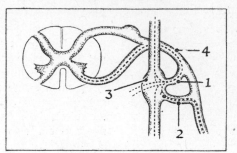

Fig. 45. *Connexion of sympathetic nerves with spinal column. The sympathetic nerve leaving the spinal column through 4, a group of spinal nerves (spinal ganglion) becomes 1, a fine strand of white fibres (white ramus communicans). This ends in 3, a cluster of sympathetic nerves (sympathetic ganglion). From there it goes forward as 2, a strand of grey fibres (grey ramus communicans).*

chial tubes, causing the muscles in their walls to relax and the tubes themselves to dilate so that more air can reach the lungs.

Sympathetic fibres to the abdominal organs form three well-defined nerves, the splanchnic, on each side. These end in some large ganglia, the prevertebral, lying in front of the spine. From these ganglia fresh relays of fibres set out and form networks, or plexuses, which supply the abdominal organs.

Solar Plexus

The chief of these is the solar plexus (Fig. 44), of which every one has heard; it sends branches to all the abdominal blood vessels and to the muscular coats of the digestive tract. A blow on the solar plexus causes widespread results, as we all know. In the ordinary way the abdominal blood vessels are moderately dilated, but when we are in fighting trim the sympathetic system causes them to contract. This is because we need as much blood as possible in our muscles, and we get it by cutting down our blood supply to the digestive tract. When we are ready to fight, then, the blood vessels in the muscles dilate, but the blood vessels in the abdomen contract; and this has the

effect of raising the blood pressure, because the heart is pumping hard against the resistance caused by the narrowing of the blood vessels. If a man in this state is struck over the solar plexus his abdominal sympathetic nerves are paralysed by the shock, and the abdominal blood vessels, which a moment before were tightly contracted, suddenly dilate, his blood pressure falls acutely and blood drains away from his limbs and brain to collect in his abdominal vessels. No wonder he feels faint and helpless, and, as we say, "winded."

Sympathetic nerves run to all the abdominal organs; some arrest the movements of the digestive tract, some relax the bladder and contract its sphincter; others cause the liver to release stores of glycogen and convert it into glucose, and others act on the spleen, causing it to release stored red cells into the blood. In fact, the sympathetic system, wherever its fibres are to be found, induces those changes in the body which we saw to be associated with fright or with preparations for hostile action.

Finally, sympathetic fibres pass to the suprarenal glands (*see* CHAPTER IX) and cause them to pour into the blood stream a substance called adrenalin, which produces very much the same effects chemically as the sympathetic system produces by nervous action.

Unconscious Control

Just as the anterior horn cells in the spinal cord are governed by messages travelling down from the brain in the pyramidal tracts, so the sympathetic cells in the cord are probably subject to higher, though not conscious, control. The higher centres governing the sympathetic system are thought to lie among those little clusters of grey matter below the thalami (Fig. 30) at the base of the hemispheres. This region, the subthalamic, as it is called, is very little understood at present but is engrossing the interest of physiologists all over the world.

In the sympathetic system we noticed that the pathway for messages lay through two neurons, one cell lying in the cord and the other in a sympathetic ganglion. In the parasympathetic system the same general arrangement is found; two neurons carry the messages sent out, but the second cell, instead of lying in a ganglion some distance from the organ supplied, is usually found in the walls of the organ itself.

Parasympathetic Nerves

The parasympathetic fibres coming from the brain travel in four pairs of cranial nerves—the third, seventh, ninth and tenth (Fig. 19). Those running in the third nerves travel into the eye socket and supply the iris. Parasympathetic fibres cause the pupil to contract, having just the reverse effect from that of the sympathetic. The fibres travelling in the seventh or facial nerves run to the sublingual and submaxillary salivary glands; the parotid gland is supplied by parasympathetic fibres travelling in the ninth nerves.

The tenth or vagus nerves—the wanderers—are the really important members of the cranial parasympathetic group. They pass out of the skull and travel down through the neck and thorax to the abdomen, giving off branches all the way. These branches pass to the heart, bronchial tubes, liver, pancreas, stomach, intestines and kidneys, in fact to nearly all the structures supplied by the sympathetic system; and in every case the action of the vagus is antagonistic to that of the sympathetic nerves. Thus it slows the heart,

increases intestinal movement, constricts the bronchial tubes, and so on.

Now let us turn to the sacral group. These, as we have seen, travel in the second and third sacral nerves, but soon leave them, and combine to form a single nerve on each side, the nervus erigens or pelvic nerve. This nerve supplies the rectum, the bladder and the other pelvic organs; its action is the reverse of that of the sympathetic; it causes evacuation of the bladder and bowel and relaxation of their sphincters.

The sympathetic and parasympathetic systems thus have antagonistic but complementary functions. The sympathetic system, penetrating throughout the body, stimulates the action of the organs. It increases the rate of output of their special products, and puts the whole body in a state of tension. This it accomplishes by means of highly developed and specialized cells, and by an elaborate system of control which, though it may be set in being by stimuli or feelings of which we are conscious, such as the emotion of anger or fear, acts through machinery which is neither conscious nor deliberate. We cannot will our heart to beat more quickly nor our glands to produce their various fluids more abundantly; but these involuntary actions, carried out by the sympathetic system, bring about precisely the results we should have desired had we been able to control them consciously. In exactly the same way the parasympathetic nerves carry through the restoration of the system to its normal condition, again acting through a mechanism beyond our conscious control to bring about the bodily condition suited to our momentary need.

Thus these two great antagonists, the sympathetic and the parasympathetic systems, send their messages to every part of the body and between them prepare us to meet every condition of bodily peace or war. They are helped in this task by the chemical messengers which the endocrine glands send about the body.

CHAPTER IX

INTERNAL SECRETIONS

CHEMICAL SUBSTANCES IN BLOOD STREAM: HOW HORMONES ACT: PRIN-
CIPAL ENDOCRINE GLANDS: ACTION OF THYROID GLAND: PARATHYROID
GLANDS: SUPRARENAL GLANDS AND THEIR PRODUCTS: IMPORTANCE OF
PITUITARY GLAND: PRODUCTS OF PITUITARY: ACTION OF PANCREAS: SEX
GLANDS AND SEXUAL CHARACTERISTICS: THYMUS GLAND AND SPLEEN

MEN AND the higher animals are able to live in, and more harmoniously through, their environment because of a nervous system which enables the animal as a whole to respond to an event affecting only a part. The nervous system has been compared with a telephone service, keeping all outlying parts of the body in effective communication with the great central exchange, the brain.

Chemical Messengers

The body has a second great communicating system, the blood stream. Blood vessels travel as freely into every outlying structure as nerves, and may be compared with the canal system of a well-watered country such as Holland. Nature is economical: such an excellent method of transport can be made to fulfil a dual role, and so we find the blood carrying messages from one part of the body to another and acting as an auxiliary service to the nerves. These messages are delivered in the form of chemical substances which act only on the organs or tissues for which they are intended. They have been given the name of hormones, derived from the Greek word meaning to excite, because they excite the organs of the body to action. The action may be as sudden as the contraction of a group of blood vessels, or as prolonged as the slow steady growth of the bones, which goes on for years; and it may be speeded up or retarded by an excess or deficiency of the hormone concerned.

One of these hormones, called secretin, acts in a relatively simple way. Secretin, as such, does not ordinarily exist in the body, but a substance called prosecretin is always present in the cells lining the duodenum (see CHAPTER V).

Action of Hormones

During the process of digestion, food is retained in the stomach until it is thoroughly mixed with hydrochloric acid and partially digested; then the pyloric sphincter relaxes and some of the acid food passes into the duodenum. As soon as the acid comes into contact with the cells lining the duodenum, a chemical change occurs in the prosecretin which they contain. It is converted into secretin, which is absorbed by the blood vessels lying in the duodenal wall and carried off in the blood. It is carried right round the body but has no effect until it reaches one organ, the pancreas (see CHAPTER V). As soon as the pancreatic cells receive secretin from their blood supply they become active and pour out pancreatic juice; and this juice passes by way of the duct of the gland into the duodenum, and helps to digest the food. In this way the acid food entering the duodenum will set going the machinery necessary for its own digestion.

There are plenty of hormones similar to secretin; for example, products of tissue breakdown act as hormones on the liver, causing it to build up new substances; in the same way, carbon dioxide acts as a hormone to the respiratory centre in the brain, causing us to breathe more deeply.

Many important hormones are prepared by the endocrine or ductless glands, which pour their juices directly into the blood stream instead of into ducts. These juices maintain health, control growth and help the nervous system in its work.

The glands themselves are scattered about the body, and some have another function to perform besides that of producing an endocrine hormone or hormones. The pancreas, for example, is an endocrine gland, or gland of internal secretion, but in addition to the digestive juice it pours into the duodenum, it delivers into the blood stream a hormone (insulin) which prevents diabetes. So the adjective ductless for the glands in this group is really inaccurate; the pancreas has a perfectly good duct travelling to the wall of the duodenum and opening there, and though this duct has nothing to do with the part of the gland forming insulin, it is nevertheless a duct. The name endocrine gland is therefore more appropriate than ductless gland for this group.

At present the following endocrines are recognized: the thyroid, the parathyroids, the suprarenals, the pituitary, the pancreas, the sex glands (and placenta) and the thymus.

The endocrine gland whose function was first recognized was the thyroid (Fig. 1). It lies in the neck and consists of two lobes connected by a bridge. Under the microscope the thyroid is found to consist (Fig. 2) of cavities filled with a gelatinous material and lined with approximately square cells. The gelatinous material contains the thyroid hormone, thyroxin, which is necessary to normal development and health. Methods of studying the effects of an endocrine hormone are as follows:—

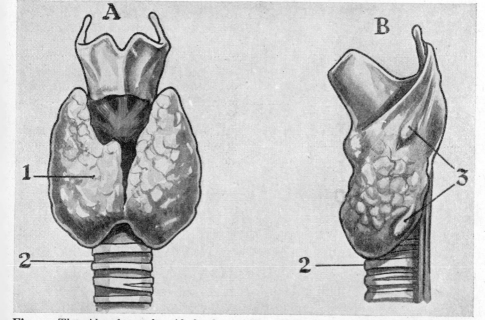

Fig. 1. *Thyroid and parathyroid glands.* (A) *Thyroid gland from front: 1, Thyroid gland; 2, part of windpipe (trachea).* (B) *Thyroid gland from side: 2, Trachea; 3, parathyroids. The thyroid gland lies in the neck, and consists of two lobes connected by a bridge.*

1. The gland producing the hormone can be removed from an animal, and the effects noted.
2. A normal animal can be given the hormone, so that it possesses an overdose.
3. The effects of diseases of the gland can be studied.

The thyroid has been investigated thoroughly along all these lines. If the thyroid of a tadpole is removed, the unfortunate creature will not develop into a frog. If thyroid extract is added to the water in which he lives, however, he resumes his growth in the normal way. If a normal tadpole is given extra thyroid in his water, his development speeds up enormously, and he becomes a frog, so to speak, by leaps and bounds. These experiments give us an idea of what to expect

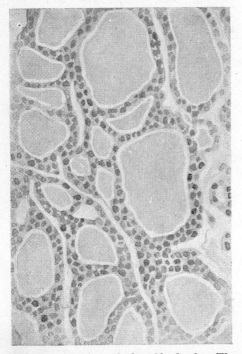

Fig. 2. *Section of thyroid gland. The cavities of the thyroid gland are filled with gelatinous material containing thyroxin, which is essential to normal development and health. Its deficiency produces cretinism.*

when the thyroid is diseased, absent or over plentiful in humans.

Sometimes children are born in whom the thyroid is absent or inactive; these children become cretins (Fig. 3). At birth, and for about six months afterwards, they appear to be normal healthy infants; then the signs of cretinism develop. The reason for the time lag is not perfectly clear. Perhaps before birth the baby receives enough thyroid from his mother's blood stream to carry him through the first six months, perhaps he receives for a time sufficient thyroid in her milk.

Inactive Thyroid

The thyroid deficiency usually begins to show itself during the latter part of the first year of life, and unless the child is treated, his development will be gravely affected. His growth, both physical and mental, is retarded; he becomes stunted, stupid and feeble. His muscles are so weak that they cannot maintain his bones in the proper positions; consequently the bones become bent and deformed. His tongue becomes too large for his mouth and protrudes, his nose is snub like a pig's, his hair is dry and scanty, his eyelids are swollen, and pads of fat develop on his shoulders. His abdomen swells, the navel protrudes and the skin all over the body becomes dry and coarse.

Happily, cretinism is rarely seen in England today, because doctors are so much on the look out for the signs of its onset. Consequently, every baby who shows mental and physical backwardness is likely to be given thyroid at once. Quite a small daily dose is enough to keep the symptoms at bay and restore normal growth and development.

Occasionally the thyroid gland of an adult person ceases to do its work, and a disease then develops which is in some ways the counterpart of cretinism. Obviously, since growth is complete, the patient will not become a dwarf, but he eventually becomes stupid and retarded mentally, his skin becomes dry, his hair falls out and he develops pads of fat over his collar bones and puffy swellings round his eyes. Like the cretin, the patient suffering from this condition, which is called myxœdema, can be cured by small doses of thyroid extract. The change in such cases is startling and delightful; the patient becomes his old self again, and grows fresh hair and eyebrows.

Thyroxin is a very important hormone; it is not only necessary to normal growth and development but essential to physical and mental health. It contains iodine in relatively large quantities, and so, in districts where the soil is deficient in iodine, disease of the thyroid is common; in the Alps and Himalayas, for example, goitre is commonly seen among the inhabitants. The thyroid may be so large as to hang down upon the chest, but in spite of its size the gland in such cases is often inactive and the patient may show signs of cretinism or myxœdema.

Over-active Thyroid

The signs of an over-active thyroid are quite different (Fig. 4). Patients who suffer from this condition have an anxious startled look, because their eyes become prominent and their eyelids are retracted. They are nervous, tremulous, and excited upon little provocation. The enlarged thyroid gland produces a swelling on the front of the neck, the heart always beats too fast, and patients often suffer from palpitation. They can usually be cured only by the removal of part of the too active thyroid gland.

Four more small glands lie in the neck close behind the thyroid; these are the parathyroids. If these glands are removed from an animal, the nervous system and muscles become highly excitable and various twitchings occur which may finally take the form of fits. This state of neuromuscular irritability is known as tetany; the animal cannot long survive without the parathyroid hormone, and

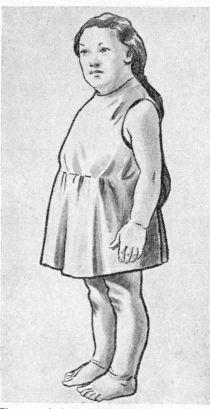

Fig. 3. *A cretin, suffering from the absence or inactivity of the thyroid gland. This shows itself in the retarding of growth, both physical and mental. Cretinism is rare in England.*

eventually will die from the convulsions.

The task of the parathyroid glands is to maintain the calcium in the blood stream at a steady level. When this level falls too low, tetany develops. Tetany may also develop in children as an accompaniment of rickets, but the parathyroids are not to blame in such cases, the calcium in the blood being diminished for other reasons than parathyroid deficiency. The treatment in either case is to inject calcium.

When the parathyroids become over-active, a rare disease develops. The active glands raise the calcium in the blood far above its normal level, by draining calcium out of the bones, which become soft, and bend or break following the slightest injury. People so affected are as a rule completely crippled. In some cases a tumour of one of the parathyroids is present, and when this is removed patients recover their normal health.

The suprarenal glands lie one on the top of each kidney, fitting like a small cocked hat. Each gland consists of two parts, an outer portion called the cortex and a central part called the medulla. The origin of these two parts shows that in effect each suprarenal gland is two glands which have different origins and different tasks to perform (Fig. 5).

The medulla produces a hormone called adrenalin, which acts chemically to produce exactly the same results as the sympathetic system produces by nervous action. The medulla is, in fact, nervous in origin. It develops from cells derived from the original neural groove, which give rise also to the sympathetic ganglia.

The cortex has a very different history.

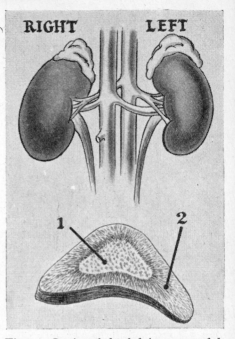

Fig. 5. *Section of glands lying on top of the kidneys (suprarenal glands). 1, Central portion (medulla); 2, outer portion (cortex). These are really separate glands. The medulla produces adrenalin, and helps the nervous system; the cortex produces cortin, which is concerned with sex development.*

It derives from the group of embryonic cells which give rise to the sex glands.

Remembering the sympathetic system, we can foretell what adrenalin will do. It raises the blood pressure by causing the abdominal blood vessels to contract, dilates the pupil of the eye, increases the blood supply to muscles, brings digestion to a stop by inhibiting movements of the intestinal wall, contracts the sphincters, and causes the liver to release supplies of sugar into the blood. The medulla of the suprarenal is our friend in emergencies by reinforcing the sympathetic system and preparing us to meet dangers.

The cortex of the gland has nothing to do with all this, and we know far less about it. We do know, however, that it is essential to life. If it is removed from an animal,

Fig. 4. *Effects of over-active thyroid gland. This results in nervousness and liability to over-excitement. The enlarged gland produces a swelling on the front of the neck.*

the appetite is lost, body weight falls and the creature becomes weak and apathetic and finally dies. Similar signs are seen when destructive disease of the cortex appears in man; tuberculosis of the suprarenals is usually responsible for this condition, which is known as Addison's disease. The patient becomes languid and steadily weaker, the skin becomes bronzed and the blood pressure is very low. At one time patients who suffered in this way invariably died, but now it is possible to make an extract from the suprarenal cortex which restores them to health. The extract contains cortin, the hormone of this part of the gland.

When this part of the gland becomes over-active in children, precocious development of the sexual organs follows, and a boy of four may show the development and secondary sexual characteristics of a full-grown man. Women with an over-active cortex become masculine in appear-ance and develop a moustache, a beard and a deep voice. The change also affects their character; from being normally feminine they become mannish and adopt the behaviour of the opposite sex.

The pituitary (Fig. 6) is the most remarkable gland of a remarkable series. It lies at the base of the brain, attached to it by a stalk called the infundibulum, and enclosed in a tiny bony box, the Turkish saddle (see CHAPTER I). It is made up of two lobes which have different origins and different functions. The anterior lobe develops from the embryonic mouth cavity and grows upwards to join the posterior lobe, which grows downwards from the brain to meet it. The anterior lobe becomes divided from the mouth cavity by the bones of the base of the skull, but the posterior lobe remains attached to the brain.

The more we learn about this gland, the more astonishing it appears. It is no bigger

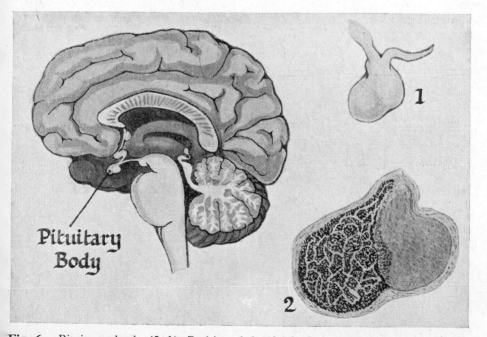

Fig. 6. *Pituitary gland. (Left) Position of the gland. It is enclosed in a bony structure lying at the base of the brain, to which it is attached. It governs activity of all the other glands, and maintains balance between them. (Right)* 1, *Pituitary gland enlarged;* 2, *section.*

than a pea and yet it produces more hormones than any other endocrine gland; moreover, it governs the activity of all the other glands and helps to maintain the balance between them. If it fails to do its work efficiently, the body's development becomes distorted.

Action of Pituitary

If the pituitary is removed from young animals (Fig. 7), the sex glands fail to develop, and the thyroid and the cortex of the suprarenals atrophy. If extracts of pituitary are injected into normal young rats they become nearly double the size of their brothers and sisters in the same litter. The pituitary manufactures a growth hormone, and also a number of other hormones. Two of these act on the thyroid and suprarenal cortex, and have been named respectively the thyrotropic hormone and the adrenotropic hormone. The pituitary affects the sex glands by two gonadotropic hormones. It produces a hormone called prolactin, which causes the mammary glands to secrete milk, and

there is evidence that the parathyroids are controlled by a parathyrotropic hormone. Finally, a hormone is present which raises the sugar content of the blood (thus antagonizing the action of insulin) which may be called the diabetogenic hormone.

All the hormones so far mentioned are made by the anterior lobe of the gland, and have been discovered only in comparatively recent years. The posterior lobe has been useful in medicine for a much longer period; it contains a hormone which acts on smooth muscle, especially that of the uterus, causing it to contract, and it can often be administered to advantage in the late stages of labour. In addition, the posterior lobe can cause a rise of blood pressure by stimulating the blood vessels to contract, and it also reduces the production of urine. Like the anterior lobe, it has the power of increasing the amount of sugar in the blood.

Disorders of the pituitary lead to surprising effects. All the giants (Fig. 8) seen in circuses possess an over-active anterior lobe. They can become tall only if the

Fig. 7. *Effect of removal of pituitary gland. If the pituitary is removed from young animals other glands fail to develop, and growth is retarded. The illustration shows two dogs from the same litter at one year old. (Left) Pituitary gland has been removed, as a result of which the animal has not grown to its normal size. (Right) Normal growth.*

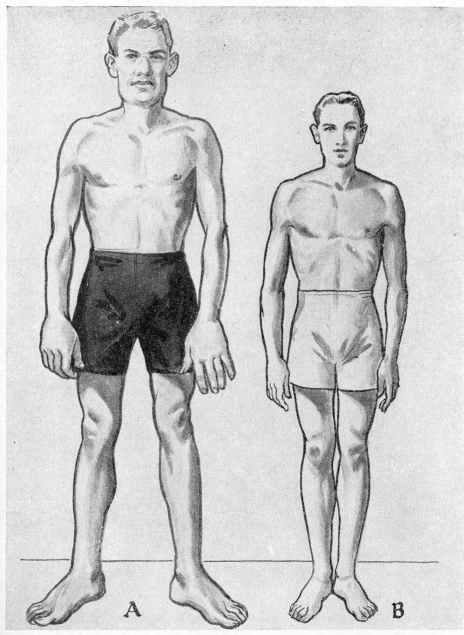

Fig. 8. *Effects of over-active pituitary gland. If over-activity of the pituitary sets in before the normal growing period of the individual concerned is ended, abnormal growth will take place and the condition known as gigantism will result. The illustration shows:* (A) *Gigantism compared with* (B) *normal growth. Notice the large face, even in relation to the over-developed body, heavy jaw, fleshy nose and lips and large hands and feet. If the over-activity occurs after the normal growth period is ended, it will not result in tallness, but in deformed over-development of these features. This condition is called acromegaly.*

over-activity sets in before the normal growing time is ended. An over-active pituitary in later life leads to a condition called acromegaly; the bones cannot grow in length but they become thicker and stronger, the jaw bone and head being particularly affected, so that the patient develops a heavy jowl and jutting brows. Hands and feet also become large, nose and lips thick and fleshy. The disease is progressive, and the patient goes on growing more and more deformed until the day of his death.

Under-active Pituitary

If the pituitary becomes under-active, dwarfism is likely to result. Pituitary dwarfs are of two types. In one, the patient has the appearance of a graceful child; he is intelligent and agreeable to look at, but he remains throughout life a sort of Peter Pan. The other type is fat and sleepy. The fat being rather feminine in distribution, he looks rather like a too plump girl.

Anterior lobe deficiency occurring later in life produces the same type of obesity, but without dwarfing. Complete atrophy of the anterior lobe occurring early in life causes a terrible condition of premature senility; thus a child of eight may show the sallow wrinkled skin, sparse hair and fragile bones of an old man.

Another disease due to deficiency of the posterior lobe is diabetes insipidus, in which the patient experiences extreme thirst and passes large quantities of very dilute urine. The condition is more annoying than dangerous, and can be relieved for several hours at a time by an injection of posterior lobe extract.

The Pancreas

Mention has been made already of the fact that the pancreas is an endocrine as well as a digestive gland. Embedded in its substance are small groups of cells which differ from the rest. These are the islets of Langerhans (see CHAPTER V), which produce insulin, a hormone having the task of converting glucose into a form in which the body cells can use it. When the islet cells cease to function the patient develops diabetes.

The ovaries in the female and the testes in the male (see CHAPTER XII) are not merely responsible for making reproductive cells. They are endocrine glands as well, and are responsible for those changes (secondary sexual characters) which occur at puberty and denote sexual maturity. These include breast development and the onset of menstruation in the female, deepening of the voice and development of the genital organs in the male.

Action of Sex Glands

If the sex glands are removed from immature animals, the organs of reproduction fail to develop properly and there are also changes in growth and the distribution of fat. The ovary produces two hormones called œstrin and progestin. Dotted about in the ovary are circular clumps of cells called Graafian follicles; every month one of these follicles grows larger and finally forms a tiny spherical cavity containing a ripe ovum. The cavity also contains fluid, and at this stage, the lining cells produce the hormone œstrin, which passes into the blood stream.

The Graafian follicle in the ovary ruptures, and the ovum passes into the Fallopian tube and thence into the uterus. Meanwhile the Graafian follicle has become filled with large yellow fatty cells derived from the lining, and at this stage is given the name of corpus luteum, or yellow body. The corpus luteum produces the second ovarian hormone, progestin. This is carried by the blood stream to the uterus, and causes it to prepare for the reception of the ovum.

If the ovum is not fertilized by a spermatozoon, it is discharged at the next menstrual period in company with the discarded uterine lining; in that case the corpus luteum soon disappears from the

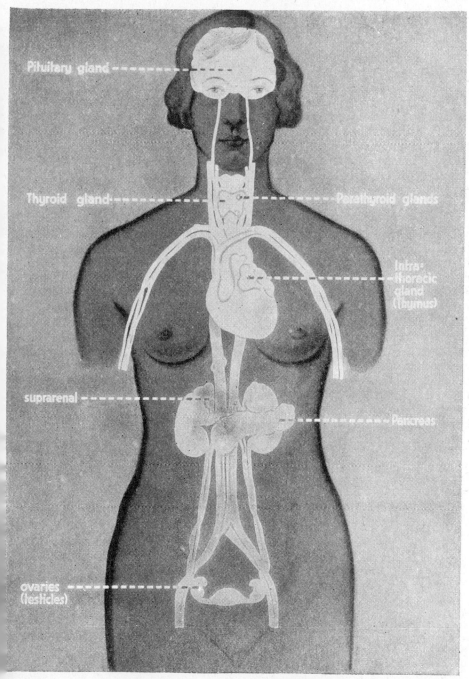

Pituitary gland

Thyroid gland

Parathyroid glands

Intra-
thoracic
gland
(Thymus)

suprarenal

Pancreas

ovaries
(testicles)

GLANDS OF INTERNAL SECRETION

This diagram shows the position of the chief glands which produce hormones, or chemical substances, which flow through the blood stream and affect the action of various organs.

ovary. But if the ovum is fertilized, the corpus luteum grows steadily larger throughout pregnancy, and the progestin which it pours into the blood stream is responsible for the growth and efficient activity of the placenta, or afterbirth.

The placenta is itself an endocrine gland. It produces two hormones, one of them being identical with œstrin and the other helping to maintain the growth of the corpus luteum. Thus the placenta and the corpus luteum are able to supplement each other's activity.

Sexual Development

During pregnancy large quantities of œstrin, derived from the placenta, appear in the urine. This has been made the basis of a test for pregnancy devised by Aschheim and Zondek, two German scientists. They injected a small quantity of urine from a pregnant woman into a sexually immature female mouse. After a few days the mouse was killed and its ovaries examined. Signs of sexual maturity were present in them: that is to say, some of the Graafian follicles had ripened and corpora lutea had been formed. This test has proved very useful, enabling doctors to make a diagnosis of pregnancy much earlier and more certainly than formerly.

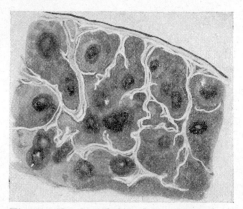

Fig. 9. *Section of the spleen. Bands from the capsule which encloses the spleen form a framework, in the interstices of which is a pulpy substance composed of lymphoid tissue.*

The œstrin produced by the Graafian follicle is responsible for the development of the secondary sexual characters in the mature female. The ripening of the Graafian follicles at puberty sets in train the physical and mental changes which convert the little girl into a young woman. The hormone of the male sex gland is prepared by the interstitial cells which lie between the groups of cells that are later to develop into spermatozoa. The hormone is called testosterone, and it is responsible for the normal development of the sex organs and for the secondary sex characters, such as the breaking of the voice and the growth of the beard. It does not appear in the urine of boys until they are about ten or eleven years old, but curiously enough it is present in the urine of normal women, though at present we do not know where it is formed in the female body or what purpose, if any, it serves there.

Of the two gonadotropic hormones produced by the anterior lobe of the pituitary which act on the sex glands, one causes the Graafian follicles of the female to mature and is thus responsible for the production of œstrin, and the second comes into play when the ovum has been discharged from the Graafian follicle and stimulates the growth of the corpus luteum, thus being responsible for the formation of progestin.

Both gonadotropic hormones act upon the testes, one stimulating the cells producing spermatozoa and the other the interstitial cells. Thus the pituitary plays a part in every endocrine activity.

Thymus Gland

In the infant the thymus gland lies in the lower part of the neck and extends down into the thorax behind the breast bone. It is made up of a cortex composed of cells resembling lymphocytes, and an inner portion in which round clusters of flattened cells, called the corpuscles of Hassall, are found. Their function, and

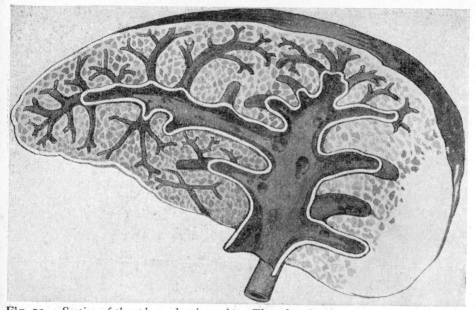

Fig. 10. *Section of the spleen, showing veins. The spleen is situated on the left side of the abdomen, its lower part resting on the left kidney. It manufactures white blood corpuscles (lymphocytes), and also acts as a reservoir for red corpuscles, which it liberates into the blood stream when need arises. It is also concerned with the destruction of worn-out red corpuscles.*

indeed the function of the whole gland, is not known. In any case, at puberty the thymus begins to get smaller, and by adult maturity has disappeared altogether. At one time an enlarged and persistent thymus used to be blamed for deaths under anæsthesia, though the mechanism by which disaster came about was never made very clear. Nowadays even that theory has fallen into disrepute, and we have to confess our ignorance of the purpose of the thymus.

The spleen (Figs. 9 and 10) is the largest of the ductless glands. It is of a dark purplish-grey colour, being gorged with blood, is about five inches long, weighs some six ounces, and in shape is an elongated ovoid. It is situated on the left side of the abdomen, close to, and just behind, the cardiac end of the stomach, the lower part resting against the left kidney. It is covered by a capsule from which bands pass into its substance, forming a kind of framework, in the interstices of which is a pulpy substance composed of lymphoid tissue. Distributed in this tissue are numerous small, round, whitish bodies known as Malpighian bodies or corpuscles.

Lymphocytes are manufactured in the spleen, and it also acts as a reservoir for red blood corpuscles, a supply of which it liberates into the blood stream when need arises, as after hæmorrhage. During fœtal life, the spleen plays an important part in blood production; but later, in addition to its storage function, it is concerned with the destruction of worn-out red corpuscles. This gland does not appear to manufacture any special hormone.

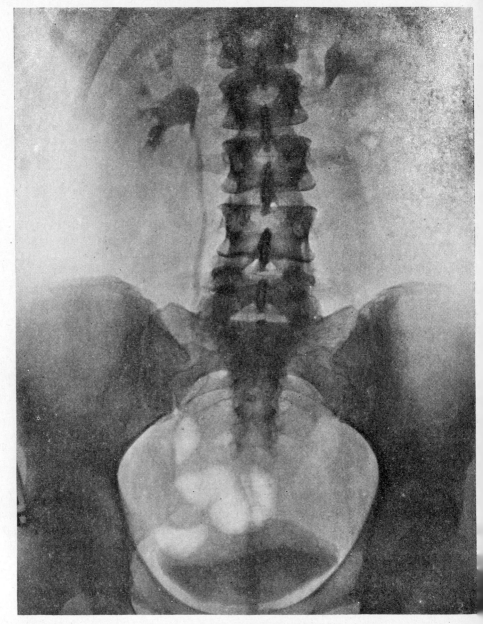

RADIOGRAPH OF THE KIDNEYS

This is a radiograph of the urinary tract, taken fifteen minutes after an intravenous injection, with iodine preparation as the opaque medium. The picture, which is reproduced by courtesy of Ilford Limited Radiographic Department, shows the lower ribs with lumbar vertebrae, sacrum and coccyx below; the pelvic bones are on either side. The outline of the kidneys can be faintly seen under the lowest ribs, the thin light line on one side of the spine being a ureter, with the bladder below as a light shadow within the pelvic bones.

CHAPTER X

THE KIDNEYS AND THEIR FUNCTION

LOSING MATTER FROM THE BODY: FUNCTION OF KIDNEYS: POSITION AND
COMPOSITION OF KIDNEYS: URETER AND KIDNEY PELVIS: BLADDER AND
URETHRA: CONSTRUCTION OF BLADDER: TUBULES AND GLOMERULI: BLOOD
SUPPLY OF KIDNEYS: HOW THE KIDNEYS WORK: URINE AND URINATION:
EFFECTS OF EXCITEMENT ON THE KIDNEYS, TEMPERATURE AND DISEASE

IN THE course of a year, an average man takes into his body in the form of food, water and oxygen, about three thousand pounds of matter. What happens to it all? Obviously he has not increased by anything approaching that amount in weight. Yet we may be quite sure that no matter has been lost (that is, utterly destroyed), though it may have changed its form; and we find, as a matter of fact, that a man loses from his body every year in material pretty much the equivalent in weight of what he has put into it. He may be a few pounds heavier or lighter by the end of the year, but that is neither here nor there; at most he will have gained or lost, except in cases of serious illness, about the equivalent of a day's intake of matter.

Bodily Expenditure

Four principal means by which matter passes from the body are the lungs, the intestines, the skin, and perhaps most important of all, the kidneys. A nursing mother in addition loses a certain amount of matter in feeding her child, and there are various minor ways whereby loss is experienced, but normally the four methods named are the principal instruments of bodily expenditure.

Water and carbon dioxide are, perhaps, the commonest products of all combustion. We get rid of these by our lungs.

We may lose as much as a pint of water a day in our breath alone, and normally we lose about the same amount in the form of invisible perspiration from the skin. On a hot day, or if we engage in strenuous exercise, the loss of water in the form of sweat may be very much greater. A certain amount is regularly lost from the bowels in the acts of excretion; but the principal system by which water is normally passed from the body is that which includes the kidneys and the bladder.

Function of Kidneys

The waste that is got rid of by means of the intestines is ordinarily matter that never in a strict sense entered into our bodily systems at all; that is to say, it has never been digested and carried away in the blood stream. The fæces are, in a real sense, the incombustible ashes, the roughage, which passes through the alimentary canal unchanged. The great energizer of our body is the substance called glucose. The usable parts of most starchy and sugary foods, such as bread and rice, are converted into glucose. As a result of its combustion, that is, its combination with oxygen in the body itself, energy is liberated and the glucose and oxygen are converted into water and carbon dioxide. But the body needs for its health and maintenance something more than sugar or

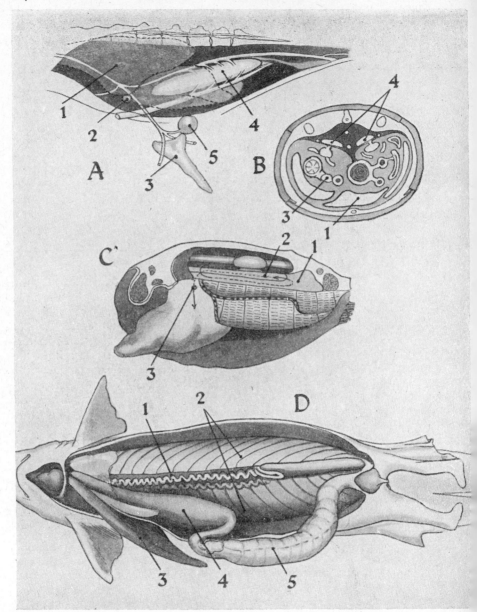

Fig. 1. *Kidneys and adjoining organs of various vertebrate animals. All vertebrate possess some kind of kidney or organ corresponding to it and fulfilling the same function though they are very different in shape from human kidneys. (A) Internal organs of frog (the overlying organs have been removed): 1, Liver; 2, gall-bladder; 3, pancreas; 4, kidneys 5, spleen. (B) Section of body of frog: 1, Liver; 3, pancreas; 4, kidneys. (C) Organ corresponding to kidney (renal organ) of mussel: 1, Renal gland; 2, entrance or vestibule of gland 3, external aperture of gland. (D) Internal organs of shark (overlying organs removed) 1, Main kidney tube; 2, side, or lateral, tube; 3, right lobe of lung; 4, stomach; 5, intestine*

other forms of carbohydrate. It needs, especially, a certain amount of suitable nitrogenous foods in the form of proteins. The elements that make up the proteins are present in every cell in our body and in nearly all our gland secretions, and they play an important part in every one of our vital activities. Cells are constantly breaking down, and need repairing or replacing; as a result, there is a lot of nitrogenous waste to be got rid of. This waste is mostly soluble in water or blood, but cannot be reduced at body temperatures to a state of vapour, and cannot therefore be got rid of by the lungs. It is the principal function of the kidneys to get rid of the nitrogenous waste of bodily life and bodily activity.

Kidneys in Vertebrates

In all the vertebrate animals some kind of kidney or renal organ is to be found (Fig. 1). They take various shapes, and only in mammals do they closely resemble human kidneys. One would have thought that in fishes, at any rate, no need exists for the provision of a separate receptacle for the urinary fluid secreted by the kidneys. Yet, as a fact, the great majority of fishes are provided with a definite bladder into which ureters empty. Herrings and pilchards are among the few fishes that seem to have no bladder, their ureter, or ureters, opening directly at the surface of the body behind the anus.

In reptiles, the kidneys much more nearly resemble those of birds and of mammals, though in serpents there is no bladder, and the ureters, as in the herring, open on the surface.

The kidneys in man lie at the back of the abdominal cavity at either side of the lumbar region of the spine (Fig. 2). They are about four inches long and their shape (Figs. 3 and 4) is characteristic enough to have given rise to the term kidney-shaped.

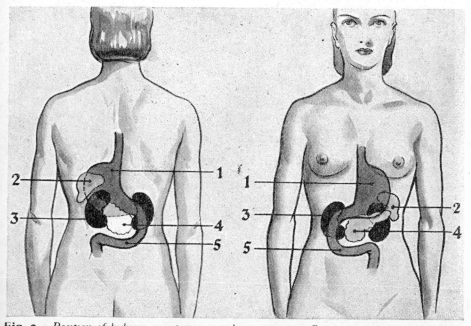

Fig. 2. *Position of kidneys in relation to other organs. 1, Stomach; 2, spleen; 3, kidneys at back of abdominal cavity; 4, pancreas; 5, part of small intestine (duodenum). The concave inside border of the kidney is called the hilum, and is attached to the canal down which urine flows to the bladder. The kidneys lie at the back of the abdominal cavity, in the loin region.*

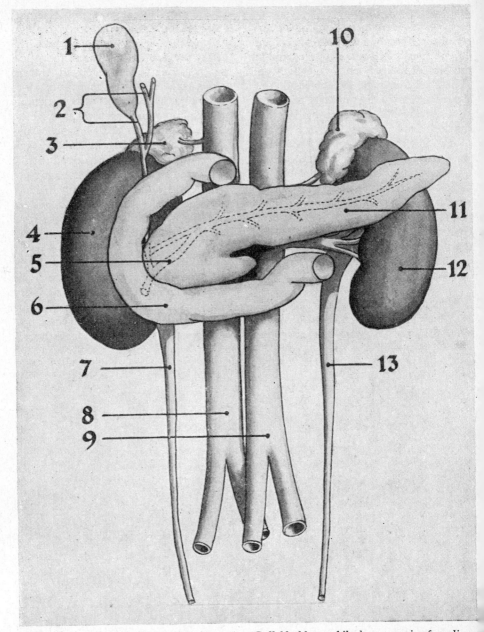

Fig. 3. *The kidneys and their attachments. 1, Gall-bladder; 2, bile ducts, running from liver; 3, gland lying on top of kidney (right suprarenal gland); 4, right kidney; 5, channel running from pancreas to small intestine (pancreatic duct); 6, first portion of small intestine (duodenum); 7, tube by which urine flows to reach the bladder (right ureter); 8, main vein of lower part of body (inferior vena cava); 9, main artery of body (abdominal aorta); 10, left suprarenal gland; 11, pancreas; 12, left kidney; 13, left ureter. The kidneys and their connexions with the bladder are the principal system by which the body gets rid of excess water*

Each of them is vertically placed alongside the spine (Fig. 5), with its concave border facing inwards towards the mid-line of the body; this concave border is called the hilum of the kidney and affords attachment to the ureter, the canal down which urine flows in order to reach the bladder.

Before birth the kidneys develop as lobules, which finally become fused into the smooth organ which we know; occasionally the lobulated appearance persists but gives rise to no ill effects. Sometimes the two kidneys are fused together at their upper poles—a condition known as horseshoe kidney from the shape of the united

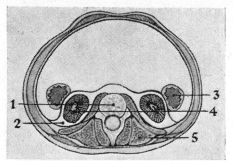

Fig. 5. *Cross-section of abdominal cavity, showing position of kidneys. 1, Spinal column; 2, layer of fat enclosing kidneys; 3, large intestine; 4, kidneys; 5, muscles of back.*

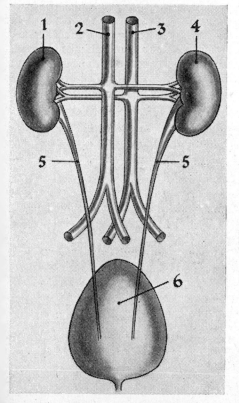

Fig. 4. *Kidneys, ureter and bladder. 1, Right kidney; 2, main vein of body (inferior vena cava); 3, main artery of body (aorta); 4, left kidney; 5, tubes running from kidneys to bladder (right and left ureters); 6, bladder.*

organs; this, again, causes no trouble unless it becomes necessary to remove one kidney for disease. Very occasionally one kidney fails to develop, in which case the other is likely to be specially large, and will apparently have no difficulty in efficiently carrying out the work of two.

The kidneys are embedded in a thick layer of fat and are enclosed in closely fitting fibrous capsules: a sheet of fascia stretches in front of them and anchors them to the vertebral column and the lumbar muscles. All the other organs in the abdominal cavity have a certain degree of freedom of movement, and can shift gently in relation to each other, like boats riding in a harbour. But the kidneys are fixed in place by the fat surrounding them and by their restraining sheet of fascia. Occasionally a kidney may slip its moorings, and be found wandering round the abdominal cavity as a so-called floating kidney. Floating kidneys rarely give rise to trouble, but if they do they can be stitched into position again at operation.

Each kidney is capped by a suprarenal gland (Fig. 6), a little triangular mass of glandular tissue which sits on the top of the kidney like a cocked hat. The suprarenals have nothing to do directly with the function or activity of the kidneys.

When a kidney is cut across (Fig. 7), it is found to consist of a thick mass of

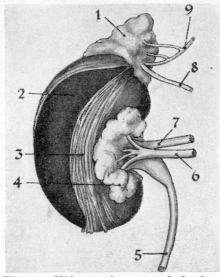

Fig. 6. *Kidney and suprarenal gland. 1, Gland lying over kidney (suprarenal gland); 2, outer part of kidney (cortex); 3, fibrous capsule containing kidney; 4, fat layer; 5, ureter; 6, vein of kidney (renal vein); 7, artery of kidney (renal artery); 8, suprarenal vein; 9, suprarenal artery.*

glandular tissue surrounding a cavity which opens at the hilum; this cavity is called the sinus, and is lined by a fibrous membrane continuous with the closely-fitting capsule covering the kidney. Urine is carried from the kidney to the bladder by means of the ureter (Figs. 6 and 7), a thin-walled narrow duct about twelve inches long, composed of unstriated muscle fibres and lined with mucous membrane.

Pelvis of the Kidney

At its upper end, the ureter widens into a funnel-shaped dilatation, which occupies the whole of the sinus and is called the pelvis of the kidney (Fig. 7). Below, the two ureters open into the urinary bladder near its base. The bladder (Fig. 8) is a highly muscular reservoir lying deep in the pelvic cavity between the pubic bones, in front, and the rectum behind; in woman, the uterus lies between the bladder and the rectum. A canal called the urethra carries the urine from the bladder to the outside of the body; in woman the

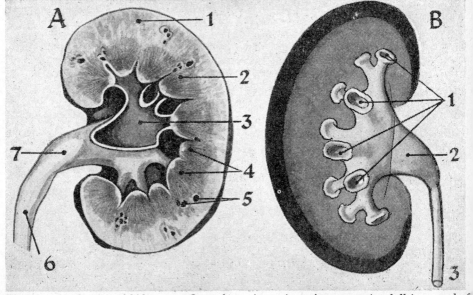

Fig. 7. (A) *Section of kidney: 1, Outer layer (cortex); 2, inner part (medulla); 3, end of ureter (cut open); 4, cone-shaped sections of kidney tissue (pyramids); 5, blood vessels; 6, ureter; 7, funnel-shaped end of ureter (pelvis of kidney).* (B) *Pelvis of kidney with tissues removed: 1, Cup-shaped growth at ends (calyces); 2, pelvis; 3, ureter.*

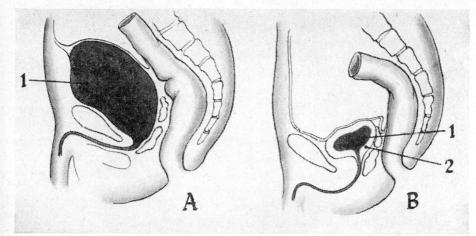

Fig. 8. *The bladder* (A) *distended, and* (B) *contracted. 1, Bladder; 2, muscular bladder wall. The bladder becomes distended if it is not emptied in the normal way through the urethra.*

urethra is only about an inch long, but in man (Fig. 9) it measures seven or eight inches. The openings of the two ureters and of the urethra all lie within an inch of one another, forming a triangle at the base of the bladder. Urine passes down the ureters at intervals, propelled by the involuntary muscle fibres in their walls. The urethra is closed by a sphincter which is under the control of the will. The bladder is lined with mucous membrane (Fig. 10), resting on a submucous layer; it is invested in a muscular coat consisting of three layers of unstriated or involuntary fibres—an outer and an inner layer of longitudinal fibres and a middle layer of circular fibres. It is thus, like the stomach, an extremely stout and resistive organ, which is rarely ruptured except when the pelvis itself is fractured. When escape of urine through the urethra is prevented, the bladder may become greatly distended (Fig. 8), rising up into the abdominal cavity as a smooth rounded swelling. Normally the bladder remains a pelvic organ; when it reaches a certain degree of distention, the desire to micturate is experienced; the sphincter of the urethra is voluntarily relaxed and, by a reflex action, the involuntary muscle fibres

in the bladder wall contract, forcing the urine through the urethral canal.

Urine is derived from the blood and formed by the activity of the cells of the kidney. When a kidney is cut across it is found to have distinctive markings which

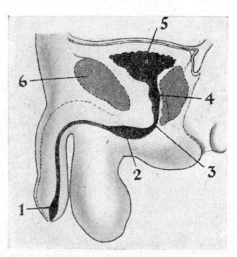

Fig. 9. *Canal connecting male bladder with outside of the body (urethra). 1, Front end (fossa navicularis); 2, bulbous portion; 3, membranous portion; 4, section connected with prostate glands; 5, bladder; 6, section of pelvic arch. The male urethra is about seven inches long, the female only an inch.*

are visible to the naked eye. Near the concave border is the irregular cavity, the sinus, lined by the dilated upper portion of the ureter (the pelvis of the kidney); projecting into this cavity are many little conical prominences of kidney tissue, the pyramids (Fig. 11). Each of these pyramids lies with its apex in the pelvis and its base embedded in the substance of the rest of the kidney; together the pyramids make up the inner or medullary part of the kidney (Fig. 7). The cortex, or outer part, is darker in colour than the medulla, and forms a comparatively narrow layer lying near the surface of the kidney just under the capsule.

Blood Vessels

Under the microscope the difference in appearance between cortex and medulla is explained. The kidney is entirely made up of minute uriniferous tubules (Fig. 12) lined with epithelial cells. In the cortex these tubules are closely associated with blood vessels and follow a tortuous course. In the medulla the tubules are straight and unite with each other to form larger tubules which eventually open on the endings, or apices, of the pyramids.

Each tubule begins as a rounded dilatation folded in upon itself to form a cup. In this cup lies an intricate knot of capillary blood vessels derived from the rich blood supply to the kidney. These tufts of capillaries are called glomeruli (Fig. 13), and the cup in which each of them lies is called the glomerular capsule. Glomeruli are found only in the cortex of the kidney and are responsible for its darker colouration. The capsule, as we have seen already, is only the dilated beginning of a tubule destined to carry

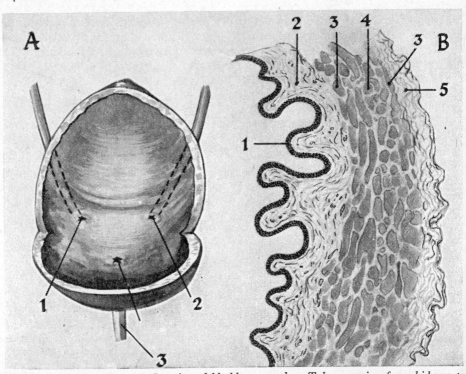

Fig. 10. *The bladder.* (A) *Interior of bladder: 1 and 2, Tubes running from kidneys to bladder (right and left ureters); 3, canal from bladder to outside of body (urethra).* (B) *Section of bladder tissue: 1, Submucous layer; 2, mucous membrane; 3, 4 and 5, layers of muscle fibre.*

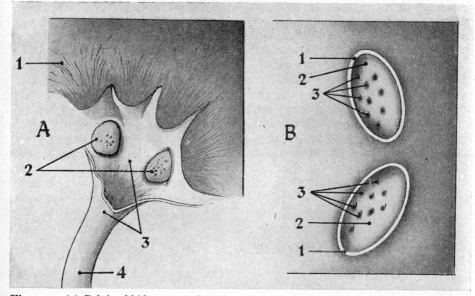

Fig. 11. (A) *Pelvis of kidney opened to show endings of pyramids: 1, Outer layer (cortex); 2, endings (apices) of pyramids forming inner part; 3, ending of ureter (pelvis of kidney); 4, ureter.* (B) *Apices of pyramids of kidney: 1, Edge of cup-shaped tubes at end of ureter (calyces); 2, apex of pyramid; 3, endings of tubes.*

urine to the pelvis of the kidney; the first part of this tubule is twisted but it soon straightens out and becomes narrower, forming a deep loop which dips down into the medulla, the loop of Henle (Fig. 12). The ascending limb of the loop of Henle runs up into the cortex again, until it is almost alongside the glomerular capsule from which it arose. Here the tubule again becomes twisted for a short distance before entering a straight, or collecting, tubule, which plunges straight down through the medulla to open on the apex of one of the pyramids.

The complicated course of the kidney tubules has a purpose; the manufacture of urine is no simple feat, and each part of the tubule has a special task to perform.

The blood supply of the kidney reaches it through the renal artery (Fig. 6), which divides into a series of arches running between the cortex and medulla. From these arches smaller vessels are given off which penetrate the cortex and send out the twigs which form the glomeruli; the blood leaves a glomerulus by way of a small vessel which quickly branches to form a network round the uriniferous tubule. Thus the blood vessels of the kidney are associated in the closest possible manner with the capsules and tubules in which the urine is formed.

Action of Kidneys

Physiologists have had many disagreements as to the way in which the kidney does its work. Of late years, however, it has been more or less agreed that it manages to produce urine partly by allowing it to filter through the glomerular capsules and partly by manufacturing or secreting it through the cells of the tubules. From the vessels forming the glomerular tuft, water containing salts in solution filters into the capsule and passes into the uriniferous tubule. This water solution has to be concentrated as it passes down towards the collecting tubule, because if passed in bulk, as it filters through the capsule, it would drain too much fluid out of the blood and leave us dehydrated and perpetually thirsty. Water is therefore re-absorbed into the blood-stream through the walls of the tubules.

The substances in solution which filter through the capsule are simple inorganic salts of sodium, potassium, calcium and ammonia, mostly in the form of phosphates. Sodium chloride, or common salt, is present in the urine in considerable quantity, being taken abundantly in an ordinary diet. Urine is normally acid in reaction, thanks to the presence of acid phosphates; its pale yellow colour is derived from bile pigments in the blood.

In addition to inorganic salts, urine contains the organic products of protein breakdown, chiefly in the forms of urea and uric acid (Fig. 14). These substances do not filter through the capsule but are secreted directly into the tubules by the cells lining their walls. The process of secretion is not a passive oozing, like the process of filtration, but the result of definite activity on the part of the tubules —a process of biochemistry which can

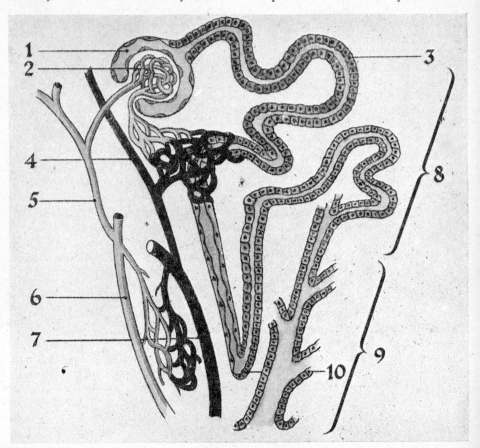

Fig. 12. *Small tubes which make up kidney (tubule). 1, Capsule containing blood vessels (glomerular capsule); 2, knot of blood vessels (glomerulus); 3, tube producing urine; 4, vein running between tubes of kidney (interlobular vein); 5, artery running through kidney (interlobular artery); 6, renal artery; 7, renal vein; 8, outer layer of kidney (cortex); 9, inner layer (medulla); 10, loop of tube running into medulla (loop of Henle).*

only be carried out by living cells. The cells of the kidney tubules are the only cells in the body which can extract the end-products of protein metabolism from the blood; their importance is therefore enormous. If, owing to failure of these cells, urea and uric acid are retained in the blood stream the unfortunate sufferer from uræmia, as this disorder is called, is slowly poisoned by the products of his own activity. Luckily, nephritis, or inflammation of the kidneys, rarely damages all the tubules, of which there are some thousands in each kidney.

The average amount of urine passed by an adult in twenty-four hours is about three pints; but the individual amount varies enormously according to season and personal habit. On hot days, when we lose a lot of water by perspiration, the urine is comparatively scanty. The man who drinks a pint of beer every two or three hours will need to pass a lot of fluid. But we must drink more fluid than will barely replace our loss by the lungs and by the skin, to meet the demand of the kidneys for enough water to dissolve and get rid of the nitrogenous waste substances,

Fig. 14. *Uric acid crystals. These crystals, contained in urine, are the organic products extracted from protein by the kidneys.*

which would be poisonous if they remained in the body.

It takes a pint and a half of water to get rid of 500 grains of urea, which is about the average amount eliminated by a healthy man every day. A patient living without water or food of any kind lost nearly a pint of water daily through the kidneys alone. Fasting men can lose nearly all their stored glycogen, and nearly half the protein and fat built into their body structure, without running any great risk to life, whereas a loss of even twenty per cent of the body's water content is invariably fatal. The danger of dysentery and of cholera lies largely in the incessant diarrhoea which often characterizes these diseases. The important thing is that the fluidity of the blood shall be kept in uniform condition; and it is notable that when the total amount of water in the body falls below normal, the last tissue to become modified is the blood. The kidneys cannot help when there is a deficiency, but when there is an excess, their function is important.

Children, who normally take a good deal of fluid in their diet, manufacture more

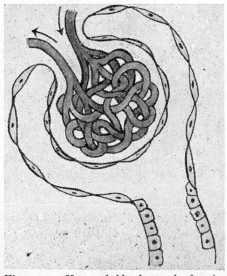

Fig. 13. *Knot of blood vessels forming beginning of tubules of kidney (glomerulus).*

urine than adults in proportion to their size; a child of five, for example, will manufacture nearly half as much as an adult. An increase in blood pressure will increase the flow of urine, so that exercise, anxiety and excitement may be counted upon to have this effect. Exercise acts in two ways, by raising the blood pressure and hence increasing the rate of filtration through the glomerular capsules, and by throwing into the blood stream those products of protein breakdown which are generated by muscular activity; the cells of the kidney tubules, stimulated by the presence of these products in the blood, hasten to remove them.

Effect of Excitement

The effect of excitement on the secretion of urine is well known to any one who has taken a child to the pantomime. The urine on such occasions is abundant and pale, consisting mostly of water which has filtered through the capsules as a result of a rise of blood pressure. Cold weather also provokes an increased flow, and so does a moist atmosphere. Both of these act by reducing the loss of moisture from the skin in the form of sweat; the kidney accepts the task of eliminating the extra fluid. The body needs to be constantly flushed through with water if it is to remain healthy. If the skin will not help to maintain this flushing process, the kidney must do extra work.

Conversely, anything which increases the loss of water in the form of sweat will reduce the output of the kidneys. After a hard bout of exercise the urine is scanty and dark in colour, being concentrated by the absorption of much urea as it passes down the tubules. Medicines given to promote sweating have the same effect, and so do Turkish baths. The kidneys, ever prepared to give and take as body economy demands, balance the loss of fluid in the form of sweat by allowing a larger proportion of the fluid which has filtered out of the blood to be drawn back

into it. These activities make it clear why such a complicated blood supply is necessary to the kidneys. The capillary tufts in the glomeruli pour fluid in bulk into the capsules; the network of vessels round the tubules perform the double function of receiving back the excess fluid and of providing the tubule cells with an opportunity of extracting waste protein products from the blood stream.

Effects of Disease

In fevers, the urine is notoriously scanty and concentrated, owing to the loss of fluid by sweating and by increased activity of the lungs. In diabetes the flow of urine is increased; it is pale in colour, and judging from its watery appearance, might be thought to contain few substances in solution. When it is examined, however, it is found to be heavily loaded with sugar, a constituent absent from normal urine; in order that the urine may carry this dissolved sugar the kidney must allow far more water than usual to pass unabsorbed down the tubules. The urine is dilute as far as its other constituents are concerned.

In nephritis, albumen appears in the urine, showing that the tubule cells, instead of exercising their usual powers of discrimination, are allowing substances to escape which ought to be retained in the blood. Albumen is an important constituent of blood plasma, and the healthy kidney never permits it to pass into the urine. The presence of albumen in the urine therefore is generally a sign of damage to the kidney, though it sometimes appears temporarily in the course of fevers or following general anæsthesia, and in these circumstances has no serious significance. Inflammation of the bladder may also cause albumen to appear in the urine; but in this case it is derived from the blood and pus cells which are also present, and disappears as soon as the inflammation subsides, and the bladder recovers its normal condition of health.

CHAPTER XI

THE SENSES AND SENSE ORGANS

SENSE OF TASTE: TASTE AND SMELL: SENSE OF SMELL: OLFACTORY
NERVES AND NASAL MEMBRANE: IMPORTANCE OF SCENT: SENSE OF SIGHT:
CONSTRUCTION OF EYEBALL: RETINA AND OPTIC NERVES: DEFECTS OF
THE EYE: SENSE OF HEARING: OUTER, MIDDLE AND INNER EARS: VIBRA-
TION AND SOUND: SENSE OF BALANCE: SENSATION AND CONSCIOUSNESS

THE PRINCIPAL sensory organs associated with the skin have been already mentioned. The importance of these organs can hardly be exaggerated. Much less important to man from the point of view of self-preservation is his sense of smell, though in other animals it is extremely valuable, and in some cases of at least equal value with the senses of sight or hearing so prized by humans.

When our evolutionary ancestors took to walking on their hind legs only, using their fore-limbs for clutching and seizing, lifting their noses high in the air and, at the same time, greatly extending the area of possible vision, their sense of smell became less helpful to them. Gradually it began to be rather a source of æsthetic gratification than a guide to edible prey or to the proximity of dangerous neighbours. Yet, in what we may call our sensory world, our olfactory structures continue to play a quite important part. It is still no small deprivation to lose the sense of smell.

Taste and Smell

We owe more to this sense than many of us are aware. Nearly all the gratification that we commonly attribute to our sense of taste is not due to that sense at all, but to the sensitiveness of the olfactory receptors in the nose. Professional tasters of tea and of fine wine are accustomed to place some of the fluid in their mouths and then to breathe out from the nostrils, thus causing the vaporous aroma to pass over the olfactory membrane. The range of sensibility of the receptive organs of taste proper is very limited, although taste and discrimination are now identical in meaning.

Taste-buds

The gustatory receptors are the taste-buds (Figs. 1 and 2). These are arranged about the so-called vallate papillæ situated near the middle of the upper surface of the tongue. There are two or three hundred taste-buds to a single papilla. The taste-cells with their fine nervous connexions are inside these taste-buds. The chemicals which give rise to the sensation of taste enter the taste-buds through minute pores opening into the cavity of each. Not all these taste receptors are equally susceptible to the stimuli giving rise to the four elementary taste sensations of sweetness, bitterness, sourness and saltness. Those taste-buds towards the back of the tongue are more sensitive to bitter taste stimuli; those near the tip are more sensitive to sweet and salt; and those at the sides to sour and salt. It is because the sense of taste is so limited that most people find that what they call their

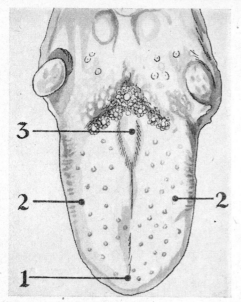

taste almost completely disappears when they have a bad cold in their nose.

The nose is separated from the mouth by the palate, to which in ordinary conversation we attribute a sensitiveness to which it can lay no claim. The palate ends before we come to the point at which the nostrils join the mouth cavity. So, also, does the septum (Fig. 3) of the nose which divides the anterior space into two nostril cavities. From this point onwards the nasal passages are to be regarded merely as passages for air on its way to the lungs. It is only at the topmost part of the nostrils that the receptive surfaces reactive to smells exist; that is why we sniff slightly when we wish to enjoy the fragrance of a rose or lily.

In order to be smelt by us, any external object, be it a spray of lilac, a rasher of bacon or a cake of soap, must give off particles of vapour, and this vapour must be soluble in, or mixable with, the mucus with which the sensitive

Fig. 1. *The tongue, showing parts susceptible to particular tastes. 1, Part of tongue chiefly susceptible to sweet and salt taste; 2, sour and salt taste; 3, bitter taste.*

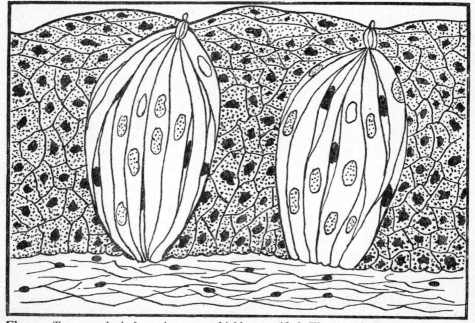

Fig. 2. *Two taste-buds from the tongue, highly magnified. The taste-buds are situated near the middle of the upper surface of the tongue, and contain minute taste-cells, which have delicate nervous connexions and which are responsible for the various sensations of taste.*

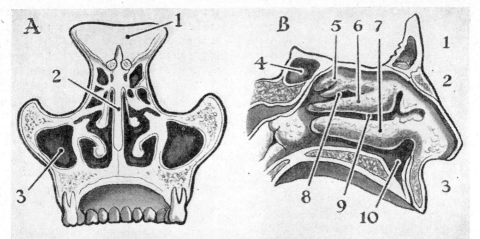

Fig. 3. (A) *Back view of vertical section of cavities of nose (nasal fossæ): 1, Wedge-shaped bone, at back of nose (sphenoid bone); 2, division between nostrils (nasal septum); 3, air space, or sinus, in upper jawbone (antrum of Highmore).* (B) *Outer wall of left nostril: 1, Bone of forehead; 2, nasal bone; 3, upper jawbone; 4, air space in sphenoid bone (sphenoidal sinus); 5, 6 and 7, projections from the wall of the nostril (superior, middle and inferior turbinate bodies); 8, 9 and 10, recesses between the turbinate bodies (superior, middle and inferior meatuses). The front passages of the nose are merely air passages.*

olfactory membrane is kept covered. The immediate provocants of the receptors of smell are thus more tangible than those vibrations of air or ether which provoke the receptible nerve endings of sight or of hearing, though even less tangible than are those solids or liquids which provoke the few true sensations of taste.

Of course, not all gases and vapours are odorous. The normal constituents of the atmosphere do not produce any impression on our olfactory sense. From a utilitarian standpoint, it is not difficult to realize how desirable it is that smells of decomposing meat should be repellent to us, but it is not immediately obvious why the smell of lilies of the valley or of other flowers that we class as agreeably fragrant should seem to us as pleasant; for these things are not edible nor, so far as we know, can they be in any way helpful to our bodily functioning.

The external nose, which we all take for granted as the most prominent feature on the human face (Fig. 4), is a sort of pyramidal triangle composed partly of bone, partly of cartilage, both tissues being covered with muscles and skin. The bridge, or bony part of the nose, is made up of parts of the superior maxillary bone and of the two nasal bones (*see* CHAPTER I). Extending from them forwards are two lateral cartilages which make up the basic structures of the ridge and tip of the nose. Smaller cartilages, attached to these form the so-called wings, or alæ. Internally, the cavity is divided into two by a septum (Fig. 3), the chambers on either side of which are wide at their outer end. The external openings, or anterior nares, measure in the average adult about one inch from front to back and about half an inch across. The hindermost openings of these two nostril tubes are called the posterior nares, and there they connect with the nasal pharynx at the back of the nostrils.

Between the anterior and the posterior nares the nasal canal, or fossa, communicates also with air spaces, or sinuses,

(Figs. 5 and 6) situated in the spongy parts of four bones, the frontal, the ethmoid, the sphenoid and the superior maxillary. The dividing septum is partly bony, partly cartilaginous. The septum is rarely placed strictly in the centre, being almost always a little deflected to one or the other side, thus dividing the nasal passage into two unequal parts. The walls of these parts are uneven in structure owing to the projection of small rounded structures known as the turbinate bodies (Fig. 3). These partly divide each fossa into three recesses, termed the superior, middle and inferior meatuses (Fig. 3). The superior meatus, which is very small, lies between the superior and middle turbinate body; the middle meatus lies between the middle and inferior turbinates, and the inferior meatus, which is the largest, lies between the inferior turbinate and the floor of the nostril. It is into the inferior meatus that the nasal duct, leading from the lachrymal gland at the inner corner of the eye, opens. The lining membrane of the nasal cavity is continuous with that of the pharynx, the Eustachian tubes (Fig. 19) and the four accessory sinuses in the spongy bones adjacent to the nose. By a reverse route, infection may pass from the nostrils themselves.

The largest of these accessory sinuses is that in the superior maxillary bone, and is known as the antrum of Highmore (Fig. 5). Into it often project the roots of the molar teeth covered with but a thin membrane. Owing to this fact, infection of the antrum may arise through septic condition of the teeth. As compensation, an infected antrum can sometimes be successfully drained by extracting one of the

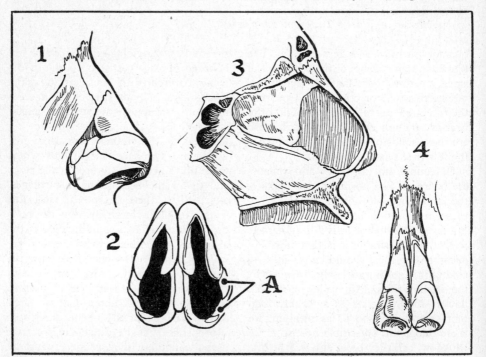

Fig. 4. *Bones and cartilages of the nose. 1, Side view of outer nose. The upper part, or bridge, is made up of part of the upper jawbone and the two nasal bones. From them extend cartilage structures; 2, view of the cartilages from below, showing nostrils and (A) the wings of the nose (alæ); 3, division between nostrils (nasal septum); 4, front view of nose.*

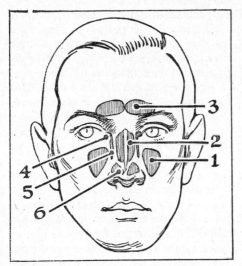

Fig. 5. *Parts of nose.* 1, *Air space in upper jawbone (antrum of Highmore);* 2, *cartilage;* 3, *air spaces in bones of forehead (frontal sinuses);* 4, *tear gland;* 5, *channel from tear gland (nasal duct);* 6, *wings of nose.*

molar teeth. The frontal sinuses are, as their name implies, situated in the forehead above the orbits. They are separated from the brain by very thin bony plates. As a consequence, infection of these sinuses is to be regarded as a grave matter. The plates of bone which separate the ethmoidal and sphenoidal sinuses from the brain cavity are also thin; consequently infection of these also involves very serious possibilities.

Olfactory Nerves

It is in the mucous membrane lining the surfaces of the ethmoid bones at the higher parts of the nasal cavity that the sensitive endings of the olfactory nerves (Fig. 7) are situated. When we are breathing quietly and ordinarily, potentially odorous particles, unless present in large quantity, are likely to be held up by the intrusive turbinate bodies. Therefore, when we deliberately want to smell something, we repeatedly sniff more or less vigorously, so that the air in which these particles are suspended may pass to the higher regions of the nasal canal, where they can come into contact with the endings of the olfactory nerve. In so doing, we usually close the mouth so that all the inhaled air may pass through the nose, with the certainty that some of it will replace the stagnant air in contact with the olfactory membrane.

A word as to the microscopic structure of the lining membrane of the nasal passages. The lower part of the nostrils has no function in relation to the sense of smell; it closely resembles the lining of the windpipe and other breathing passages. On the surface, it consists of a wall of minute columnar cells provided with cilia, or microscopic surface brushes, which sweep along the mucus with any particles entrapped in it. Beneath this layer, or interspersed in its course, are to be found the goblet cells which secrete the mucus. Deeper still is a layer of fibrous tissue containing many lymph corpuscles, some aggregated into masses of adenoid tissue, which is similar to that of the tonsils.

The lining membrane of the upper part of the nasal cavity is different from that of the lower part, being brownish in

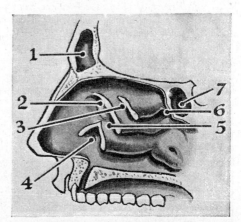

Fig. 6. *Openings of sinuses into nose.* 1 and 2, *Frontal sinus and opening;* 3, *opening of sinus in ethmoid bone;* 4, *opening of channel from tear gland;* 5, *opening of sinus in jawbone;* 6 and 7, *sphenoidal sinus and opening.*

colour, and rarely furnished with cilia. The surface cells in this region are spire-shaped, with the point directed away from the surface. Between the apices of these cells are to be seen spindle-shaped sensory cells, from each of which protrudes towards the surface, between the bodies of the spire-shaped cells, a microscopic rod which opens out into several fibres where it emerges on the surface. It is by coming in contact with these tiny fibres that aromatic particles stimulate the olfactory nerve and produce in our mind the sensation of smell.

The fine olfactory nerve fibres which

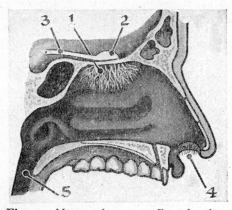

Fig. 7. *Nerves of nose. 1, Branches from nerve of smell (olfactory nerve); 2, nerve structure (olfactory bulb) connected with brain; 3, connexion with brain (olfactory tract); 4, air passage; 5, throat.*

constitute the receptor organ are associated with, or incorporated in, the projecting rods. These terminal nerve fibres (Fig. 8) are branches of fusiform nerve cells lying directly beneath the surface layer of cells. Branches from these cells run to join a nerve structure called the olfactory bulb, which is in direct nerve relation with the interpreting olfactory centre in the brain. There the message is decoded, with the resulting effect on our consciousness which we call this or that smell or fragrance. This olfactory lining membrane in the upper part of the nose is kept constantly moist by mucus, and over it air passes in the process of inspiration and expiration, though there is very little movement of air in the layer immediately adjacent to the surface membrane.

We have said that the sense of smell in man today is very much less acute than in many other animals. It is thought, for example, that the acuteness of the olfactory sense of a dog may, in some cases, be many thousand times greater than that of the average man. But even man can recognize by smell the presence of one twenty-five-thousand-millionth of a gramme of the alcohol called mercaptan diffused in a quart of air, or one part of vanillin diffused in ten million parts of air.

No one who has learned to appreciate and discriminate between the almost unlimited variety of fragrances yielded by flowers and leaves can doubt for a moment the greatness of the possibilities of pleasure afforded by the sense of smell.

Variety of Scents

Most people are acquainted in a general way with the characteristic smells of violets, of hyacinths, of pinks and of lilac; and all these are delicious. But the dozen or two sweet scented flowers which, for most people, complete the tale of garden fragrance, give but the merest hint of the multitude and of the variety of scents which the garden can be made to yield. The distinctive scents of the roses alone cannot be counted on the fingers of the two hands. The daphnes, the honeysuckles, the different kinds of clematis, the mignonette, the cowslip—but the list is endless. And when we have finished with the flowers, there is the lengthy catalogue of plants whose aromatic leaves are no less satisfying and stimulating. A garden of scented plants is as charming and almost as interesting at night as in the day; and may give almost as much happiness to the blind as to the seeing.

Yet it is doubtful if man's longevity would be materially lessened if his sense of smell disappeared altogether. Our real danger is not one of over-valuing an unimportant possession, but of neglecting and wasting a possible source of infinite pleasure and æsthetic enlightenment. No doubt the sense of smell owes its somewhat lowly place in our scale of values largely to its failure to get the credit for the impressions it enables us to receive, nine-tenths of our olfactory sensations being customarily put down to the account of taste. But remembering the

hours earlier—by the stag or the hare; but are we so sure that we are comparing identical senses? In any event, it must be recognized that we apply our sense of smell—as indeed our other senses—to a great many purposes unknown in the life of our evolutionary ancestors.

Neither knowledge, nor even sensation, was the original purpose or function of sense organs. At first, their only function was as what have been called "triggers of reflex action." Sensation was a

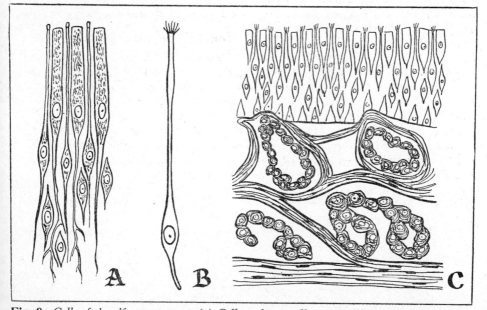

Fig. 8. *Cells of the olfactory nerve.* (A) *Cells and nerve fibres; particles coming into contact with these fibres stimulate the olfactory nerve.* (B) *Single nerve fibre enlarged.* (C) *Section of olfactory mucous membrane showing nerve fibres. These cells are in the upper part of the nose.*

tea taster and the wine taster—to say nothing of the gastronome—it may well be doubted if our olfactory sense has really degenerated. All those flavours and aromas, the recognition of which makes up the taste of the epicure, are not really matters of taste in the least; they are all matters of smell.

It is true that none of us can, like the spaniel, scent the footprints left by the pheasant; or, like the hound, run unerringly along the line followed—perhaps

later, and knowledge a much later development. Biologically, the sense of smell is intimately related to two great primal facts of human existence, food and sex; and it is still with the physiological æsthetics of these aspects of life that it is largely associated.

All the same, we should be in a bad way if we relied solely on our noses to tell us what foods to eat and what to avoid. The attraction of cyanide of potassium, with its suggestion of almonds, would outclass the perfectly conditioned gorgonzola every time. Nevertheless, the sense of smell does still serve a useful purpose in connexion with food and eating. For it is in great measure the flavours and aromas of food which, in a purely reflex manner, set into activity the processes of the digestive machinery.

Sense of Sight

The sense of sight is in many ways the most wonderful, as it is certainly the most valuable, of all our senses. Since our assumption of the upright position, we have come more and more to rely upon our eyes, and less and less on our nose, or even our ears, for guidance as to the nature and position of external objects. We have shown ourselves persistently anxious to improve and extend our senses of sight and sound by means of scientific inventions—spectacles and earphones, microscopes and microphones, telescopes and telephones—whereas we have devoted little, if any, ingenuity to the discovery of means whereby our sense of smell may be amplified, or our senses of touch and of temperature intensified.

By practice and special training nearly all our senses can be rendered more acute and more discriminating. Through sheer necessity, almost all blind people develop a sensitiveness of touch that appears almost uncanny to those who have eyes to see with. So also often with their other senses. Blind masseuses and blind piano tuners afford obvious instances. Epicures in wine often close their eyes almost unconsciously when savouring a fine vintage; the same trait may often be observed among keen appreciators of music and those wishing to extract the maximum of pleasure from the fragrance of a flower. It seems that the intensity of a sensory impression is increased by the closing down of other sensory gateways.

Differences between Individuals

There is, especially in the case of sight and sound, a marked difference in the impressions created in the mind by the same sensory impact on different individuals. There is little resemblance between the physical aerial vibrations set up by the instruments of an orchestra and the varying sound reactions and interpretations provoked in the minds of the listeners. Nor is there any obvious resemblance between the assumed vibrations of equally assumed ethereal particles said to occupy space and to stimulate our receptive organs of sight, and the mental impressions which we call "things we see." We certainly do not see the vibrations or the ethereal particles; we see oranges, or cornfields with poppies in flower, or tables, or words in a book. No more is the decoding of the visual impressions performed identically by all human individuals, so large a part is played in the act of interpretation by association, by experience, and by what we must call abstract thought. The real mystery lies not so much in the receptive organ of sight, the eye,

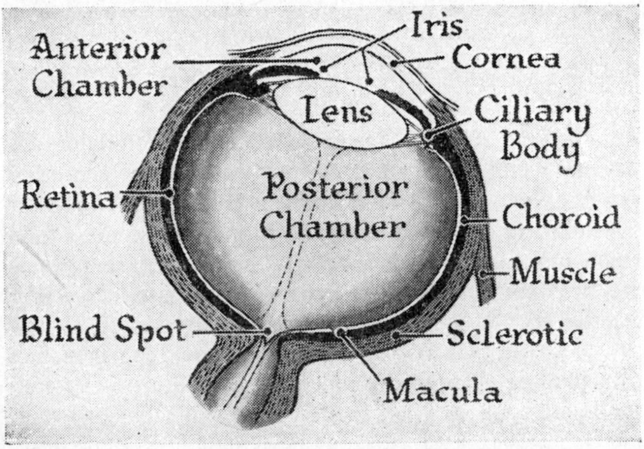

Fig. 9. *Section across the eyeball showing names of its parts.*

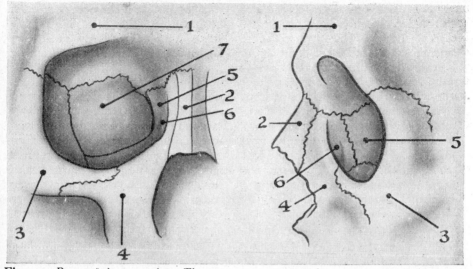

Fig. 10. *Bones of the eye socket. The eye socket is contained in a cavity made up of seven bones of the face. 1, Bone of the forehead (frontal); 2, bone of the nose (nasal); 3, bone of the arch of the cheek (zygomatic); 4, jawbone (maxillary); 5, bone containing sieve-like (cribriform) plate through which smell nerves pass (ethmoid); 6, bone containing channel from tear gland (lachrymal); 7, wedge-shaped bone of face (sphenoid).*

as in the interpreting organ where mind and body, by means incomprehensible to us, become inter-blended or continuous.

What we call the eyeball (Fig. 9) is an almost spherical structure protectively situated in a ball-shaped socket of the skull (Fig. 10), the walls of the cavity being made up of parts of seven bones of the head and face. It is padded round with fatty tissue which prevents it from being bruised against the bony walls of the eye socket. At the back it is directly connected with the brain by a sort of stalk, the optic nerve. Its most essential part is, indeed, a direct outgrowth of the brain.

Eyelids and Eyebrows

The eye is still further protected in front by the structures we know as the eyelids and the eyebrows (Fig. 11). The eyebrows form a protective ridge which is furnished with a linear growth of hair serving to divert particles of dust and drops of sweat from the forehead which otherwise might fall into the eye. Only

people who avoid physical activity can have their eyebrows plucked without risk of injury. The eyelids are thin, flexible shutters which protect the front of the eyeball. They are composed outside of skin, and are lined on the inner side with a delicate membrane called the conjunctiva, which is continuous with the membrane covering the front of the eyeball. At the margin of the eyelids are narrow strips of cartilage which tend to stiffen them and make them fit well together when closed. The edge of the lower eyelid is nearly straight, that of the upper one is arched. Both lids can be moved in the process of bringing them together so as to close the eyes, but the upper one moves much more freely than the lower, and can be lifted considerably at will. The upper lid has a special muscle to draw it up, but when the eye is closed a single muscle tends to bring the lids together.

The edges of the lids are fringed with lashes designed to entangle and arrest particles of dust on their way into the eye, but fortunately we need not depend on the lashes alone for this service; the eyelids themselves are the most effective defence of the eye. The lid muscles are under the control of the will, but they are also executors of the fastest reflex movement in the body. When a flying particle approaches the eye the lids clap themselves together and save the precious eyeball from harm well before the brain is notified of the danger.

Under each lid is a kind of pouch into which particles of dirt or small insects are apt to make their way, causing much irritation. These can be dislodged only by folding the upper lid upwards on itself, or by drawing the lower lid down with the finger until its lining is exposed. Within

small tubes, one in the upper lid and one in the lower. These soon join to form a single tube leading to a small cavity known as the lachrymal sac. From here proceeds the nasal or tear duct which opens below into the inferior meatus of the nose (Fig. 3). The tears, in passing across the surface of the eye, help to keep it clean, washing along all minor particles that fall on it. Normally, the lachrymal fluid is sufficient only to keep the surface moist, but greatly increased production of tears results when an irritating foreign body impinges on the eye, when irritating vapours are inhaled through the nostrils, or under the stress of emotion. The production of this fluid may be so great as to

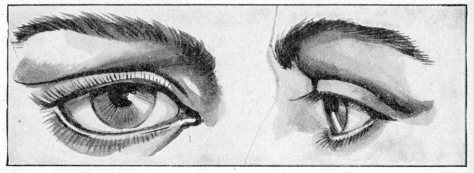

Fig. 11. *Eyelids and eyebrows. The eyebrows form a protective ridge above the eyes with a growth of hair to divert dust and sweat. The lids and eyelashes protect the front of the eyeball.*

the row of eyelashes are the openings of little sebaceous glands, the so-called Meibomian glands, which produce an oily secretion that keeps the surface pliable and prevents the lids from sticking together. Sometimes one of these tubes becomes blocked, and the gland consequently enlarged. We then have either a small abscess—a stye—or what is known as a Meibomian cyst.

Underneath the bony projection at the outer corner of the eye socket is the lachrymal gland (Fig. 12), which secretes or manufactures the thin watery fluid we know as tears. This fluid passes constantly across the surface of the eye to its inner corner, whence it is carried off by two

outdo the carrying capacity of the nasal duct. Tears then overflow from the eyes and stream down the face, resulting in the phenomenon known as crying.

The eyeball itself (Fig. 9) is about an inch in diameter, and its limiting wall consists of varying layers, each of which has its distinct and important function. The outer layer is called the sclerotic coat. This is very tough, being composed of fibrous and elastic tissue. What we call the white of the eye is a part of the sclerotic membrane. In the very front of the eye, this tissue is continuous with the circular transparent plate called the cornea. The cornea together with the white of the eye is covered by a layer

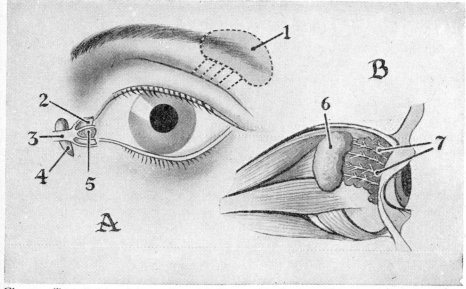

Fig. 12. *Tear gland and connexions.* (A) *Front view of eye: 1, Tear gland and its channels; 2, tube carrying tears from the eye (lachrymal canal); 3, muscle tendon; 4, papilla; 5, cavity in which tears collect (lachrymal sac).* (B) *Side view of eye: 6, Tear gland; 7, channels leading from tear gland and carrying its fluid to the eye (lachrymal ducts).*

of the conjunctival membrane continuous with that lining the eyelids.

Within the sclerotic layer is a second coat known as the choroid, more delicate in structure and richly furnished with blood vessels and nerves. It has a black lining, the function of which is to absorb such rays of light as would otherwise confuse vision. The choroid continues towards the front in the form, first, of what is called the ciliary body, incorporating the important ciliary muscle (Fig. 13), and then, in the very front of the eye, as the iris. This is the coloured part of the eye, and is what we refer to when we speak of a person having brown, or blue, or grey eyes. It has an aperture in its centre which can be made smaller or bigger, much as can the iris diaphragm in a camera. In bright light the aperture is made smaller, in dim light larger. Doctors often test the contractability of the iris by turning a light on to the eye and then shading the eye with the hand. The round hole in the centre of the iris is

called the pupil (Fig. 15). This small round hole is the little disc which to any one who looks into the eye of another seems black. Actually it is transparent, and the blackness is due to the lining of the choroid membrane, which is so constructed that it reflects no rays of light.

Almost immediately behind the iris is a transparent body, somewhat jelly-like in composition, called the crystalline lens. This is shaped rather like the lens of a camera, and is curved convexly both in front and behind. It is surrounded by a fine membrane, and is attached above and below by slender ligaments. The convexity of the lens can be increased or diminished by the muscles which are attached to it (Fig. 14).

Between the cornea and the lens is a cavity known as the anterior chamber, containing a watery fluid called the aqueous humour. It is in this chamber, just in front of the lens, that the iris is situated. Behind the lens there lies another and much larger cavity called the posterior

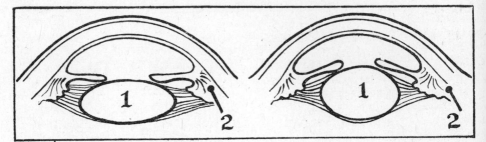

Fig. 13. (Left) Eyeball contracted; (right) eyeball relaxed. The lens (1) is controlled partly by the action of the ciliary muscle (2) which forms part of the second coat of the eyeball (the choroid). The black lining of the choroid coat, by absorbing light, helps to clarify vision.

chamber. This is filled with a semi-solid substance which is called the vitreous humour.

The innermost lining of the eye wall is the retina (Fig. 16). This is really a delicate nerve film, covering the posterior two-thirds of the eye cavities, and is far and away the most important and most complicated part of the eye. It receives the impressions of light, and transmits them through the optic nerve to the brain, where they are interpreted.

The retina may be compared to the film of a photographic camera. It is a sort of nervous net, highly sensitive to light, and is really an outgrowth from the sur-face of the brain. It is composed of numerous microscopic cells of two kinds, called from their shapes the rods and the cones. The rods are of importance when we are seeing in a dim light, the cones in a bright light. In the centre of the retina there are nothing but cones, round the margin there are nothing but rods; in between, the rods and cones are mixed in a sort of mosaic. From this it follows that in a dim light we can usually see more out of the corner of the eye than out of its centre. The cones alone enable us to distinguish colour, which is why we find it difficult to distinguish colours at night, even though we may see their shapes

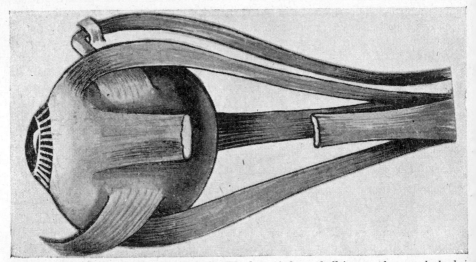

Fig. 14. Muscles controlling the eyeball. The lens of the eyeball is curved convexly both in front and behind; its convexity can be increased or diminished by muscles attached to it.

fairly clearly. The nerve fibres of the retinal cells run towards the back of the eyeball and finally converge to a single thick bundle which leaves the eye as the optic nerve itself. There are no sensitive nerve cells at the point where the optic nerve plunges backwards through the retina to escape from the eyeball, and so there is no vision in this tiny area of the retina, which is therefore known as the blind spot.

Clearness of Vision

A blind spot is to be found in each eye, but we do not notice it because we use both eyes at once, and what one eye misses the other sees. The optic nerve leaves the eyeball towards the inner side; the point of most acute vision is exactly in the middle at the back of the globe and is called the macula (Fig. 9); here the rays of light entering the eye are brought to a focus by the lens. We know that we can see a wide field of vision, but that we can see distinctly only those objects at which we are looking directly. That is to say, the only part of the retina receiving a clear-cut image is the macula, and objects seen by the rest of the retina are out of focus; if we want to see them distinctly we have to turn our eyes so that they are brought into the centre of the field of vision.

The optic nerves run backwards towards the brain and presently unite with each other to form the optic chiasma (Fig. 17); they divide again immediately to

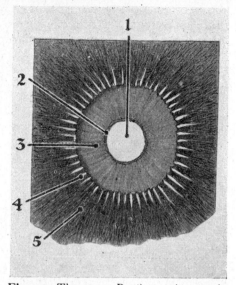

Fig. 15. *The iris. 1, Pupil; 2 and 3, muscles (circular and dilator) of the iris; 4, continuation of coating of eyeball (ciliary muscle); 5, second coat of eyeball (choroid).*

form the optic tracts, which plunge into the brain and pass to the visual cortex of the occipital lobes.

The course of the fibres in the optic chiasma is interesting, because the fibres from the inner half of each retina cross in the chiasma to run in the optic tract of the opposite side. Thus each optic tract is made up of fibres from the outer half of the retina on its own side and fibres from the inner half of the retina of the opposite side. In this way each occipital lobe of the brain receives messages from half of each eye.

The stimuli to which the sensory cells of our eyes react are due to the impact of rays of light emanating either directly from some luminous object, such as the sun or a burning lamp, or from such light falling on external objects as is reflected by them. A large proportion of the light falling on a white surface is reflected, whereas very little is reflected from a black surface. Between the two there are infinite shades of gradation.

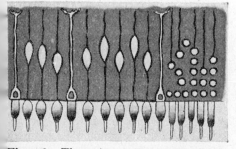

Fig. 16. *The retina, a nervous net, highly sensitive to light, an outgrowth from the brain.*

A black surface seems actually to absorb most of the light. From a luminous object light rays (which travel in straight lines) proceed in all directions. These rays may be either reflected or absorbed, directly transmitted, or refracted, that is, changed in direction.

An object which reflects no light, and does not transmit or refract it, appears black. The reader is only able to see the letters in front of him because of the

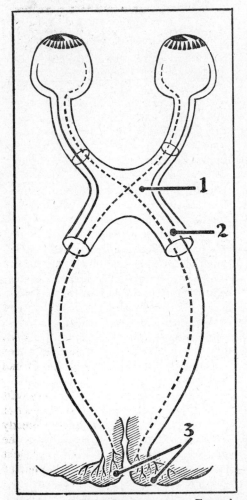

Fig. 17. *Path of the optic nerves. From the eyeballs the optic nerves run to the optic chiasma (1) through the optic tracts (2) to the visual cortex of the brain (3).*

spaces between the letters. The letters themselves are invisible. What we call transparent substances allow light rays to pass through them. Generally they are not absolutely transparent; if they were we should not be able to see them at all. We cannot see air when it is free from moisture, but we can see water, because water is not quite so transparent as air; nor is glass, even at its clearest.

When rays of light pass from a less dense medium to a denser one, for example, from air to glass, or from air to water, the rays are refracted, or bent towards a line perpendicular to the common surface of the two media. If they again pass from the denser medium to the rarer one, they are bent away from the perpendicular. A ray of light passing through a pane of window glass obliquely from the sun, is first bent upwards and then again downwards, so that its passage through the room is identical with, or parallel with, the line of its approach from the sun to the window.

Defects of the Eye

These elementary physical facts are important if we are to understand the functions of the different parts of the eye and the defects which sometimes exist in that functioning. Rays of light falling on the eye, if they are to reach the sensitive retina at the back of that organ, have to pass through various transparent media of varying densities. All these media are denser than the air. Therefore the rays are at each stage bent to a varying angular extent towards the central line of the eye from front to back. First of all, we have the membrane of the cornea; then the aqueous humour; then the lens, and finally, the vitreous humour behind it. All these play a part; but it is chiefly owing to our power, by the relaxation and contraction of a little muscle, of altering the shape of the crystalline lens, making it a little less or a little more convex, little flatter or a little rounder, that w can accommodate our vision to near and distant objects.

Our aim is to focus on to the sensitive retina as many as possible well defined rays of light proceeding from the object we are looking at. From distant objects, the rays impinging on our eye are more or less parallel; from objects near our eye, they are more divergently oblique. The purpose of the lens is to bend these rays towards one another, so that they meet in a point. If we are to see a thing clearly this point must be on the retina, neither in front of it nor behind it. To bring this about the lens has to be made more convex when we are looking at near objects, less convex when we are looking at distant objects. In the normal, or what we call perfect, eye, the shape of the lens is quickly adapted to meet the occasion. But the lens is constructed by nature on the assumption that the distance between it and the retina is uniform. Unfortunately, not all eyes are of the same depth; some are shorter, some are longer than what we call the normal. Individuals so handicapped may have quite normal lenses, but such people constitute a large proportion of the long-sighted and the short-sighted.

Short and Long Sight

In earlier and simpler times the eyes of our ancestors were concerned rather with distant objects and with things of appreciable size than with small near objects, such as printed letters, and the mechanical minutiæ and fine work of today. Considerable muscular effort is called for if we are constantly to observe small objects near to us. This fact alone no doubt, accounts for many of the refraction troubles of today. People who can see things near to them, although their vision for distant objects is confused, are called short-sighted. Commonly, they are people with over-long eyeballs. They cannot reduce the convexity of their lenses sufficiently to effect

that degree of refraction of the rays entering the eye which will bring them into suitable conjunction at the level of the retina. Oculists accordingly prescribe for them supplemental aid in the form of concave lenses to correct the over-convexity with which Nature has furnished them. In the opposite case, that of those who are long-sighted, seeing clearly objects at a distance, yet indistinctly objects near to them such as printed words, the oculist prescribes glasses which are convex.

Kinds of Lenses

It is easy to tell whether a lens is convex or concave by moving it along in front of the eye and observing whether the objects seen through it appear to move with it in the same direction or contrariwise. Objects seen through a concave lens seem to move to the right or to the left as moves the lens, whilst things seen through the convex lens seem to move in the opposite direction.

Another refractive error which is far from uncommon is known as astigmatism. This may be associated with some degree of short sight or of long sight, but its essence consists in an irregularity in the convexity of the crystalline lens. Human ingenuity has found a means of correcting even this defect of Nature by means of artificial lenses.

Clouding of Vision

Some reference should be made to the incidence, common in old age, of clouding or loss of transparency of the lens through which rays of light reach our sensitive nerve cells. Such a clouding naturally causes progressive diminution of vision, and ultimately, complete blindness. Surgeons can without much risk remove the obstructive lens which is the cause of the defect, and can thus restore to the individual, with the help of powerful glasses, an acceptable and reasonably efficient measure of sight.

Our apparatus for hearing is composed of several parts. A defect in any one of these parts almost inevitably leads to some impairment of hearing. The main function of the external ear (Figs. 18 and 19), the pinna, is to catch those aerial vibrations which give rise in our mind to the sensation of sound. These vibrations enter the little external canal, at the end of which is a stretched membrane, corresponding to the parchment covering of a drum, spoken of as the tympanic membrane. This separates the external ear from a tiny chamber known as the middle ear (Fig. 20), the essential part of which is a fragile bridge of three minute bones, or ossicles, the end of one of which rests against the tympanic membrane, whilst the head of the one most remote fits accurately into a passage leading to the so-called inner ear (Fig. 23). The only connexion of the middle ear with the out-side air is through a fine tube called the Eustachian canal (Fig. 21), which opens into the pharynx at the back of the mouth. If this tube becomes blocked through inflammatory trouble in the throat or other cause, the air pressure within the ear drum falls, and the tympanic membrane tends to be drawn out of shape and to lose its tension, so that it no longer conveys sound vibrations.

Fig. 18. *The external ear. The illustration shows a human external ear, the external ear of an Alsatian and of a hare, and a human external ear which has been damaged, the so-called cauliflower ear. The function of the external ear is to catch vibrations in the air, which are translated in the mind into the sensation of sound.*

The Eustachian tube allows air to enter the middle ear from the throat and so keeps the pressure equal on the two sides of the ear drum; were it not for the Eustachian tube, our ear drums would be likely to burst every time we went up a mountain or down a mine. Unfortunately other things besides air can get up the Eustachian tube—notably bacteria. In some people, especially children, inflammation is liable to spread up from a sore throat until it involves the middle

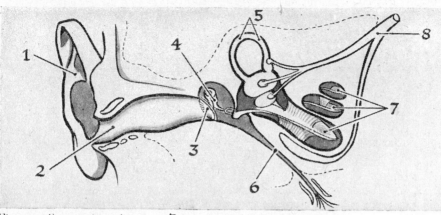

Fig. 19. *Section through ear. 1, External ear; 2, passage running from external ear; 3, ear drum; 4, bridge of tiny bones resting on ear drum (ossicles); 5, semicircular canals forming part of inner ear; 6, tube connecting middle ear with outside air (Eustachian canal); 7, spiral tube in inner ear (cochlea); 8, auditory nerve.*

ear, and an abscess may form there which can only escape by bursting through the drum. This is the cause of running ears not uncommonly seen among children. Sometimes the drum proves too tough to burst, and in that case infection spreads into the air cells of the mastoid process of the temporal bone, producing a mastoid abscess (Fig. 22). This needs immediate surgical treatment because the pus cannot escape except by tracking inwards to the brain; the surgeon opens the bone behind the ear and allows the pus to escape outwards.

The middle ear is designed to transmit sound from the drum to the inner ear. The ossicles form a chain across the middle ear and carry vibrations from the

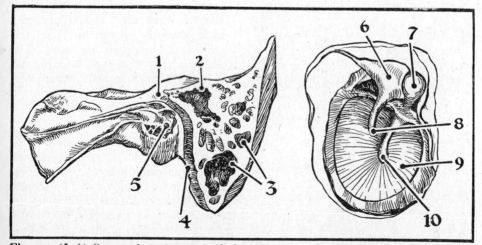

Fig. 20. *(Left) Section through inner half of middle ear. 1, Canal carrying the facial nerve; 2, cavity in the mastoid projection of the temporal bone (mastoid antrum); 3, air cells in the mastoid; 4, outer surface of facial canal; 5, spiral tube (cochlea). (Right) Interior surface of left ear drum showing small bones (ossicles). 6, Body of anvil bone; 7, head of hammer bone; 8, attachment for stirrup bone; 9, ear drum; 10, handle of hammer bone.*

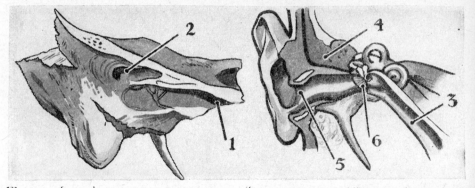

Fig. 21. *Eustachian canal and ear drum. 1, Tube connecting middle ear with outside air (Eustachian canal); 2, opening of Eustachian canal into air cells of mastoid bone; 3, Eustachian canal; 4, mastoid cells; 5, channel from outer ear to ear drum (auditory meatus); 6, ear drum. The Eustachian canal equalizes pressure on the two sides of the ear drum.*

drum to a little oval window in the inner wall which communicates with the inner ear. These ossicles (Fig. 23) have been named the hammer, the anvil and the stirrup bones, from their fancied resemblance to these objects.

The hammer bone is fastened firmly by its handle to the drum and by its head to the anvil bone; this in turn is fitted to the arch of the stirrup bone, and the foot of the stirrup fits into the oval window communicating with the inner ear. Sound

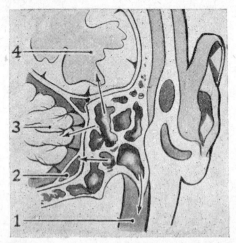

Fig. 22. *Connexions of mastoid, showing how infection is transmitted from it. 1, Tissues of neck; 2, air cavity (sinus); 3 and 4, parts of brain. Arrows show infection path.*

waves pass down the meatus and set the drum vibrating, and these vibrations shake the ossicles, causing the stirrup bone, which is held in position by an encircling ligament, to move up and down in the window like the plunger of a piston.

The inner ear (Figs. 24 and 25), lying embedded in the temporal bone, consists of a tiny bag filled with fluid. The central part consists of two small chambers, the utricle and the saccule, connected by a Y-shaped passage; from the saccule springs a hollow spiral tube, the cochlea; the utricle gives rise to three curving passages called the semicircular canals. The cochlea is concerned with hearing, and the utricle, saccule and semicircular canals are organs of balance.

The Cochlea

The spiral canal of the cochlea (Fig. 26) makes two and a half turns; it is supported on a central pillar of bone, the modiolus (Fig. 26), round which a thin bony shelf curls, like the corkscrew track round the tower at a fun fair; the tube of the cochlea embraces the edges of this shelf. A delicate membrane, the basilar, sensitive to sound, stretches from the edge of the shelf to the far wall of the cochlea, thus dividing it into two canals along its whole length. A branch of the auditory nerve passes up the middle of the modiolus and sends fibres out through the shelf to the basilar membrane.

The sound waves travel down the meatus till they reach the drum and set it oscillating; the ossicles transmit the vibration across the middle ear and set the foot of the stirrup bone moving in the oval window; this movement stirs the fluid in the cochlea and waves are generated which set the basilar membrane vibrating in its turn; these vibrations stimulate the auditory nerve fibres and are transmitted to the brain, where the messages are interpreted as sound.

Vibration and Sound

What we know as sound is, until the terminals of the auditory nerve have been reached, composed of vibration only. The nature of the excitement that passes along the nerve—the nerve impulse—we do not clearly know. It is only when the nerve impulse reaches the special auditory cells in our brain that it becomes interpreted as the sensation which we call sound.

The ear is not only the organ of hearing, but also what may be called the organ of balance. The mechanism of hearing is complicated, and the balancing mechanism of the ear is no less so. The utricle,

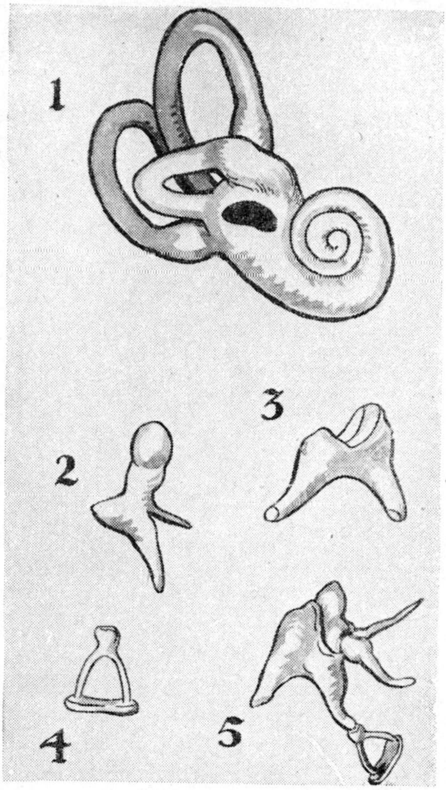

Fig. 23. *Inner ear and bones of middle ear (ossicles). 1, Internal ear; 2, hammer bone; 3, anvil bone; 4, stirrup bone; 5, hammer, anvil and stirrup bones, forming bridge.*

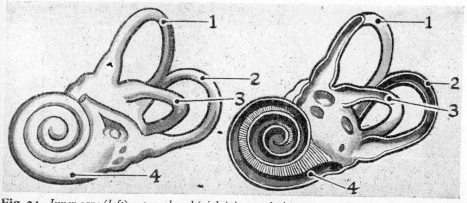

Fig. 24. *Inner ear: (left) external and (right) internal views. 1, 2 and 3, Semicircular canals, concerned with balance, lying one in each dimension of space; 4, spiral canal (cochlea); concerned with hearing; vibrations transmitted by ossicles affect the cochlea, which sends on waves, eventually to the auditory nerve and to the brain, which interprets them as sound.*

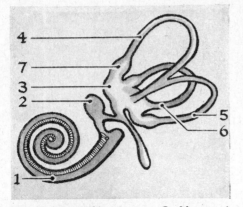

Fig. 25. *Parts of inner ear. 1, Cochlea canal; 2, chamber from which cochlea springs (saccule); 3, chamber from which semicircular canals, 4, 5 and 6, spring (utricle); 7, swelling at end of canal (ampulla).*

saccule and semicircular canals all have a share in it. The three semicircular canals lie in three different planes, corresponding with the three dimensions of space. At one end of each canal there is a swelling called the ampulla (Fig. 25), and inside each of these is a minute ridge covered with stiff microscopic hairs which project into the cavity of the ampulla. The fluid in the neighbourhood of the hairs is sticky and glutinous. When a man changes the position of his head, he sets up waves in the fluid in his semicircular canals, and these waves agitate the glutinous fluid into which the ampullary hairs project. Fibrils of the eighth cranial nerve (*see* CHAPTER VIII) lie at the roots of the hairs, and every time the hairs are stirred by movements of the fluid the nerve fibres send a message up to the brain. Since the canals lie in three different planes, movements in any direction can be recognized.

Sensing Position

But this is not all. In the simple nervous system of the jelly fish, certain sensitive cells have particles of calcium in association with them, and as the weight of these very tiny particles shifted, the

animal was able to appreciate changes of position in its progress through the water. In the utricle and saccule of the ear we have exactly the same device, serving exactly the same purpose. On the floor of the utricle and on the inner wall of the saccule are round patches of stiff hairs, like those in the ampullæ, and again the fluid in the neighbourhood of the hairs is thick and sticky; but, in addition, minute calcareous particles are tangled among the hairs and kept in position by the sticky fluid. When the position of the head is changed the weight of these particles pulls on the hairs, and fibres of the eighth nerve lying at their roots transmit information to the brain. The semicircular canals record movements of the head, while the saccule and utricle send in news about position. We learn from the semicircular canals that we have turned the head suddenly to one

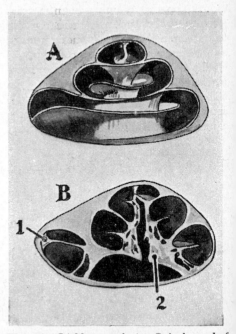

Fig. 26. *Cochlea canal.* (A) *Spiral canal of cochlea, showing central pillar of bone (modiolus).* (B) *Section of cochlea: 1, Membrane connecting cochlea with auditory nerve (basilar membrane); 2, modiolus.*

side, but when we wake up in the morning it is the utricle and saccule which inform us that our heads are lying on our pillows. The news sent by these organs is accurately interpreted by the brain.

The sensations which we experience have been grouped into two classes, known as general and special. The former have their origin within the body itself; under this heading are included hunger, thirst, fatigue, faintness, and so on. Special sensations are such as are directly caused by objects or forces outside the body. It is only through such sensations that we are made aware of the outside world, all our knowledge of which is based on stimuli to which our special senses react. Our direct knowledge is limited to that part of the external universe which is able to ring one or other of our sensory door bells.

Limits of Consciousness

We know that vibrations of a certain rapidity and wave length, falling on our eyes, give rise in our consciousness to a sensation of "redness," vibrations of another wave length produce an impression which we call blue; and so on through the entire spectrum of visible light. But there are light rays both of shorter and of longer wave length than any of those which, through the medium of our eyes, are directly perceptible to us. So with those aerial vibrations which cause in us the sensation of sound. Individuals vary very much in their sensitivity to sound; but the most aurally sensitive amongst us can directly perceive only those vibrations whose wave lengths fall between comparatively narrow limits. Other animals whose ears are differently constructed, can hear sounds which are inaudible to humans (Fig. 27).

These particular physical impressions are signalled to our brain by nerves whose names, optic and auditory, indicate their special purpose. The queer thing about these nerves is that apparently they are fundamentally identical with one

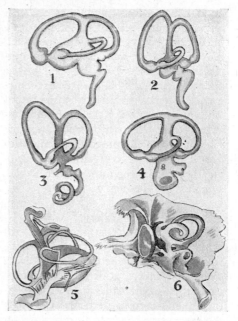

Fig. 27. *Aural structures of various animals. These varying constructions make it possible for some animals to hear sounds inaudible to humans. 1, Membranous labyrinth of reptile; 2, bird; 3, mammal; 4, frog; 5, organ of hearing of fish; 6, organ of hearing of owl.*

another and with all the rest of our nerves, with one or other of which practically every cell in our body is in touch. It is the receptor or "distal" terminals of these nerves and the "interpreter" or "central" connexions that vary and so enable our senses to work.

Interpreting Sensations

There is nothing about the bundles of fibres that we call nerves that may not, for practical purposes, be regarded as analogous to electric cables. Their uses and functioning can, for the most part, be considered as physio-chemical phenomena. So may those of the receptive organs which transform this or that vibration or other impact or stimulus into "nerve impulse."

It is only when we reach the other end of the nerve fibre, where matter and mind become transfused, that the real miracle begins. There is seemingly little in common between the vibrations which fall on our ear drums and the pseudo-electric current which passes up our auditory nerve. This unlikeness, however, becomes relatively insignificant when we try to trace the connexion between these electric messages, or the vibrations which provoke them, with our conscious interpretation of them, whether it takes the form of a Beethoven symphony or the hoot of a motor.

Local Sensations

Though the "electric movement" set up in any nerve fibre, no matter what the stimulus, seems to be the same in every case, yet, whatever the nature of the provocant, the sensation has its own peculiar quality and its own peculiar location. If the optic nerve be cut in a surgical operation, the sensation is not that which we commonly think of as the pain of a tissue being cut, but that of a flash of light. Each distal ending of a sensory nerve fibre is peculiarly responsive to one sort of stimulus, and its central end gives rise to one special sensation.

It is not only with regard to light and sound that our sensibility is specialized and localized. Thus our hands, which are so sensitive to touch, are less so to warmth than are many other parts of the body. That is why the comfortable temperature of a bath cannot easily be gauged by plunging the hand into it. If we put to our lips the two points of a pair of compasses, they can be recognized as separate points even though they are placed very close together. If, however, they are applied to the back, they must be placed very wide apart if they are not to give the impression of a single point.

The External World

Ordinarily we receive at the same instant thousands of different messages from the sensory nerves of the skin, and from the optic nerves; and it is only by arranging these that we form any idea of the world about us, and of the shape and size of external objects. The only reason we have for believing an apple to be green is that it affects our organ of sight in such a way as to cause a sensation which we have decided to call green. Its other characteristics, as we call them, are all built up in like manner. It is quite possible that to another creature, with senses differing from ours, the apple which we see would appear to be an altogether different thing.

It is commonly imagined by people not given to reflecting on such matters, that colour, taste, shape, consistency, smell, sound, temperature and one or two subsidiary qualities are the sum of the attributes which a material object can possess. This is not so.

The slowest vibrations which perceptibly affect the retina of our eye are those of about four hundred million million to the second. These give rise to the sensation which we call red. More rapid vibrations cause severally the sensations of orange, yellow, green, blue and violet, beyond which our eyes fail us. Our ears are adapted to be affected by vibrations up to about forty thousand a second. Above this number we can hear nothing. We have no organs for detecting vibrations between forty thousand and four hundred million million. Yet it is certain that such vibrations exist.

Development of Senses

It is quite possible, or even probable, that sensibility to qualities unknown to us exists in various animals, especially in such highly-developed insects as the bees. There seems also some reason to suspect, though there is no conclusive evidence of it, that certain human beings, especially among those deprived of the use of one or more of the customary senses, not only possess an exaggerated development of one or more of the other customary senses, but actually are able to sense certain vibrations which to ordinary folk are non-existent.

Civilized man, with his comparatively high development of reasoning faculty, has to some extent made himself independent of various senses which are in habitual use among more primitive people. Thus, the native African, his senses unblunted by civilization, has an immediate sense of direction which seems almost uncanny to the European; and many explorers and travellers have themselves experienced such a development of this sense as to be able to rely on it without hesitation.

In many animals, especially among insects, we find elaborate sense organs of whose function we have not the slightest notion. To them, the world must present an altogether different aspect. They may be aware of music and of beauty of kinds such as we cannot even imagine. There is no limit to the range of possible colours, tastes and scents, to speak only of sensations similar in kind to our own. When we remember that the honey-bee possesses two hundred "conical structures" each with a nerve-ending, and twenty thousand specialized flasks and pits, we are clearly faced with an organization of almost infinite potentialities. It is only necessary to observe the purposive accuracy of the bee's flight, remembering that its eyes, unlike our own, are fixed in their sockets and have no power of focus, in order to be convinced of the presence of senses outside our knowledge.

It is difficult to be sure of the extent to which consciousness accompanies the stimulus of external objects on the senses of other animals, even when followed by definite reactions. The earthworm, for example, distinguishes between light and dark, reacting to each differently; yet it has no eyes, and the effect, whatever it is, is apparently brought about by the action of light on any part of its surface. Even plants bend towards, or from, the light according to the self-preservation indications of the occasion, yet it is difficult to think of them as experiencing sensation in our meaning of the word.

Limitations of Normality

On the other hand, whenever there is a specific reaction in any living organism to a specific external stimulus, it is quite beyond our power of proof to assert that the reaction is entirely unconscious, and that no true sensation is present. To a creature furnished with additional instruments of sensation, the world would inevitably present aspects differing profoundly, both quantitatively and qualitatively, from any of those which we customarily regard as altogether making up the whole. It is therefore rash to scoff too whole-heartedly at the seeming miracles of telepathy and of the queer sensory phenomena which we sometimes hear reported in connexion with those deprived of one or more of their normal senses. Even the least imaginative of us can scarcely fail to have his complacency disturbed when, in the most silent and solitary place, he switches on a wireless receiving set, and is at once brought into relation with a world until that moment entirely beyond his perception.

CHAPTER XII

REPRODUCTION AND SEX

METHODS OF REPRODUCTION: CELL DIVISION: BEGINNINGS OF HUMAN
LIFE: FEMALE SEX ORGANS: PROCESS OF IMPREGNATION: MALE SEX
ORGANS: SEMINAL FLUID: DEVELOPMENT OF FERTILIZED OVUM: STAGES
IN GROWTH OF EMBRYO: NOURISHMENT OF EMBRYO: DEVELOPMENT OF
ORGANS: DETERMINATION OF SEX: THE BREASTS: EMOTION AND SEX

ONE OF the most striking characteristics of all living organisms is the capacity to produce living copies of themselves. There are many varieties of the process of reproduction, but they may all be grouped under two heads, asexual and sexual.

Very simply constructed plants and animals reproduce their kind by the elementary method of dividing into two parts, each of which is indistinguishable from the other. This form of reproduction is in the main confined to lowly organisms composed of a single microscopic unit, or cell; and though it seems very different from the complicated process of human reproduction, it nevertheless embodies the same fundamental principle, that of growth by cell division.

Division and Fusion

As we rise higher in the plant and animal kingdoms, complications begin to be introduced into the process of reproduction. There are, for example, organisms which at some times reproduce by simple cell division, at others by two units fusing together.

A little further up the evolutionary scale we find differentiation between individuals of the same species. Each of the individuals starts as a single cell, and grows by cell division, but a number of cells remain adherent to each other to form a composite plant or animal, and these plants or animals are not all alike in function or in form. In particular, a group of cells is set apart for purposes of reproduction, and according to the nature of that group the individual may be classed as male or female. When this stage is reached, offspring can result only if a reproductive cell from the body of a male establishes contact with a reproductive cell from the body of a female.

Asexual Reproduction

Many plants and animals are capable of both asexual and sexual reproduction. Among many plants the two methods may be adopted respectively at different seasons, the asexual being more usual in the spring, the sexual in the autumn. In the case of many mosses and ferns, the choice of method seems to be related to the amount of moisture available.

In other cases, the different methods are used in alternate generations. Jelly fish, or medusæ, for instance, develop male and female reproductive organs and then separate from the parent hydroid, which they in no way resemble, and from which they originate by budding. By the sexual method they in turn produce hydroids, from which, again, medusæ are produced.

In higher animals the differentiation between the male and female becomes

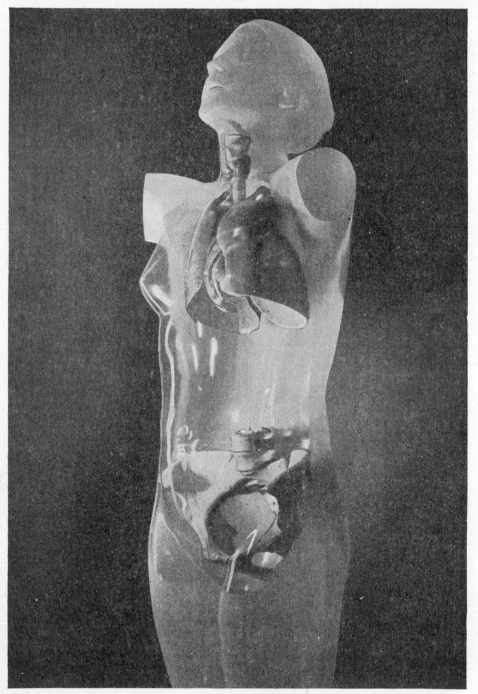

ORGANS OF THE FEMALE BODY

This giant model shows the position and the construction of the heart, the lungs and the pelvis.

absolute. There are, it is true, even among human beings, very rare cases of hermaphrodites, or creatures possessing the reproductive organs of both sexes, but such instances form so infinitesimal a proportion of the whole as to be negligible. The main difference between various classes of higher animals lies in the method of gestation; birds and reptiles disgorge their young from their bodies in a very immature state but protected by shells and equipped with food, mammals retain their young in their bodies until the latter are physically complete in form—though not, of course, in size.

Beginning of Life

Every living thing, plant or animal, begins its life as a single cell, which contains within its microscopic self all the mysteries and magic of life. Man, in common with all other life, begins his earthly career as a single cell, the fertilized ovum. This particle, which is but one hundred-and-seventy-fifth of an inch in diameter, just visible with the aid of a normally powerful magnifying glass, is itself the product of the union of two diverse cells, a spermatozoon separated from the body of a male human being, and an ovum from a female. This fertilized ovum, which is retained in a special organ, the uterus or womb, in the female body, divides into two cells, and these again into four, and so on until the many million-celled body which we know as a human being has thus been built up.

The distinctive physical characteristics of male and female among humans are accompanied by psychological differences little less marked. In this chapter we shall confine ourselves to a description of their basic physical reproductive organs.

The essential reproductive organs of woman are the ovaries, the oviducts or Fallopian tubes, the uterus or womb, and the vagina (Figs. 1 and 2). The reproductive function of woman is to produce an egg or ovum, to afford facilities for the fertilization of this ovum by the male reproductive cell, to mature this fertilized egg, and then to nourish the still immature new individual until it is capable of nourishing itself, even after it has left the mother's body.

The ovaries (Fig. 2) are two small rather flattened oval bodies lying one on each side of the lower part of the abdominal cavity. In front, they are attached to, and held in position by, a flattened band stretching across the abdomen, called the broad ligament. At their back and sides they are unattached. They are somewhat larger in the virgin than in a woman who has borne children. Roughly, they are about an inch and a half long, half an inch thick, and three-quarters of an inch wide. The ovaries are covered with a rather thick membrane, immediately beneath which is a layer in which are embedded a number of small follicles or vesicles known as the Graafian follicles, each containing fluid and a microscopic body which is an immature ovum (Fig. 3)

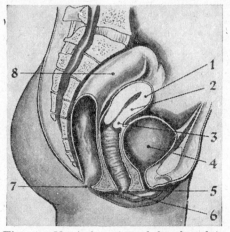

Fig. 1. *Vertical section of female pelvis, showing position of reproductive organs. 1, Head of womb, or uterus; 2, body of womb; 3, short tube at end of womb (neck of uterus); 4, bladder; 5, channel by which urine leaves the bladder (urethra); 6, channel leading from womb to exterior of body (vagina); 7, end of digestive tract (anus); 8, last section of large intestine (rectum).*

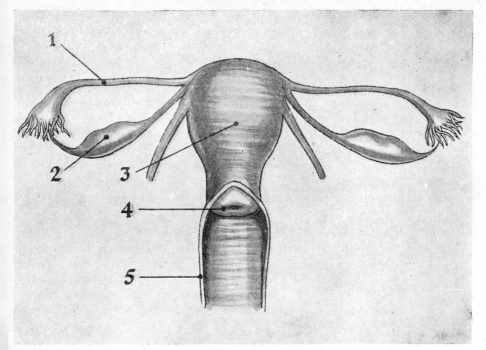

Fig. 2. *Female reproductive organs. 1, Tube by which discharged particles from the ovary are sucked up and carried into the womb (Fallopian tube); 2, egg-shaped bodies, lying at the side of the lower part of the abdominal cavity, containing microscopic immature ova, or eggs (ovary); 3, body of uterus; 4, neck of uterus; 5, channel from uterus to exterior of body (vagina).*

or egg. At birth, it is estimated that there are in the ovaries of a female child about thirty thousand ova or eggs. No fresh ova are formed after birth.

The reproductive life of woman does not normally begin until she is from thirteen to sixteen years of age; it terminates usually between the ages of forty-five and fifty-five. During the reproductive period the cells from which the ova develop, together with the follicles in which they are embedded, progressively come nearer the surface of the ovary, where they mature and increase in size.

About every twenty-eight days one of these Graafian follicles bursts, and the ovum which it contains, together with the fluid surrounding it, is expelled into the abdominal cavity. Near to each ovary is the funnel-like opening of a tube, the oviduct or Fallopian tube, the end of

which is broken up into a sort of circular fringe with threads, called fimbriæ, arranged rather like the opening of a trumpet. The lining of the Fallopian tube is furnished with microscopic hairs or cilia which are in constant movement, thereby causing an inward current, which draws into the tube particles floating near the opening. By this action the discharged ovum is sucked into the tube and drawn along to the uterus in which the Fallopian tube terminates. The Fallopian tubes are each about three and a half inches long. The ripe ovum itself is spherical and about one hundred and twentieth of an inch in diameter.

The uterus, except during pregnancy, is roughly pear-shaped and about three inches long. Its walls are very thick, and its cavity so small that the walls are almost in contact with one another. Its broader

Fig. 3. *Human ovum, highly magnified. The ovum consists of a nucleus surrounded by granules. The ovaries of a female child contain, at birth, about thirty thousand ova.*

blood and the unfertilized ovum constituting the menstrual flow. The preparation and ripening of a new Graafian follicle and ovum at the surface of the ovary begins anew and, in a few weeks, the whole process is repeated. The bursting of the Graafian follicle and the setting free of a ripe ovum is called ovulation, and it is believed that it usually takes place at about the middle of the period which elapses between menstruations.

Impregnation

The act of impregnation by the male consists first in the ejection of seminal fluid from the penis into the vagina of the female. This seminal fluid contains a large number of male reproductive cells, or spermatozoa. The spermatozoa are capable of independent movement and make their way towards the mouth of the womb into which some of them succeed in making an entry. When one of them succeeds in effecting a junction with the ovum, the process of impregnation is complete. Ovulation and menstruation then cease and do not recur until after the birth of the child nine months later. Usually cessation of ovulation and menstruation

end, the fundus, lies uppermost. Below, the uterus ends in a short conical thick-walled tube called the cervix or neck. This projects into the vagina into which it opens by a small central aperture called the os uteri or mouth of the womb. The vagina is a sort of canal or tube, some four inches long, leading from the womb to the outside of the body.

When the ovum discharged from the ovary every month makes its way to the uterus, it finds the lining membrane thickened and well supplied with blood for its reception. If a male reproductive cell, or spermatozoon (Fig. 4), meets and unites with it on its course, the ovum takes root in the prepared uterine seed bed and there develops. The woman is now pregnant, and the creation of a new human individual has begun.

If, however, the ovum does not encounter a spermatozoon, within a few days it is cast off, and the process called menstruation is initiated. In this process the whole lining membrane of the uterus separates and a variable loss of blood occurs, the dead membrane with the

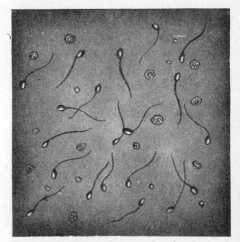

Fig. 4. *Human male reproductive cells (spermatozoa) highly magnified. The spermatozoon is about one-five-hundredth of an inch long. It moves by vigorous lashing of its tail.*

continues whilst the breasts are actively secreting milk and while the baby is being suckled.

The essential reproductive organs of man (Fig. 5) are the testes, from each of which proceeds a tube called the vas deferens, the prostate, the seminal vesicles, certain small glands, the principal being known as the glands of Cowper, the ejaculatory duct, and the penis. The reproductive business of the male consists in the manufacture of male reproductive cells, in furnishing them with suitable media in which they can live and move, and in injecting them into the body of the female where they may establish contact with the female ovum. With the act of impregnation, the reproductive task of man is finished.

The Testes

The testes, or testicles, are two oval glandular structures, each in the adult about an inch and a half long, and about an inch thick from front to back and from side to side. They each weigh normally about an ounce or a little less. They are suspended in a small bag, or pouch, called the scrotum, which may be regarded as a small extension of the abdomen, its cavity, however, being in adult life separated from that of the abdomen. Through the partition between the two cavities certain structures pass on each side. The passage way is the inguinal canal.

The more characteristic part of the testis consists of a large number of small lobes, each composed almost entirely of minute tubes known as the seminiferous tubules, in the interior of which tubes the seminal fluid is secreted. The separate tubules of each lobe unite to form one large tube, and these larger tubes again join together, constituting the first part of the convoluted tubular structure called the epididymis. This is closely attached to the testis on each side, and is generally considered as forming a part of it. It is really the beginning of the vas deferens,

folded again and again on itself, and connects the testis with the seminal vesicle of its own side. The vas deferens, then, together with certain arteries, veins, nerves and lymphatic vessels constituting, with it, the spermatic cord, passes through the inguinal canal and enters the pelvic part of the abdominal cavity. At the back of the lower end of the bladder, the vas deferens joins with a small tube leading from the seminal vesicle, the canal which they form together being known as the

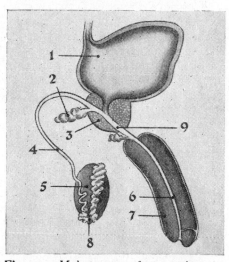

Fig. 5. *Male organs of generation. 1, Bladder; 2, membranous receptacle at side of bladder (seminal vesicle); 3, glands surrounding neck of bladder (prostate); 4, tube leading from testicle (vas deferens); 5, testicle; 6, urethra; 7, penis; 8, tubular structure forming beginning of vas deferens (epididymis); 9, tube formed by joining of vas deferens and seminal vesicle (ejaculatory duct).*

ejaculatory duct. The ejaculatory duct on each side passes for an inch of its way through the prostate gland, ending in the upper part of the urethra, the canal which runs through the centre of the penis, and thus serves as a common medium for the ejection of urine and of the seminal fluid.

The seminal vesicles are two membranous receptacles situated one on each side of the base of the bladder at the back. They are about two inches long and about a third of an inch wide. Each consists of a tube coiled and re-coiled on itself, ending in an opening into the vas deferens, with which it forms a single tube, the seminal or ejaculatory duct.

Prostate Gland

The prostate gland is composed of thirty or forty small glands. It is about the size of a chestnut, which it resembles also in shape. It surrounds the neck of the bladder and the front part of the urethra, weighs rather less than an ounce, and is about three-quarters of an inch thick, an inch long from base to apex, and about an inch and a half wide at its base. Its situation in relation to the basic structures of the body is about half an inch below the symphysis of the pubic bones, that is, the lowest bony point which can be felt with the hand in the front of the body in the central line.

The Urethra

The first part of the urethra and the lowest part of the neck of the bladder are enclosed in the prostate. The seminal or ejaculatory ducts also pass through the prostate to join the urethra about an inch from its beginning. The secretion of the seminal vesicles appears to help the mobility of the spermatozoa, as does also the secretion of the prostate. There are almost certainly subtleties in the action of these secretions which we have not yet fathomed. The so-called Cowper's glands, which are adjacent to the first part of the urethra, also secrete a fluid which is passed into the urethra. The function of this is not established, but it is thought probable that its main purpose is to neutralize the acidity of the urine, thus helping to make the environment more favourable to the activity and the mobility of the spermatozoa in the seminal fluid when it is expelled through this organ.

The penis, the most obvious external part of the male reproductive organs, is composed of three almost cylindrical collections of tissue, one on each side known as the corpora cavernosa, and one behind, enclosing the urethra, called the corpus spongiosum. The main body of the penis consists of the corpora cavernosa; but it is the corpus spongiosum which forms the enlarged and rounded extremity known as the glans penis. At the summit of the glans penis is a vertical slit which is the external opening of the urethra. The rounded terminal border of the glans penis is known as the corona glandis, behind which there is a constriction known as the cervix, or neck. At the back of the cervix below is a fold of skin which forms the posterior part of the frænum. The circular fold of skin covering the glans is known as the foreskin, or prepuce. This is freely movable over the corona except in the middle line below, where it is attached by the frænum.

A marked characteristic of the penis is its capacity for rapid change of form and size in obedience to emotional or sensory stimulus. The corpora cavernosa include blood spaces which are usually practically empty, but are capable of becoming gorged with blood in times of sexual excitement. This engorgement, combined with the activity of certain erectile muscular tissue, causes the penis at times to increase in size and rigidity, and thus it becomes possible for it to be introduced into the vagina of the female.

Seminal Fluid

The seminal fluid ejected from the penis into the female vagina consists of the external secretion of the testes together with that of the seminal vesicles, of the glands of Cowper and of the prostate. It is a viscous fluid, somewhat milky in appearance, consisting of ninety per cent water and ten per cent organic and inorganic substances in solution or in suspension. Fundamentally important are the spermatozoa (Fig. 4), the active male reproductive agent. An average ejaculation of seminal fluid contains several hundred million of these mobile units. In man, the spermatozoon consists of a head-piece, a middle piece, and a long whip-like tail-piece, and looks rather like an elongated tadpole in miniature. The human spermatozoon is about one five-hundredth of an inch in length and, at its widest part, about one six-thousandth of an inch in breadth. The forms of spermatozoa in different animals vary greatly, but all are characterized by mobility. They achieve this mobility by a somewhat vigorous lashing of the tail (Fig. 6).

Pregnancy

Whenever sex intercourse results in pregnancy, it means that out of the enormous number of spermatozoa ejected into the vagina of the female at the time of coition, one has succeeded in making its way into the uterus and, generally, into one of the Fallopian tubes leading from the ovaries into the uterus; and in that tube, or earlier, has encountered a ripe female ovum with which it has effectively united. It will be seen that at every act of coition, millions of living spermatozoa die and become disintegrated.

The capacity of the male testes to produce active spermatozoa begins only when the earlier years of boyhood have been passed. The period of transition is that which we characterize as the age of puberty. It varies greatly in individuals, but is usually from fourteen to sixteen. At this time, certain manifestations which we speak of as secondary sexual characteristics show themselves. Hair begins to grow on the face and on the pubes, and remarkable changes in the emotions and temperament take place; alterations occur also in the voice and in the facial expression. The capacity of the testes to produce active spermatozoa, once established, may persist throughout life; usually, however, a gradual loss of fertilizing power sets in towards the end of what is called middle age. But although it

is unusual, it is by no means unknown for men seventy or eighty years old to become the fathers of children.

Coition is the term applied to the union of the sexes by the introduction of the male reproductive element into the body of the woman. To this biological end the penis is constructed for insertion into the vagina. Under the influence of physical and emotional stimuli the penis becomes congested with blood and consequently swollen. Various muscles contract and this normally flaccid organ becomes comparatively rigid.

While physical contact with, or even propinquity to, the body of a member of the other sex may act as a definite provocant of erection, especially during virile youth, there is an individuality, a particularity, which determines the intensity of the stimulus and, consequently, of its effectiveness. Not all males are equally

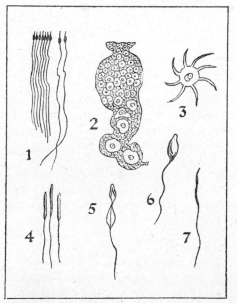

Fig. 6. *Sex units of various animals. 1, Spermatozoa of snail; 2, ovary of earthworm; 3, spermatozoon of crayfish; 4, spermatozoa of worm; 5, spermatozoon of guinea pig; 6, spermatozoon of man; 7, spermatozoon of rat. Notice tail of spermatozoa, the vigorous lashing of which produces movement.*

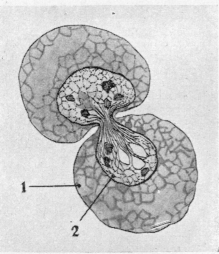

Fig. 7. *Division of a cell. The fertilized ovum, consisting of 1, protoplasmic surrounding network, and 2, nucleus, splits into two cells, each possessing this same structure.*

attracted by the same females, and vice versa. The whole phenomenon strikingly illustrates the difficulty, if not the impossibility, of drawing any hard and fast line between the physical and the psychological elements of human physiology.

Union having been established, wave-like contractions occur in the muscles of the seminal vesicles which cause the semen loaded with spermatozoa to be forced into the urethra. Rhythmic contractions of the muscles surrounding the urethra then expel the semen from that canal into the vagina. The mechanical stimulus of the surface nerves of the penis are commonly the immediate cause of the motor activity of these muscles, the spinal cord acting as the nervous intermediary. These nerve centres can, however, be brought into activity without direct sensory stimuli. This occurs sometimes in dreams, when sexual images appear in the mind though no physical contact exists. The first stages of the normal coitive reactions, indeed, occur not infrequently as a result of the contemplation of ideas or images possessing sexual significance.

In many—probably most—animals the female part in the sexual act would seem to be a much more passive one, from the emotional or psychological point of view, than that of the male. In man, however, as in certain other of the nearly related mammals, psychic and physical events occur in the female not dissimilar from those which take place in the male. As a result of sexual excitement, the clitoris, like the penis (of which it is the female counterpart), becomes swollen and erected, whilst the muscles of the Fallopian tubes and the uterus contract and pour down copious fluid into the vagina. The walls of the vagina are stirred into activity and flood it with mucus secretion, generally at the time that semen is ejaculated into the vagina. The spermatozoa emitted by the male thus find themselves in a suitable environment for their progress towards the cavity of the uterus and thence into the oviducts.

Sex Attraction

One of the most remarkable phenomena in all bi-sexual fertilization is the attractive force that seems to operate between the male and the female sex elements, that is, between the spermatozoa and the ova. It is hard to comprehend this attractive force if we exclude conscious purposiveness on the part of the individual cell.

Before the spermatozoon enters the ovum, the latter throws out bud-like projections which become separated from the main body of the cell. From the time that the male cell fertilizes with the female one, a steady development takes place until, in the course of nine months, a minute speck of protoplasm, weighing about one-fifteen-thousandth of an ounce, becomes an elaborately organized body, weighing something like two million times as much, and possessing muscles, nerves, bones, and a circulatory system. The ovum swells, then divides into two cells (Fig. 7) and these again into four. The now multicellular embryo moves on towards the uterus. By the time it reaches its destination in the wall of that organ, it will consist of a ball, still minute, but composed of many units, all apparently similar to its original self (Fig. 8). In contact with the wall of the uterus, threads grow out from the minute ball and plant themselves in the lining tissues, and small branches of maternal blood vessels extend from the uterine walls into the growing ovum.

The blend of the threads from the developing ovum and the blood vessels from the interior of the uterus constitutes the beginning of the structure known as the placenta (Fig. 9). This becomes in time a large fleshy mass which serves as an intermediary between the growing child and its mother. Through it the embryo obtains its nourishment, and through it its waste products are eliminated. Only when the child is born, at the end of nine months, does the placenta cease to function; then it separates from the wall of the uterus and is expelled from the mother's body.

In the course of three or four days after being fertilized, the unicellular ovum is divided into a number of cells united together into a ball, the morula (Fig. 8), which under a fairly powerful microscope looks rather like a mulberry. Some of the cells forming the middle of this ball begin to move away from the centre and cluster near the edge, leaving a central space

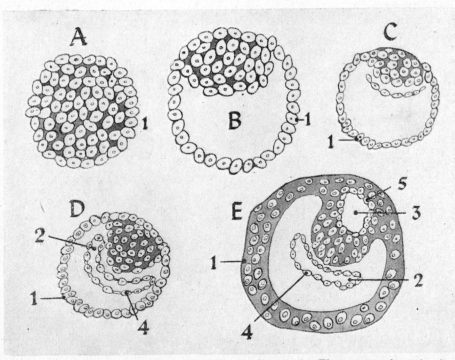

Fig. 8. *Early stages of development of the fertilized ovum.* (A) *Three or four days after being fertilized—a number of cells united in a ball (morula).* (B) *Some cells then move away from the centre and cluster round the edge, leaving central space filled with fluid (blastocyst stage).* (C), (D) *and* (E) *Subsequent stages of development, showing increasing complication.* 1, Limiting wall of embryo, through which nourishment is obtained in the early stages (trophoblast); 2, layer of cells separated from the mass, forming a yolk-sac; 3, cavity in main cluster of cells (amnio-embryonic, or amniotic, cavity); 4, layer of cells around yolk-sac (entoderm); 5, layer of cells which develop around and enclose the amniotic cavity (ectoderm).

which is filled with fluid. At this stage, the developing ovum is known as a blastocyst. The morula has been converted into a sort of bladder with a covering wall consisting of a single layer of cells, except where at one point a cluster of cells, like a miniature bee swarm, projects into the central cavity as a mass.

Nourishment of Embryo

The limiting wall is known as the trophoblast, from the Greek word trophe, meaning nourishment. This layer takes no part in the formation of the actual embryo, but is concerned only with the establishing of relations between the uterine wall of the mother and the growing child within her; through its intermediation, nourishment is, at this early stage, obtained. The embryo and certain temporary structures connected with it are formed out of the cell-mass which projects into the cavity of the blastocyst. The layer of cells of the projecting cluster furthest from the boundary rim then separates from the mass and forms

a closed sac which, later, will constitute a sort of yolk sac. Soon afterwards, a cavity develops in the middle of the projecting cluster, so that we now have three enclosed cavities. Separate from one another, but within the main cavity, are the amniotic, or amnio-embryonic, cavity formed in the middle of the projecting cell cluster, and the future yolk-sac enclosed by cells separated from the projecting cluster.

The layer of cells around the yolk-sac constitutes the entoderm, whilst that lining the amniotic cavity is called the ectoderm. These are known as germinal layers. Between these two a third germinal layer, called the mesoderm, soon comes into existence. It is out of these three layers of cells that the embryo child develops; the embryo is, as it were, suspended between the amniotic cavity above and the yolk-sac cavity below in the form of a flat double plate, known as the embryonic disc. This, to begin with, is almost circular but gradually lengthens out and becomes differentiated for the production of the various parts of the

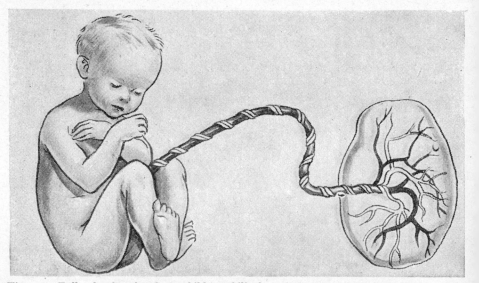

Fig. 9. *Fully developed unborn child; umbilical cord through which the embryo derives nourishment from its mother, and eliminates waste matter by means of the blood vessels passing through it; and placenta, a large fleshy mass which serves as the intermediary between the embryo and the mother, and is expelled from the mother's body after birth*

body. The entoderm is destined to form the food canal and the structures associated with it; the ectoderm layer is the starting point of the skin and its appendages and also of the brain and spinal cord. From the mesoderm spring the muscles and bones and connective tissue of the body. At this stage, the embryonic disc consists of a few thousand cells, but it still measures less than one-eighth of an inch in diameter.

Development of Head

The first part to develop in the embryonic disc is the head, which occupies practically three-quarters of its length. The proportions gradually change, but, even in a full-grown baby at birth, the size of the head in proportion to that of the rest of the body is very much greater than in the later stages of life. From the ectoderm arise the skin, the hair, the nervous system, the lens of the eye, and the nerve parts of special organs of sense; from the mesoderm the muscles, bones, blood vessels, lungs, alimentary canal, most of the glands, the reproductive organs, and the blood; from the entoderm the lining of the breathing passages and of the alimentary canal and all the glands connected therewith, as well as the bladder and the thyroid and thymus glands.

Sex Determination

Whether the child is to be male or female is probably determined at the moment of fertilization. It would seem that the spermatozoa are of two kinds, male-producing and female-producing, produced in about equal numbers. The sex of a child would appear to depend on which variety of spermatozoon succeeds in establishing union with a ripe ovum. Boys and girls are certainly born in about equal numbers. The observable differences in the sex of the embryo are generally manifest about two months after conception. By the beginning of the third month, external differences show themselves. The testes and the ovaries which, at the beginning, are placed high up in the abdominal cavity, move gradually downwards until, at the time of birth, the ovaries have reached a secure location in the pelvis, and the testes have moved down still further into the pouch prepared to receive them.

By the end of the first month of pregnancy, the main parts of the embryo—head and body and limbs—can easily be distinguished. But it is, of course, extraordinarily unlike the human baby at birth. It lies immersed in a fluid contained in a closed bag which has been made out of its own cells; and this bag is suspended within the mother's womb. With the wall of the uterus the embryo is directly connected by the umbilical cord, through which blood vessels pass, carrying nourishment from the maternal tissues to the growing child and carrying back waste products which the mother's organs gradually get rid of. The navel, or umbilicus, in the wall of the human abdomen is the scar marking the point at which the umbilical cord was attached to the fœtus during its development.

The New-born Child

At birth (Fig. 10) the cord, having been tied by thread, is cut a few inches from the baby's body. The remainder of the cord attached to the placenta is expelled with that structure from the maternal uterus very soon after delivery; and a few days later, the shorter part separates spontaneously from the child.

Up to the moment of its birth the fœtus derives all the nourishment required for its growth in a directly assimilable form through the blood passing from the mother through the umbilical cord. Its mouth and its digestive system have not yet been brought into play. With the separating of the umbilical cord this source of supply is cut off. Thenceforth, the baby must breathe oxygen for itself through its nostrils into its lungs; it must take in nourishment through its mouth and gullet, and digest it in its stomach and intestines. But it is still dependent on its mother for this nourishment, which must take one particular form, namely, that of milk. Human mothers are normally adapted to provide this nourishment.

The Breasts

On the front wall of a woman's thorax are two glands, one on each side, known as the mammary glands, or breasts. In childhood and early youth these glands are small in size both in girls and in boys. But at, or just before, the age of puberty the girl's breasts rapidly grow and become more prominent—anticipatory, as it were, of motherhood. During adolescence they develop still further.

The breasts are rounded eminences extending from the third to the sixth or seventh rib and, when fully developed, from the side of the sternum, or breast bone, to the armpit. A little below the centre of each is a small conical projection, the nipple, generally somewhat darker in colour than the adjacent skin. Around the nipple is a ring called the areola; in the young virgin it is generally rosy in colour, but it has a darkish brown shade in those who are, or who have been, pregnant.

Producing Milk

The nipples are perforated by a number of fine openings which are the endings of tubes leading to the substance of the breast. This latter consists of lobes of glandular tissue, each furnished with an excretory tube, or duct, leading towards the nipple; and each lobe is subdivided into smaller lobes, or lobules, and these again into smaller ones. The tubes leading from the smallest division join with others, and again join, until they ultimately constitute the excretory tubes leading to the openings in the nipple. The structure is not unlike that of the lungs. It is this glandular tissue which, during lactation, produces or secretes milk, manu-

factured from the blood passing through the small vessels which surround the lactiferous cells.

The full development of the female breast is completed during pregnancy. The substance enlarges and the skin of the areola darkens in colour. A few days before the birth of the child, milk begins to be produced and may even exude from the nipples. For the first few days after the child's birth the mammary secretion is thin and somewhat watery, but from about the third day true milk is yielded. As the sucking efforts of the baby act as an important stimulus to the production of milk, it is important to put the baby to the breast frequently during the first few days. Human milk secreted in the breast of a healthy woman furnishes all the nutritional needs of a normal infant.

Emotion and Sex

Although we cannot here go into any detail concerning man's emotional life, it is clear that many emotional factors play an extremely important part in the machinery of reproduction. The initial desire to reproduce one's kind, the process of selecting a mate, and the care and affection bestowed on progeny, all betoken the workings of mind and feelings which are something beyond simple physical and chemical forces. It is true that among the lower animals we find many examples of tenderness for their young. In its simpler forms, however, this amounts to little more than physical attachment to something that must seem to be an actual part of themselves. The biological value of such parental solicitude is obvious. But it is only rarely that we find, among the lower animals, any evidence of those subtle and complicated emotional constituents which enter into love between man and woman, and which have made the fact of sex differentiation into a driving force which has been responsible for some of the greatest of man's intellectual and æsthetic achievements.

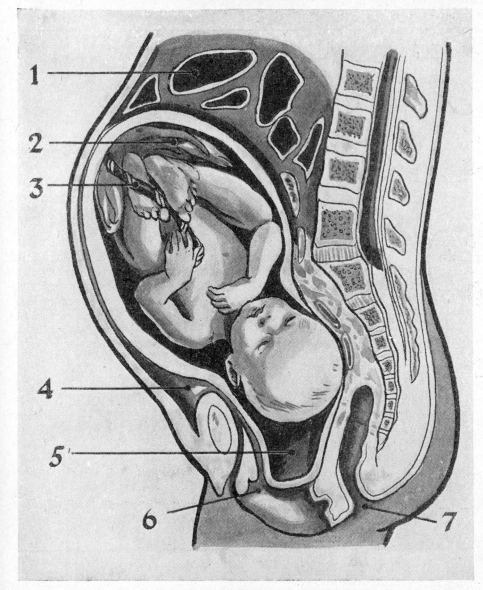

Fig. 10. *Section of womb, showing position of child, immediately before birth. 1, Stomach; 2, placenta; 3, cord attaching embryo to wall of womb (umbilical cord), the navel marks the point at which this cord was attached before birth; 4, bladder; 5, projecting bag of membrane in which the embryo is contained within the womb; 6, urethra; 7, rectum. Although the unborn child has fully developed, in immature form, practically the whole system of organs of digestion, blood circulation, nervous system, and so on, it still depends for nourishment, up to the moment of birth, on the blood supply it receives from its mother through the umbilical cord. When the umbilical cord is severed this source of supply is cut off, and the baby's own organs come into action. The sex of the embryo is probably determined at the moment of fertilization, and observable differences in its sex are generally manifest after about two months.*

CHAPTER XIII

MIND, BODY AND INHERITANCE

PSYCHOLOGY AS A SCIENCE: PSYCHOLOGY IN EVERYDAY LIFE: INTER-
ACTION OF MIND AND BODY: NERVOUS STIMULI AND CONDITIONED
REFLEXES: CONSCIOUSNESS AND MEMORY: REPRESSED MEMORIES AND THE
UNCONSCIOUS: DEVELOPMENT OF CHARACTER: CHARACTER AND HEREDITY:
GENES AND CHROMOSOMES: TRANSMISSION OF HERITABLE CHARACTERISTICS

WE HAVE, so far, been concerned with the anatomy and physiology of the human body, that is, with its structure and organs and their functions. We have regarded the body rather as a machine, and we have taken it to pieces to see how each piece works. But we have not yet inquired into the power which enables the whole machine to function. We have, it is true, examined the brain and the nervous system, which differ essentially from bones and muscle in that they are controlling and directing organs, while the others are controlled and directed, and we have discovered that the circulatory system of the blood plays a part in receiving and transmitting sensations and reactions. But we have not yet faced the problem of why man thinks and feels and acts as he does, showing initiative, judgment, and penetration of thought and capacity in action which rank him far above all other members of the animal kingdom. This problem is the province of psychology, the science of mind.

Study of Psychology

Psychology as a study has a long history. It dates back at least as far as the ancient Greeks. As early as the fifth century B.C. it was emerging as a science, with close affinities on the one hand with philosophy and metaphysics, on the other with the natural sciences—biology, chemistry and physics. But its progress along these lines was checked by two completely effective obstacles: man's ignorance of biology and his predilection for abstract thought. As a result psychology became divorced from science and wedded to philosophy. It is only within quite recent days that it has again taken its rightful place as a strictly scientific study.

Psychology and Life

During the centuries that psychology was a department of philosophy, it remained an abstract and abstruse study, woven out of the minds of subtle and erudite thinkers. From the moment when it began to be taken out of the library and into the laboratory, and later into the market place, it became not only absorbingly interesting to, but also increasingly important in, the life of the ordinary man and woman. The philosopher-psychologist expended his energy on weaving theories as to the nature of mind; the scientist-psychologist devoted himself to the workings of mind and to obtaining direction and control of those workings. Along those lines he has been, particularly during the past thirty or forty years, profoundly helpful to ordinary men and women in their everyday lives. The ultimate nature of mind is still in doubt, as we shall see, but our knowledge of how to control and direct our minds has increased almost incredibly during the present century. Unhappily, all too little use is made as yet of that knowledge, which in many quarters is still regarded with grave, though unjustified, suspicion.

At this point a warning should be entered against two widely believed fallacies: that modern psychology is only common sense translated into long words, and that it is a science which any one can master by reading two or three popularly written books. It is certainly the business of psychology to explore the truth of opinions long established by common sense, and in so far as it has confirmed such opinions, it naturally says the same thing, though as a rule more precisely.

Common Sense and Psychology

But its verdict in such cases is based on solid evidence, and can therefore be relied upon, whereas the verdicts of common sense, being based largely upon hearsay, tradition and convention, are rarely entirely reliable. For example, King Solomon delivered an opinion two thousand years ago that to spare the rod was to spoil the child. That opinion has seemed uncommonly common sense to innumerable parents and teachers ever since, and they have acted on it with gusto and without question. But it is an opinion which modern psychology emphatically does not confirm, and which it has in a few short years quite efficiently succeeded in discrediting.

The other fallacy, that psychology is easy, has resulted from its extreme popularization, largely by people who know little or nothing about the subject, during recent years. Some of the discoveries of modern psychology have made first-rate journalistic stories, and in addition, since the science of psychology has proved itself capable of improving and enriching the lives of men, the subject offers openings for all manner of pretentious but unreliable practitioners. It cannot be too strongly emphasized that

modern psychology is an exceedingly difficult and abstruse science whose study demands first-rate intelligence and highly trained powers of observation and reasoning. Those facile authors who splash about in the foam of its shore-borne wavelets can give no conception of the depth and complexity of its ocean.

Certain Knowledge

Perhaps it may be as well to add a word to those who doubt the findings of psychology. Up to a point they are in good company, for no one doubts some of the findings of psychology as much as the psychologist himself. But after many years of incessant research and experiment there exists an established nucleus of certain knowledge. That nucleus of knowledge may be accepted, and acted upon, with absolute confidence.

One established fact is that the human mind, whatever its nature may be, requires the human brain in order to manifest itself. If part of the brain becomes diseased, or has to be removed, the mind suffers. Sleepy sickness, which is an inflammation of the brain, may cause a radical change in character; other brain diseases bring about the condition known as general paralysis of the insane, when the patient may imagine himself to be God, Julius Cæsar, Henry VIII, or any other personality his disordered imagination may hit upon.

Glands and Character

Disorder of the ductless glands may also give rise to deflection of character or alteration of behaviour, which is the outward and visible expression of the workings of the mind. An over-active thyroid gland produces emotional over-activity, an under-active one slowness of thought, depression and suspicion. A woman with an over-developed pituitary gland may develop a masculine outlook on life. In one case well known to students of medicine, a girl, previously normally feminine in appearance and outlook, lost both feminine shape and tastes as the result of a tumour of the suprarenal glands. On the removal of the tumour she became once again a girl, in her figure and appearance as well as in her attitude to life.

Mind and Body

The extent of the part played by the ductless glands in the formation of character and personality is still obscure, but it is certain that normal physical growth and mental and sexual development depend largely upon their balanced functioning. It is equally certain that there is an intimate and indissoluble relationship between mental and physical activity. Mind and body are not, as some of the medieval psychologists imagined, separate entities. They are not even partners working in close co-operation. They are indivisible parts of the same organism. Mind cannot in this life be separated from body, nor body from mind.

Together they constitute the whole person. They are as inseparable as water and the waves. For convenience sake we talk about this faculty, that sense, that instinct. We isolate such factors mentally in order to examine each one in detail, we pull the machine to bits to see how each part works: but it is essential to remember that the parts work and the machine functions only when the bits are adjusted one to another and are working the one with the other. An isolated instinct, for example, simply does not exist; without a functioning body it has neither meaning nor means of expression.

Brain and Mind

Man's brain is, relative to the size of his body, the largest among the animals. Its large size is due to a great enlargement of the cerebral hemispheres, in which are situated what are called the higher centres of the brain, that is, those dealing with the superior processes of thought. One large part of the cerebral hemispheres consists of an intricate reception centre for messages coming from within the body and from without via the senses of sight, hearing, smell, taste and touch. Another part composes the executive side which translates into action the messages which it has received.

Attached to the under surface of the brain, close to the region which is concerned with emotional life and such fundamental activities as sleep and the building up and breaking down of body tissue—metabolism—is the pituitary, the most important of the ductless glands. From this part of the brain, which in an evolutionary sense is very old, is exercised control of the sympathetic nervous system.

Sympathetic System

When for any reason we are frightened or angry, the sympathetic nervous system goes into action; the heart beats more forcibly and rapidly, the blood pressure rises, extra sugar to supply energy is passed into the blood, the stomach and intestine cease work, and in extreme cases the hair literally stands on end. The pituitary gland is closely connected with the controlling centre of the sympathetic nervous system, and it also secretes a substance which can excite the suprarenal glands to activity. The secretion of the suprarenal glands has just the same action as the sympathetic nervous system.

Here, then, is a combination of ductless glands under the three-fold leadership of the pituitary, the sympathetic nervous system and the base of the brain. This trio is intimately concerned with growth and development, emotional and sexual life, and the carrying on of the basic activities of the body. If any one of the trio gets thrown out of gear, disturbance of both body and mind invariably follows.

Lower down in the brain are collections of nerve cells which control breathing, digestion and the circulation of the blood. These basic activities are carried on automatically, and life thus depends on their persistence. A man can stop thinking, and survive; but if he ceases to breathe he dies. These activities are described as reflex, that is to say, they happen automatically in response to stimuli. When a piece of grit is blown into the eye, the eyelids close, as we say, instinctively. No effort of will power can prevent the eyelids closing; they have done so before the will has any opportunity to come into action.

Reflex Action

If you have ever been through a medical overhaul by a doctor, he has probably made you cross one knee over the other and has then tapped the front of your leg just below the knee-cap with a hammer. If your reactions are in order your leg jerks upwards sharply. You cannot prevent it doing so. It has happened, so to speak, before you realize it has happened.

That is a reflex action. What takes place is as follows. The blow of the hammer stimulates sensory nerve endings in the knee-cap. From these the message "I've been stimulated" swiftly ascends the sensory nerve to the spinal cord. There a switch over from one part of the cord to another takes place, with the result that the message "jerk" travels down a motor nerve to the muscles in the front of the thigh. These muscles contract, and cause the leg to jerk forwards and upwards.

Nervous Stimulus

The elements of the reflex action are the stimulus, the message going to the centre along the sensory nerve, an adjustment at the centre, and an outgoing message which makes a muscle do something. Now consider an illustration on a higher mental plane. A door bangs unexpectedly. You start or jump. You have no power to prevent yourself doing so. If your nerves are not in too good a state at the moment your heart may beat faster for a moment or two, and you may feel cross or ashamed at having been so silly. You may even vent your exasperation on

the nearest person (particularly if this be a child) by demanding angrily why he did not shut the door when he came in. If the other person answers back a quarrel may easily ensue. Let this incident happen shortly before a meal, and you can quite well sit down without appetite and get up with indigestion. Thus do mind and body interact: your emotional disturbance has been responsible for the disorder which has occurred in bodily functions.

If you analyse such an episode, you must conclude that your reaction to the door banging was grossly exaggerated. You manifested every sign of alarm, yet a moment's cool thought shows you that the banging of a door is quite harmless. It would appear that in response to such a stimulus the adjusting mechanism in the brain provokes an interpretation which does little credit to the intelligence of the mind, since it results in the latter issuing quite foolish orders to the body.

Ancestral Memory

There must obviously be some reason for this irrational procedure. Can it be possible that these apparently stupid and unnecessary responses represent, as it were, the residue of a habit ingrained by bitter experience in those far-off days when noise really did indicate harm, when a noise in the forest spelt danger to our early ancestors, and when a split second in time or the least unpreparedness in defence might mean the difference between life and death? It seems strange that several centuries of civilization should not have eradicated such primitive traits —and yet, what are a few centuries when placed beside the vast ages of primeval time? Habits acquired in the few brief years of childhood can persist throughout a lifetime; can we expect the habits of a thousand thousand years to be eliminated in a score or so of generations?

The question then arises, what makes these habits persist? Is it a physiological mechanism, set up countless centuries ago, which continues to function though the need for it has long passed? Is it, so to speak, a system of reflex actions which has become out of date?

Or is it the result of a memory from earlier life, or even of an ancestral memory, buried deep in the mind and handed on from generation to generation? Neither theory seems impossible.

Memories of Childhood

It is surely not fantastic to suggest that the noise may remind the person who starts or jumps of some previous dangerous, or apparently dangerous, experience. May it not be that the startled jumper was as a very young child so terribly frightened by a loud noise (and babies are terrified by loud noises) that he has never since been able to control the impulse to jump whenever a door banged? The weakness of this argument seems to be that the impulse to jump, or at least to start, in such circumstances is almost universal; and this theory would imply that nearly every one had been so frightened in early childhood by a loud noise that the experience had remained unforgettable. And even so one has still to explain why every young baby is from the moment of birth terrified by loud noises. That fact rather seems to lead us back to the idea of a persisting ancestral memory.

Unconscious Activity

In either case we have to note that except in very rare instances there is absolutely no conscious memory of the original experience which (on this theory) has left the individual subject to jitters whenever a door bangs. And the usual reaction shows how much against our inclination the signs of fear are; we almost invariably reproach ourselves for having been made to appear afraid. Is there, then, an unconscious mental activity linked in some way with conscious mental activity, yet definitely different and apart from it, and as a rule hostile or opposed to it? If

it be so, is the basis of that activity physiological or psychical?

Both these last possibilities have been explored very thoroughly by modern psychologists. The work of the eminent Russian physiologist, Ivan Petrovich Pavlov (1849-1936) on reflex actions is world famous. He experimented largely with dogs. For example, he trained a dog to associate the ringing of a bell with meal times (Fig. 1). Every time a bell rang in the dog's hearing food was always there for the eating.

Conditioned Reflexes

Now with the dog, as with human beings, the sight, smell, sound or even thought of food can induce salivation. Very soon, Pavlov discovered, his dog began to salivate as soon as the bell rang. So he rang the bell, but produced no food. The dog still salivated. The animal could not help itself; salivation at the sound of a bell had become a reflex action. But it was not a natural reflex action; the ordinary dog does not salivate at the sound of a bell. Pavlov called this a conditioned reflex; it had been built up as a result of the association in the dog's mind.

A whole school of psychology has arisen on the basis of the conditioned reflex. Pavlov himself thought that every item of man's behaviour, from the simplest to the most intricate, could be explained in terms of nervous reflex to external stimuli. The behaviourists, as they are called, led by the American psychologist, J. B. Watson, have developed Pavlov's theories even to the extent of denying man anything in the way of a soul or even a conscious mind.

In their opinion the old saying: "I think, therefore I exist," is all wrong; it should read: "I act reflexly, therefore I live." The critic of this theory naturally asks, if the behaviourist denies consciousness, how can he be aware, that is, conscious, of other people's conditioned reflexes? It is an objection which has not yet been satisfactorily explained away.

Many people repudiate entirely or in part the behaviourist theory, but every student of psychology admits that the work of this school has been of immense value to the science. The behaviourists have always insisted on objective observation and measurement, and have carried out a vast number of experiments dealing and useless reaction, in that it was made to avoid a danger which did not exist. But, and here is the interesting point, the child had been so conditioned that the danger was to him as real as if it actually existed. It is obvious that a whole way of life can be built up by such conditioning, and Watson holds that many of the

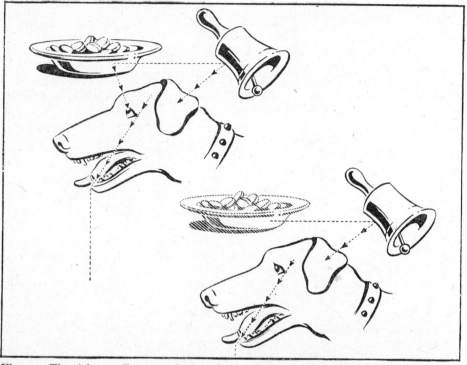

Fig. 1. *The sight, smell or sound of food induces salivation in dogs, as in humans. The illustration shows how a dog was trained to associate the ringing of a bell with meal times. Whenever a bell rang, food was present. After a short time, the dog began to salivate at the sound of the bell even when there was no food. The salivation had become a conditioned reflex.*

with sensual stimuli. Watson's experiments with young children are well known to every psychologist and teacher. Among others, he showed an infant a toy and at the same time made a loud noise. After the experiment had been repeated a few times he showed the toy but made no noise. The child was still as frightened as when the noise had first been made.

The child's fear of the toy was a conditioned reaction. It was also an irrational irrational fears of neurotic subjects are the result of progressive conditioning by a series of life experiences, and that every action is in fact a conditioned reflex.

We become aware of the world through the senses of sight, hearing, smell, taste, touch, through what are called the special senses, and through muscle sense. It is important to realize what becoming aware of the world means. To take one example, we say we see a tree. What exactly do we mean by that? Something as follows. Light reflected from the tree enters the pupil of the eye, falls upon the retina at the back of it, and there sets up a number of impulses which travel along the optic nerve to the brain. The brain fits these impulses together, synthesizes them, and so constructs the image tree (Fig. 2).

Transmitting Impulses

Note that there is no immediate contact between the observer and the tree, no first hand direct awareness of the tree. There is a reception by the brain of nervous impulses set up by an external stimulus. Without the stimulus, which in this case is light, there can be no image; equally, without the mental interpretation the image cannot materialize. When there is no light there is no image; in complete darkness a tree is invisible. If the nerve which conveys the retinal impulses to the brain be cut, the tree will not be seen; if the part of the brain concerned with seeing be removed, the tree would be equally invisible, as it is when the lens of the eye becomes opaque through cataract or some other cause. Seeing is a material act; it does not consist of a mystical relationship between the observer and the thing observed. It is dependent upon the condition of both body and mind. It is dependent to some extent even upon diet; if you do not get a sufficiency of vitamin A in your food you do not see so well in the dark as you would otherwise.

Muscle sense is important. The altered tensions of muscles in contraction and relaxation are accompanied by streams of impulses flowing to the spinal cord and the brain. These sensory impulses enable the brain to judge differences between the weights of objects, to know the positions of the limbs in space, to enable one, for example, to touch the tip of the nose with the finger when the eyes are shut, to type without looking at the keys, or to catch and hold a cricket ball above and behind one's head.

Sensations of cold, heat, touch, and pain are conveyed to the brain by nerves connected with definite and separate cold, heat, touch and pain spots on the surface of the body. Some points of the skin are sensitive to cold but not to heat, and vice versa. Touch spots are particularly numerous in the tips of the fingers, less numerous in the small of the back, where obviously they would be less useful.

This contact of the world through the senses results in a constantly changing adjustment of the person to the world. But only because the brain and the nervous system are also concerned. The purpose of sensation is to enable the body to act, to put and to keep the body in a correct relationship with the world. It could not do so without the energy generated by the brain.

Electricity of the Brain

It has recently been observed that the brain cells discharge electricity, and that this charge varies according to the part of the brain and the state of the health. The base of the brain discharges at a different rate from the cerebral hemispheres. In health the brain gives out a steady rhythmic discharge; in disease the type of discharge varies. The emotional disturbance caused by anxiety is accompanied by excessive electrical activity of the nerve cells of the base of the brain, which interferes with the rhythm of the discharge of the higher centres.

Such discoveries offer the prospect of much hope for humanity. The more we can get to know about the mechanics of mental processes, of their anatomy and physiology, the more likely we are to gain control over these processes. Even serious forms of insanity are now being cured by the production of violent chemical changes in the body. But complete knowledge of the chemistry and mechanics of mental processes would not necessarily mean that we had solved the problem of mind—unless, indeed, that school of psychology is correct which maintains that all mental activity is purely physiological.

There are many schools of psychology, and it is fashionable to emphasize the differences between them rather than the similarities. But there are essential similarities, and it is vital not to overlook these. Psychology today, of whatever school, is based upon observation. It holds, in common with all other sciences, that everything which happens has a cause,

Why, then, do their theories differ? Simply because of incomplete knowledge of the facts. So long as knowledge is incomplete it remains possible to interpret the evidence in different ways; and each interpretation must remain more or less suspect. Modern psychologists are therefore modest about their claims; it is only their ignorant disciples who are dogmatic. All that great psychologists claim as certain is that small body of knowledge

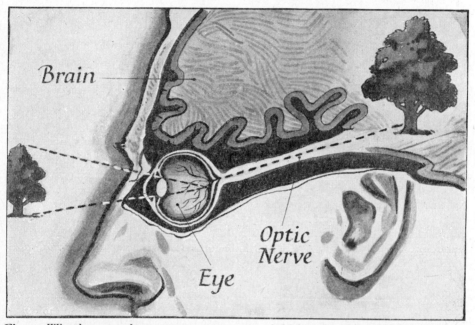

Fig. 2. *What happens when, as we say, we see a tree? Light reflected from the tree enters the eye, falls upon the retina, and sets up a number of impulses which travel along the optic nerve to the brain which synthesizes them, and builds up the image tree. We become conscious of the tree only through the stimulation of the senses and the activity of nerves and brain.*

and that the cause precedes the effect. This may seem very obvious, but more than one science has in the past been guilty of confusing the cause with the effect, and so putting the cart before the horse. It should be fully understood that today psychologists do not start off with a neat little parcel of theories and proceed to fit the facts to them; their theories grow out of their experiences and the many facts they accumulate.

common to all schools of psychology.

Until recently there appeared to be an absolute cleavage in thought between those who interpreted mental activity as a purely physiological process and those who regarded it as a process above and beyond physiology, though using physiological means—i.e. brain cells and nerves —to secure some of its effects. That cleavage is not nearly so evident today; the physiologists are prepared to admit the reality of psychic processes beyond explanation by physiological arguments, and the psychic school are prepared to admit much more than heretofore the importance of physiological processes. In part this is due to general increase in knowledge, in part to the work of the greatest revolutionary the science of psychology has ever known, Sigmund Freud, the founder of psycho-analysis.

Psycho-analysis

It is not proposed here to present the complete theory of psycho-analysis, nor to attempt to indicate more than a few of its repercussions upon psychological thought. Before doing even that, we would point out that Freud, far from being an armchair theorist, as is so often imagined, was throughout his long career a very busy consulting physician, and that his theories were all developed from his practical clinical experience.

As is well known, psycho-analysis is founded upon the theory that there exists in each of us an unconscious mind, re-pressed by and in conflict with our conscious mind. First, then, one should examine clearly what is meant when these terms are used by psychologists.

Field of Consciousness

Of what, as you read these words, are you conscious? As I write them, I am conscious of what I am setting down, of my pen, paper, the pipe I am smoking, the table at which I sit, the watch beside my manuscript, and, though less com-pletely, of various other sheafs of papers on the table. I am conscious of the chair on which I sit, the light in the room. I am conscious that someone is hoeing in the next garden, that a bird is singing outside the window, and that at this moment a motor car is passing the house.

Suppose I lay down my pen, drop my work and go out of the room to take up some other occupation. At once a whole host of other ideas comes into my con-sciousness, and the ones which previously occupied my mind begin to fade, if not into oblivion, at least into partial forget-fulness. Consciousness, you see, is very much concerned with the here and now. My consciousness will be a very different matter from what it was, by the time I reach the front door. Yet I shall be essentially the same person; my know-ledge will not noticeably have increased or decreased, my experience will not materially have altered. I could have written these words just as well yesterday as I do today; if I leave this work for an hour or a day I shall be equally able, on resuming it, to carry on. But in the mean-time my mind will not be consciously occupied with the argument of this chapter; it will be occupied with quite different matters.

Immediate Consciousness

One's immediate consciousness, then, appears to be that particular layer of the mind's content which is uppermost at the moment. That layer is capable of being changed at a moment's notice, or even, it would appear, without any notice at all. For instance, if while you are reading this book, there is a sudden cry outside of "Fire!" and a fire engine is heard rapidly approaching, you will be strangely reso-lute if you do not hurriedly put down your book, rush to the window or door, and follow the course of the engine with eager interest, all thoughts of your reading having for the moment passed from your mind and out of immediate consciousness.

Further reflection will show you that, quite apart from such sudden interruption and diversion of thought processes there is a vast host of matters—large and small, significant and insignificant—stored in your memory, which is not in your imme-diate consciousness, but which can be recalled to it on demand, so to speak, with the utmost ease. This store of knowledge and experience ranges from memories of early childhood to those of events of the immediate present and to thoughts of the future—the appointment you have made to go to the pictures tomorrow evening, for example, or the joint you must remember to order for next Sunday. The more you examine it the more you realize that the mind is like a huge department store filled with a huge and comprehensive array of goods of all kinds.

But just as not all the goods—nor even the main part of them—are on view in a department store, but are hidden away in drawers and cupboards and store rooms and warehouses, so we find that not all memories stored in the mind are, so to speak, for ever on display. We occasionally have to take them down from the shelf or out of the drawer.

Forgetting and Remembering

Sometimes little or no effort is required to bring them back; sometimes one memory recalls another ("It was the day we went to Brighton and met Aunt Mary on the West Pier; she told you how she had used Bestokur." "Oh, yes, of course I remember!"), and with the recall of what one may perhaps call a key memory, a whole flood of associated memories will return. But sometimes a memory proves difficult to recall. At times even the most concentrated mental effort fails to recover a memory, a fact, an event, you wish to recall. This often happens without any apparent reason. For example, you see in the street someone you know perfectly well; and when he stops to speak, you realize with horror that you are quite unable to remember his name. That you have not permanently forgotten it becomes obvious when, in the next street, or next day, the name slips back into your mind with the utmost ease—so easily that you wonder how on earth you could ever have forgotten it.

It would almost appear in such a case that at the moment when you met your acquaintance you did not wish to remember his name; and that, more or less, is

precisely what the psycho-analyst will tell you does happen. He will say that during the period while the name remains inaccessible, it was being kept out by a considerable force (of which you are quite unaware) resisting your earnest—and quite honest—attempt to recall the name.

Day-dreams

If you allow yourself to relax and daydream, you will find that all sorts of odd ideas and fleeting fancies will pass through your mind. They reveal a very different type of consciousness from the one which occupies itself with the practical business of everyday life. They may surprise or even shock you, just as a dream, or still more a nightmare, is sometimes a very shocking affair. This, you will say, is not your real mind at work; this is something fantastic, something more than a little mad, which has possessed you. Why should this be ? The popular explanation of a night full of weird dreams is an indigestible supper. But that completely fails to explain the day-dream, which may happen quite without reference to food, and which is essentially of the same character. Psycho-analysis offers the explanation that all the time a mental life is going on in our minds which is normally excluded from consciousness, but which comes to the surface when the usual restraints upon thought are not present, that is, during our sleep and during the more unguarded and less alert moments of our waking hours.

Repressed Memories

The importance of this unconscious mental activity was being revealed during the earlier years of Freud's professional life by investigations which he and others were making into the effect of hypnotism upon hysterical patients. It was found that when a patient had been hypnotized he could be induced to recall memories which he was quite unable to recall when fully awake. These memories were of a painful nature and referred usually to events which had happened in early childhood.

Two further striking discoveries were made. The presence of these repressed memories in the mind was responsible for the distressing traits in the patient's character and behaviour; and their recall to consciousness cured or relieved the patient. But unfortunately it soon became clear that the relief obtained through hypnotism was not necessarily permanent. The patient tended to relapse when he lost contact with the doctor who had hypnotized him. Freud therefore set out to discover a method whereby these harmful memories and wishes buried in what he called the unconscious could be brought into consciousness by the patient himself. He found it in free association, which is, in effect, the day-dream of reverie used scientifically.

The Unconscious World

Now this does not mean that any one, by simply relaxing and day-dreaming, can psycho-analyse himself and rid himself of harmful repressed memories. The aid of the skilled physician is still necessary, for the memories which are recalled have to be sorted out and interpreted before any use can be made of them. The unconscious is a wild, primitive and emotional world; it has no processes of rational thought, but deals in symbols and substitutes, and in mental pictures unknown to the conscious mind. Unknown harm may be done, and has been done, by ignorant or even semi-skilled persons attempting psycho-analysis. It is at best a long and frequently painful procedure and one which should be entrusted only to the most highly skilled and reputable practitioners.

Through the technique of analysing the memories, wishes and desires revealed in free association, a great deal has come to be known about mental activity and mental structure, and a new theory has been evolved about the nature of instinct.

This last is a subject which has engaged the attention of psychologists of all schools. Volumes have been written about it. Imposing lists of instincts have been compiled. Perhaps the best known is that of William McDougall.

The word instinct is in conversation used very loosely, being given normally a much wider meaning than it has in its scientific sense. An instinct is a fundamental drive or urge. It creates energy which must find release in action. It is primitive, and therefore the expression it would naturally crave must be curbed and restrained in a civilized society. While instinct supplies the dynamo to life, it is the function of reason to supply the steering wheel and the brake.

Instinctual Urges

Instinctual urges common to all living things are those of self-preservation and feeding. The instinct of self-preservation includes both offensive and defensive reactions against potential enemies. Modern psychologists have been so impressed by the strength and prevalence of the impulse to aggression that some of them have elevated it to the status of a full instinct. There is some justice in the argument; when in the days of long ago man was still fighting for supremacy in the world of mammals, aggression was vital to his success. He could never have become supreme merely by defending himself against his foes. Aggression, too, was necessary then if he was to get food.

Hunger and thirst drive all animals to obtain food. The taking of food is enjoyable, going without it painful. Even the imitation of taking food is pleasurable: a baby will suck anything (Fig. 3), and it would not do so unless it found pleasure in sucking. The attendance of pleasure upon the satisfaction of an instinct, seems, indeed, to be one of its hall-marks. Note how satisfying aggressive action is. War, in spite of all its horror, its inevitable and universal bestiality, its savage cruelty and its intolerable terrors, still appeals to, nay, fascinates, some minds. Civilized men and women hunt foxes and stags, shoot birds and beasts "for the fun of it," that is, for the enjoyment they get out of it. Bull fighting is the national sport of Spain. Our own British pastimes, cricket and football, harmless though they are, are based on the pleasures derived from aggression. Both bowler and crowd get a

A third instinct is that of sex, necessary for reproduction. Here again nature has contrived that satisfaction of this instinct shall be pleasurable. Upon the foundation of sex has been erected the vast and many-sided edifice of love, with all its ramifications. The love of man for his wife, of parents for their children, of friend for friend; the urge to create, the

Fig. 3. *A baby will suck anything, even its thumb, in order to satisfy its instinctual urge to take food. Instinctual urges are the fundamental driving forces of life, creating energy which must find release in action. Hunger and thirst, self-preservation, and sex are among the most powerful of these forces; they represent the primitive part of mind-body activity.*

thrill when a batsman is clean bowled; batsman and crowd are hugely pleased when a ball is hit clean out of the ground. These highly aggressive acts not merely please; they give genuine emotional satisfaction. Similarly, in football, the daring tackle and the rasping shot that leaves the goalkeeper gaping are the high spots of the game. Compare the thrill these give with that afforded by the neat bit of footwork which so often paves the way to goal. The latter often passes almost unnoticed.

willingness to sacrifice self for an ideal—all are expressions of this fundamental urge. Unfortunately, evil comes from it, too—jealousy, envy and hate.

The instincts represent the ancient and enduring part of mental activity, or to speak more accurately, of mind-body activity. They determine the direction of and give force to all those qualities of mind upon which we so much pride ourselves; the higher aspects of mind and mental activity all depend upon the dynamo of instinct. Consequently the balance of the instincts, the strength of one and the opposition afforded to another, is all-important. So too is the restraint imposed upon each and all. Instinct unbridled spells chaos for the individual and society; instinct eliminated (or repressed, for it can never be really eliminated) produces a characterless individual. Far more important than the knowledge he learns at school is the balance which the child, under the guidance of his parents, teachers and friends, learns to strike between his instinctive impulses and the obligations imposed by living in society.

The Freudian theory pays over-riding attention to the struggle between instinct and society which takes place in early life. All schools of psychology are agreed that the years of infancy and early childhood are by far the more important for character development; some psychologists go so far as to assert that character is set and fixed by the age of five, or at most by seven, and that after approximately that age only minor modifications are possible.

Character and Heredity

The growth and development of character is not, of course, so simple a matter as a straight fight between instinct and the rules of society. To what extent character is determined by heredity is as yet unknown, but sufficient has been said about genes and chromosomes to indicate that heredity must play a vital part. There is also the question of environment, by which term is meant every external influence which plays upon the child and man at every moment of his life, from the climate in which he lives to the fondness of his mother for tea or of his father for tobacco. This last is meant quite seriously; even details count—some of them much more than one would think.

People are unfortunately apt to talk very loosely about heredity, environment, eugenics, the improvement of the race and the elimination of the unfit. Such slogans

as "Sterilization of the Unfit" sound very attractive, but they are usually taken up by those with quite inadequate knowledge of the scientific problems involved.

Such people have, it is true, a very plausible analogy on which to base their argument. From time immemorial, man, in his ceaseless endeavour to improve the world and to increase his own comfort, has constantly sought to modify the life-habits of animals not of his own species in order to render them of use to himself. In very early days he tamed the horse; he has transformed oxen, elephants and camels into beasts of burden, cattle and wild fowl into domestic providers of food, dogs and cats (representative of two of the most dangerous species of wild animals) into companions and pets (Fig. 4).

Selective Breeding

In the course of turning these creatures to his desired ends, he early discovered that the results obtainable by prolonged training and environmental modification could be speeded up and secured by successional selection of the parents. A number of individual characteristics, such as size, colour, substance, and so on, were noticed to be in marked degree hereditary, and such knowledge is not only the root of all successful livestock breeding today, but has also been applied comprehensively and with striking results to the improvement of agricultural and horticultural seed and stock.

What is more natural than that, following the general acceptance of the theory of evolution and of the consequent physiological relationship between man and the rest of the animal creation, simple-minded enthusiasts should have been led to believe that all that was necessary was to apply to the human race those principles which have produced such eminently satisfactory results in the show rings of our agricultural societies and the prize tents of horticultural shows? Unfortunately, the matter is not so simple as that.

Fig. 4. *Since the very earliest times man has constantly sought to modify the characters and habits of other animals in order to make them useful to himself. The offspring of animals which are represented by the most dangerous species of wild beasts, the lion and the wolf, have been tamed by man into the cat and the dog.*

When Charles Darwin published the *Origin of Species* in 1859 he evoked a storm of protest, but he made an analysis of evolution which is accepted with very few modifications today. Darwin said that two factors were responsible for evolution: variation and inheritance. A variation implies some change in the species which can be inherited, that is to say, passed on to subsequent generations. Some inherited variations became established characteristics of the species, but others are rejected or bred out, becoming fewer and fewer in succeeding generations. Clearly this differing success of variations must be in some way concerned with the workings of heredity, but it must also have some-

thing to do with the world the animal has to live in. A variation which makes an animal incompetent in some way—which reduces, say, its ability to withstand a cold winter—will soon disappear. On the other hand every variation which promotes efficiency gives the animal a better chance of survival, and, by reason of the survival of the fittest, gradually spreads throughout the species. This effect of the environment upon variations was called by Darwin "Natural Selection."

What sort of variations had he in mind when he formulated this theory? They were nothing very startling, just tiny changes passed on from one generation to another, making the species in the long run better fitted to cope with the problems surrounding it. Outstanding variations have occurred occasionally; for example, it is said that all weeping willow trees spring from a single ancestor which appeared a few hundred years ago (Fig. 5). Before that time all willows were of the ordinary kind with upstanding branches, but this single tree, a "sport," as such eccentricities are called, was an example of a striking variation which happened to be heritable, giving rise to a new species. Possibly it was an outstanding variation of this sort which made mammals give up laying eggs in favour of the method of retaining the developing young in their bodies. But great leaps of this kind are not those which Darwin thought responsible for steady evolution.

Darwin knew nothing about the mechanism of inherited characteristics; he could only speculate about this. For the foundations of our knowledge about this important subject we are indebted to a contemporary of his whom he never met.

In the middle of the last century there lived in a monastery of Brunn, in Moravia, a patient and retiring botanist called Gregor Mendel. This studious and observant German carried out in the garden of his monastery a long series of breeding experiments with plants from which he drew certain conclusions, the significance of which went almost unrecognized for thirty or forty years. They are now universally accepted by scientists as marking one of the most profound revolutions in the science of biology.

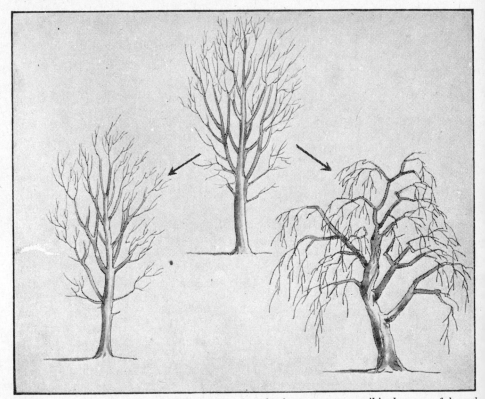

Fig. 5. *Occasionally an odd variation from standard types proves strikingly successful, and produces a new species. Originally all willow trees, for example, were upright, but an accidentally appearing weeping willow tree is said to have been the ancestor of all those now existing*

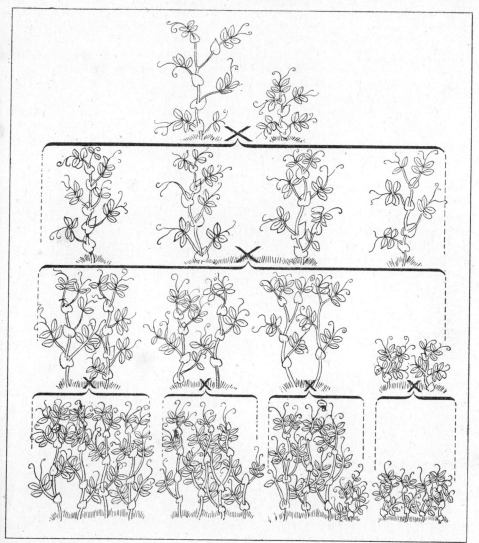

Fig. 6. *The way in which characteristics are inherited was investigated by Gregor Mendel in a series of experiments on garden peas. He mated a tall pea with a dwarf pea and discovered that their offspring were all tall, but that in the second and third generations short plants reappeared in a definite proportion, only some of the tall plants breeding true.*

Most of Mendel's experiments were carried out on garden peas (Fig. 6). In the most classic experiment of all, he mated a tall pea with a dwarf pea and found that in the first generation of descendants all the offsprings were tall. He mated these tall offsprings with each other and in the second generation tall and short plants appeared in the proportion three tall to one short. The short plants when mated with each other gave nothing but short offsprings. Among the tall plants one-third bred true, giving nothing but tall plants. The other two of the tall plants when mated together produced tall and short descendants in the same proportion as in the previous generation: that is to say, three tall to one short. As a result of these experiments he formulated the following law:—

When pure-bred individuals exhibiting a pair of contrasting characteristics are crossed, the original types separate out among the grandchildren in a definite proportion.

Dominance and Recessiveness

Among the peas grown by Mendel the two contrasted characteristics were tallness and shortness, and the proportion in which they separated out among the grandchildren (the second generation) was 3 : 1. Since tallness occurred so much more freely in the series than shortness, Mendel called tallness a dominant characteristic and shortness a recessive one.

From these experiments, scientists who followed him have argued in this way:—
1. There are characteristics which are inherited.
2. The reproductive cells must carry hereditary factors which correspond with these characteristics. The factors have been called genes.
3. Each reproductive cell carries a gene for each and every heritable characteristic which the future individual may exhibit. Thus the individual arising from the union of two reproductive cells has a double set of genes, each of the parent reproductive cells contributing one set.
4. Characteristics may be contrasting: for example, eyes may be brown or blue, hens may be black or white, peas may be tall or short. Contrasting characteristics of these kinds are said to be "allelomorphic," which simply means that they are alternative forms of the same characteristic.

Bearing in mind Mendel's findings with peas, let us try to find out what happens in the inheritance of blue and brown eyes, noting first that brown eyes are dominant to blue ones. If a brown-eyed man mates with a brown-eyed woman all their children will have brown eyes; and so long as their descendants go on mating with brown-eyed people the stock will remain brown-eyed. The same is true when two people of pure blue-eyed stock mate together; their children will be blue-eyed and blue-eyed only. But if a blue-eyed person mates with a brown-eyed person the children (first generation) will be brown-eyed, because brown is dominant to blue. If those brown-eyed children mate with others with a like family history, their children (second generation) will show brown and blue eyes in the ratio of three brown-eyed children to one blue-eyed.

Blended Characteristics

Dominance is not an essential of Mendelian inheritance. Sometimes two contrasting characteristics are so evenly balanced that they produce an appearance of blending in the offspring. If a black Andalusian fowl is mated with a white one, the offspring (first generation) are coloured an attractive shade of grey. Breeders used to hope that by mating these grey fowls they would establish a new grey strain but they were disappointed, for in the second generation the original characters re-appeared in the proportions of one black, two grey, one white. The black and the white offspring, when mated with their own colour bred true but the grey fowls, when mated with each other, continued to produce offspring in the ratios of one black, two grey, one white. This shows clearly a most important point, namely: that though the *characteristics* (black and white) became blended, the *genes* carrying them did not. The original characteristics appeared in the second generation, showing that the genes were still acting as individual units.

The reader cannot fail to see the bearing of the Mendelian theory on the practical problems of eugenics. It throws light on those mysterious reappearances of ancestral traits which seem to have skipped

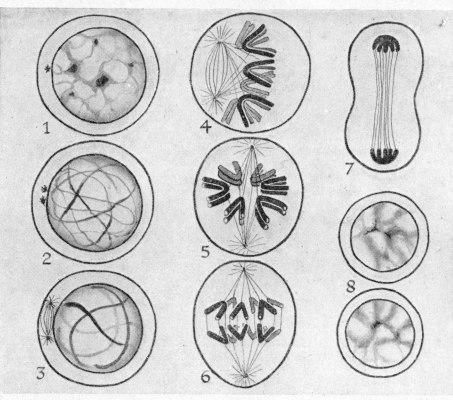

Fig. 7. *The genes that carry inheritable characteristics are transmitted in chromosomes, which are the strands formed by the change in the cell nucleus during the process which takes place when the cells making up the body divide into two. The illustration shows the stages in this division. 1, Cell nucleus; 2, spireme; 3, chromosome forming; 4 and 5, stages of settling; 6, chromosome splitting; 7, nuclei reforming; 8, completed daughter nuclei.*

several generations. The factor responsible for them has in truth been the recessive member of a pair present in the germ cell of each member of the intermediate ancestry. Only when union has occurred between a germ cell containing that factor and another germ cell similarly furnished has the outward appearance been able to manifest itself. To understand how this is possible one must inquire into the workings of the genes, or hereditary factors in the reproductive cells.

No one so far has seen a gene; but we know a good deal about them for all that. They are carried in the nuclei of the reproductive cells, and are so small that

they cannot be seen even with the most powerful microscope.

Every cell in the body, except the red cells of the blood, contains a nucleus, a little mass of granular material, called chromatin. When a cell is about to divide a change occurs in this granular material; the chromatin forms a long chord which then splits up into short lengths or strands. These strands are called the chromosomes. Before the cell divides each chromosome splits in two along its whole length and one-half of it goes into each of the two new cells (Fig. 7).

The number of chromosomes in any species is constant and the characteristic of that species. In man there are forty-eight chromosomes in every cell of the body. The chromosomes in each cell can be arranged in pairs which resemble each other, so that every cell in man contains twenty-four pairs of chromosomes. This has nothing to do with the splitting of the chromosomes which occurs when a cell divides. Every cell before division con-

tive cell is being formed by the ovary of a female drosophila.

To form this cell a special type of division occurs which has been called "reduction division" because in it the number of chromosomes is reduced to half in the process. When a parent cell from the ovary of drosophila is about to divide to form two daughter cells (ova),

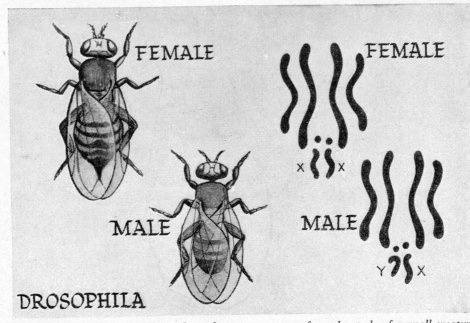

Fig. 8. *Much of our knowledge about chromosomes comes from the study of a small creature called drosophila melanogaster, in which there are only eight chromosomes.*

tains forty-eight chromosomes (twenty-four pairs); when the cell divides every member of the forty-eight splits longitudinally so that each of the new cells receives forty-eight chromosomes (twenty-four pairs).

In man the chromosomes are so numerous that experimental study of them is difficult. Students of heredity have accordingly concentrated on drosophila melanogaster (Fig. 8), in which there are only eight chromosomes (four pairs). Its chromosomes are not identical in the male and female; but at the moment let us consider what happens when a reproduc-

instead of splitting longitudinally, after the usual plan, the chromosomes remain intact, but one member of each pair passes into each of the daughter cells. Thus every ovum contains only four chromosomes. The same is true of every male reproductive cell; by a similar process of reduction division the number of chromosomes in each spermatozoon is also halved.

The purpose of this arrangement is not far to seek: when the ovum is fertilized by the spermatozoon the nuclei of the two cells fuse together, and the normal number of chromosomes (four pairs) is restored. In this way the characteristic number of chromosomes is maintained in every member of the species. Were it not for reduction division the number of chromosomes in the species would be doubled at every mating. This process is common to all animals, man included. The human ovum and spermatozoon each contain twenty-four chromosomes and the fertilized ovum contains the characteristic forty-eight (twenty-four pairs).

Transmission of Genes

When students of heredity came to consider Mendel's work in the light of all this information about the chromosomes they were struck at once by the correspondence between the two. They had only to suppose that the genes were carried by the chromosomes to understand the principle lying behind Mendel's ratio. Let us see how this can be worked out (Fig. 9). Suppose that in the case of the black and white Andalusian fowls the genes for blackness are carried in a pair of chromosomes BB in the parent fowl; when that fowl is forming reproductive cells, one chromosome of each pair will pass into each new cell. Assume that this is the cock bird, and that each spermatozoon contains chromosomes WW which are responsible for whiteness, and that each of her eggs will contain one chromosome W. Now if an egg containing W is fertilized by a spermatozoon containing B the resulting cell will contain a pair of chromosomes one of which is a B chromosome from the father and the other a W chromosome from the mother. Thus the fowls of the first generation will all carry B and W chromosomes and as we know already they will be grey.

Now look what happens when these fowls come to form their reproductive cells. At reduction division one of the new cells will get a B and the other a W chromosome. Suppose we now mate fowls of this generation together; when a B spermatozoon fertilizes a B egg we shall

get a BB individual, which will be black. Similarly when a W spermatozoon fertilizes a W egg the individual will be WW (white). When a W spermatozoon fertilizes a B egg a BW individual is produced, which is grey. By the laws of chance there will be twice as many BW matings as there will be either black or white.

The facts are just as reliable if we consider a case in which one gene is dominant

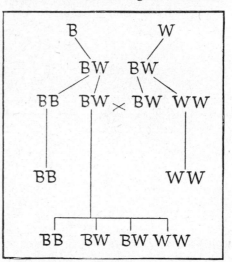

Fig. 9. *The diagram illustrates the process of reduction division in the case of black and white fowls, and shows how the genes which are responsible for blackness and whiteness are transmitted from generation to generation.*

to another. Take the case of brown and blue eyes, representing the genes for brown eyes (the dominant) by BB and the genes for blue eyes (the recessive) by bb. In the parents we have BB (the father) and bb (the mother). By the reduction division we get spermatozoa containing B and ova containing b. In the first generation we get Bb. In the second generation we get BB, Bb, Bb, bb. Now owing to the fact that brown eyes are dominant to blue eyes all the offspring in the first generation who carry a B will have brown eyes. In the second generation the same rule holds and as three out of four carry a B, three out of four will have brown eyes. Only those children who carry bb will have blue eyes.

After considering these facts students of heredity were able to say confidently that the genes are resident in, or borne upon, the chromosomes. Moreover, by a close study of drosophila they have been able to show that each chromosome carries a given group of genes and that each gene has its own place upon its own particular chromosome. From this it follows that genes carried in the same chromosome will be transmitted together as a linked group; and observations prove this to be true. In drosophila it has even been possible to make a map of the chromosomes showing how the genes carrying various characteristics are strung along the chromosome in definite positions like beads.

Sex Determination

Drosophila has also helped us to understand how sex is determined. In the female the members of the four pairs of chromosomes are identical, but in the male one member of one of the pairs is unlike its partner. Since the sexes differ in relation to these two pairs of chromosomes the latter are called the sex chromosomes. The three chromosomes which are alike—two in the female, one in the male—are called the X chromosomes. The odd chromosome found only in the male is called the Y chromosome. Since only one member of each pair of chromosomes is found in each reproductive cell all the eggs will be alike, each containing one X chromosome. The spermatozoa, however, will be different, half of them containing X chromosomes and half of them having one Y chromosome apiece.

Now if an (X-bearing) egg is fertilized by a Y-bearing spermatozoon an XY embryo will result, giving a male individual. If an (X-bearing) egg is fertilized by an X-bearing spermatozoon an XX (female) individual will result. Thus the chances of producing a male or a female drosophila are equal.

Exactly the same system is followed by other animals. In man it is the male who carries the Y chromosome just as it is in drosophila, but in some animals and in birds the female carries Y. The sex chromosomes may carry other genes—in fact they generally do—and so certain characteristics may be sex-linked, that is, they can appear only in males or only in females. A characteristic which is carried by the Y chromosome, for example, can appear only in a male.

Mutations

We can now study the problem of variation in the light which recent work has shed upon the genes. In the first place, the genes are not immutable; they can vary in themselves; and we can now say fairly confidently that a heritable variation is due to a change (mutation) in a gene.

Such mutations are exceedingly rare; they occur only about once in 50,000 to 100,000 individuals. We do not know what causes a gene to mutate or what the nature of the change is, except that we suspect it is chemical. Moreover, the mutations which occur in the laboratory are nearly always unfavourable to the animal and therefore tend to be bred out in course of time. It is logical to suppose that favourable mutations are even rarer, but that when they occur they are bred into the stock and become incorporated in it. Here we can see the principle of natural selection at work; the successful mutation is the one which environmental conditions favour.

It may be useful at this point to summarize the facts so far studied. Inherited characteristics depend on pairs of genes, and these are carried in paired chromosomes, one of which is derived from each parent; the chromosomes separate out again in the reproductive cells.

The characteristics carried by a pair of genes may be alike or contrasted. When two individuals with contrasted characteristics are crossed it is then the original characteristics separate out in definite proportions in the grandchildren.

The number of chromosomes in a given species is constant, and each carries a great many genes. If two genes are carried on the same chromosome they are said to be linked, and the characteristics to which they give rise will be transmitted together.

Sex depends on a particular pair of chromosomes, represented in the female by the symbol XX and in the male by XY. The presence of the Y chromosome determines maleness in humans. Other genes are carried in the sex chromosomes and hence are linked with sex.

Genes are arranged in a definite order along the chromosomes like beads on a string, and the position of the various genes in drosophila melanogaster have been mapped out.

Heritable variations depend on mutation (change) in a gene. The change is probably chemical in nature. Mutations, although they occur exceedingly rarely, are probably responsible for nearly all heritable variation and so for all evolutionary change.

At the same time certain hereditary anatomical freakishnesses seem to be due to the absence in an individual of some regulating factor which, in the course of embryonic growth, determines further development of this or that particular feature; with the result that the feature stops at an immature stage of its embryonic progress. Hare-lip affords a striking example of this embryonic developmental arrest (Fig. 10).

Environment

Let us now consider exactly what we mean by environment. Each animal has an optimum environment: that is to say, an environment in which it feels at its best and is able to behave most capably. Natural selection tends to breed animals which are more and more suited to their particular environment; the process is very successful so long as the environment

remains unchanged. When the environment changes the animal may find itself handicapped, and if the handicap is severe it may even die out.

The environment of an animal is both internal and external. The external environment includes all the surrounding conditions; the internal environment is dictated by the particular gene pattern

Fig. 10. *Some deformities, including hare-lip, are due to the absence in an individual of some regulating factor during embryonic growth, resulting in arrested development.*

which it has inherited. A moment's thought will show that this pattern is different in every animal; it is made up of chromosomes derived from the father and mother and through them of chromosomes derived from the four grandparents, the eight great-grandparents and so on.

Now suppose a gene carrying a relatively unfavourable characteristic is transmitted through several generations, it will find itself in a fresh gene pattern in every animal which inherits it, and it may be that it fits into one of these patterns so well that, instead of being unfavourable

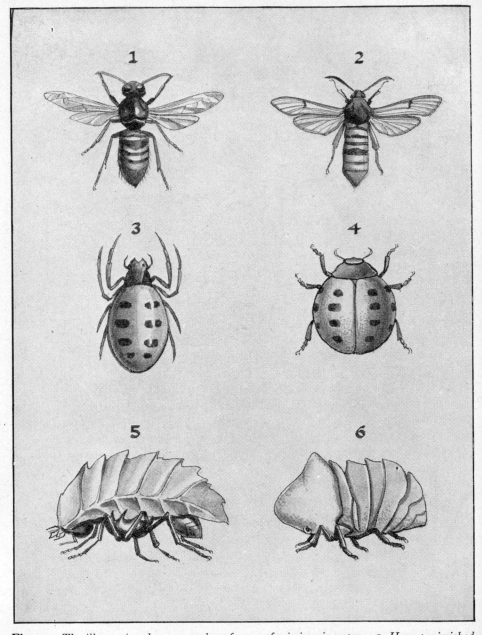

Fig. 11. *The illustration shows a number of cases of mimicry in nature. 1, Hornet mimicked by 2, moth; 3, ladybird mimicked by 4, spider; 5, coushie, or leaf-carrying ant, mimicked by 6, membracid. Over a very long period of time and as the result of tiny mutations, some insects, which are liable to attack by birds on account of their palatability, have succeeded in modelling themselves very closely on less palatable insects, so protecting themselves from attack. In this process, the genes which have made possible this successful mimicry have enabled the imitators to cope more efficiently with their environment.*

Fig. 12. *The transmission of characteristics through the genes sometimes seems to result in the possession of features which are anything but useful. The unwieldy mass of horn carried by the reindeer, the peculiar appearance of the mandrill, the disproportionate neck of the ostrich, seem to be freaks of nature. It may be, however, that these features are only part of the content of a single gene. A gene may carry more than one characteristic, and although part of its content may be unnecessary or even hampering, some other part will be a vital and fundamental part of the species' make-up and essential for its survival.*

in its effects, it turns out to be quite useful to the animal after all. It may even be selected as part of a particular gene complex and embodied as a characteristic of the species. In this way a change in the internal environment can alter the effect of a gene. It should be noted that this is different from a mutation: the gene itself has not changed, only the situation in which it finds itself.

It is easier still to see how a change in the external environment may alter the effects of a gene. Consider the case of one of those insects which mimic the appearance of another species. As a rule birds find the insect which provides the model unpleasant to eat whereas the imitator is highly palatable. Over a long period of time, and as a result of tiny mutations, the palatable insects have slowly evolved a resemblance to the unpalatable ones. Those which looked a little like the unpleasant species survived better than those which did not, and propagated further generations which, by the same gradual process, came to resemble the model even more closely. Finally the likeness became so close that birds would hardly look twice at the imitators (Fig. 11).

Now suppose that the successful imitators have become so free from attack that they multiply rapidly and greatly outnumber the models. Birds are no fools; they quickly discover that most of these insects are pleasant to eat after all, and the nasty ones comparatively rare. They take a chance, and start snapping up all that come their way.

What is the position of the unfortunate imitators now? Those which look most like the model are quickly devoured: the very genes which made for their safety now make for their destruction. Thus a change in the external environment has altered the favourable effect of a gene to an unfavourable one.

The genes and the environment, both internal and external, react together to produce the characteristics of the individual. We can form no first-hand idea of the effect of any single gene; all we can say is that a given gene will evoke certain characteristics in the presence of a particular external environment and in the presence of the particular gene pattern which the animal has inherited.

Fig. 13. *1, Spiny ant-eater, an egg-laying mammal found in Australia; 2, spiny ant-eater curled up. Many odd species of animals, which have died out in other parts of the world, have survived in Australia, which became an isolated continent at a very early period.*

Fig. 14. *Duck-billed platypus, another egg-laying mammal, or monotreme, which has survived in Australia alone. The monotremes are the most primitive surviving mammals.*

Sometimes the results of evolution seem rather staggering. Is it possible, we ask ourselves, that it really has been to the advantage of an animal to look like the mandrill or to have a neck like an ostrich or to carry an unwieldy quantity of horn upon its head like a reindeer? (Fig. 12). The answer is that an animal sometimes has to pay a price for survival, and the explanation is to be found in the fact that a single gene does not necessarily carry a single characteristic, but may be responsible for several characteristics, some of which may be unnecessary and even hampering, but at least one of which is vital if the gene has become permanently incorporated in the species. An unfavourable, or merely silly, characteristic may be perpetuated simply because it is carried in the same gene as a favourable one; this probably accounts for the film-star quill eyelashes of the hornbill.

We have seen that the evolution of any single species can be explained in terms of Mendelian inheritance; can the same process account for the divergence which has led to the appearance of thousands of different species of animals living today?

A powerful factor in the origin of new species is isolation. When animals are cut off from their fellows by a geographical barrier the two groups have to adapt themselves to differing environments, and their evolution is bound to differ accordingly. A characteristic tending to make one colony better adapted to its environment will spread very quickly; the same characteristic may hold no advantage for the other colony, and so the two stocks, though identical to start with, will become partially or totally unlike one another.

Australian animals are full of surprises. Many strange creatures have survived there which have gone down in the struggle for existence in other parts of the world. Australia harbours to this day two egg-laying mammals—the spiny anteater (Fig. 13) and the duckbilled platypus (Fig. 14). Isolation can be responsible for maintaining an old species as well as encouraging the formation of new ones.

No discussion of heredity would be complete without some reference to the vexed question of the inheritance or otherwise of acquired characteristics. In its crudest form this question is raised in such queries as: because his mother was frightened by an air raid will the baby have a birthmark like a bomb? Or, if breeders go on docking puppy-dogs' tails will they at last be able to breed dogs ready docked? The answer to such inquiries is quite definite: evolution does not work that way. You can spend your life docking puppy dogs but you will never be able to breed a single Manx dog on that system. But this does not by any means dispose of the problem of the inheritance of acquired characteristics. We can say confidently that mutilations will not be inherited; the genes responsible for the development of a dog's tail are not going to be affected by an accident happening to the tail long after their work is done. We can affirm equally that no fright experienced in an air raid by an expectant mother will cause birthmarks. We can also feel fairly certain that the giraffe (Fig. 15) did not develop a long neck by reaching up for leaves above his head and passing on the effects of his diligence to his little ones: on the contrary, it was because the giraffe which happened to have a longer neck than his fellows got more food than the others, lived longer and produced more offspring, who in turn passed on the advantage to their offspring, that the neck grew longer and longer. The better equipped were selected by nature in the usual way, tiny gene mutations gradually accumulating and achieving the final highly successful result.

Fig. 15. *The giraffe developed his long neck not by stretching it to reach for leaves and passing on the effects to his offspring, but because the giraffes who had short necks and were unable to reach the leaves died off, while those who had longer necks survived and passed on to their offspring the gene responsible for this characteristic.*

We cannot say, however, that because no method of transmitting an acquired characteristic has so far been discovered that such a mechanism could not exist; we can only go on piling up evidence until we reach a point at which we feel convinced we can offer a fairly definite conclusion. So far all we dare say is that no perfectly clear and unquestionable evidence of the inheritance of an acquired characteristic has been produced. This seems to indicate that if acquired characteristics are transmitted at all, it must be very rarely, and can have no influence on the normal evolution of a species.

No one any longer doubts the part which inheritance plays in the determination of the characteristics of every living organism. But there is still a tendency to overlook the fact that although the principal physical elements and the unconscious nervous and instinctive psychic reactivities of man are thus transmitted by means of the germ plasm, nearly everything that makes man peculiar among animals is developed after birth, and is dependent on the whole complex of his social and environmental influences.

The Social Heritage

That, even in the most general sense, individuals inherently vary in their capacity to learn, is true: but neither Newton nor Einstein, had either been born in the Stone Age, would have known—though he might have devised—even the multiplication table or the second proposition of Euclid. How enormous is our present-day social heritage, and how very large a part the momentum of this heritage plays in each further invention, discovery or advance, is apt to be overlooked by those unduly impressed by the relatively slight unusualness of the individuals who take precedence in the human procession.

Bound up with the general vague ideas about eugenics is the notion that a man's or a woman's character was inherent in the germ plasm from which they severally sprang. We say of a boy that he inherits his father's bad temper, or of a girl that she was born with her mother's querulousness. Are we sure of our facts ? Had these children been removed at birth from their parents' influence, and been exposed to a domestic atmosphere characterized by generosity, affection and intelligence, is it not quite likely that their environment would have proved more potent than their inborn tendencies ? The few experiments which have been carried out seem to suggest that such is the case.

Environment and Character

Many parents who do, to some extent, realize that procreation does not mark the end of their duties, and that they have a responsibility in this matter of character building, have very uninformed and very unsound notions as to the sort of training that is helpful. It is impossible to make a child generous, for instance, by forcibly compelling him, against his screaming will, to give half his bar of chocolate to the little boy next door: but rather by showing full appreciation of every spontaneous impulse of helpfulness, and by oneself exhibiting that generosity of soul which is as infectious as smallpox. Discipline and obedience, again, are among the most misunderstood of virtues. Any sort of order given by a parent to a child, however young, should be a reasonable and defensible one. In small matters, orders are best reduced to a minimum: in bigger matters, they should have for their aim either the well-being of the individual to whom they are given or that of the group of which he is a part. A child should not grow up with the notion that obedience and discipline are things to which a weak person has to submit for fear of punishment from a stronger person whose authority consists entirely in his superior strength. Reasonable self-confidence, self-respect, and self-assurance are essential ingredients of the soil in which ideals of fine individual character may be sown

Fig. 1. *The gorilla and man are both very highly developed manifestations of life; they stand at the end of a very long process of evolution, which has taken many millions of years. In comparison with the age of the earth, and the length of time during which life of one sort or another has manifested itself, both man and the ape are recent phenomena. Many types of animals flourished and became extinct before the primates appeared. The complex physical and mental life of the primates is the result of innumerable evolutionary experiments.*

CHAPTER XIV

THE STORY OF EVOLUTION

BEGINNINGS OF LIFE: PRIMITIVE LIFE-FORMS: ANIMAL AND VEGETABLE: PROTOZOA: CONSTRUCTION OF THE AMŒBA: CELL COLONIES AND MULTI-CELLULAR ORGANISMS: ARTHROPODS AND ECHINODERMS: THE FIRST VERTEBRATES: THE FIRST LAND ANIMALS: TADPOLE AND FROG: REPTILES AND BIRDS: FIRST MAMMALS: EVIDENCE OF FOSSILS: FORERUNNERS OF MAN

MENG, THE GORILLA at the Zoo, was one day seen tracing his shadow on the wall. Was this pure accident? Or was Meng showing artistic ability, and thus one more characteristic in common with man? Was the desire for art born in the ape mind, to come to the full flower of its development in the human?

Man and the Earth

Meng and man (Fig. 1) are comparatively recent manifestations of the mysterious phenomenon we call life. We have inherited the fruits of the earth, but the fruits were there many millions of years before we were there to enjoy them.

Every man in his heart of hearts believes in the ancient doctrine and the modern heresy—that the earth is the centre of the universe; and we all behave as if it were true. Yet once upon a time, so the scientists tell us, there was no earth. Ages ago—it may be as recently as 1,500 million years ago, or as long ago as 3,000 million years—the earth was just part of a wandering mass of gas, of what the astronomers call an island universe. There are millions of these gas masses. In the midst of this gas were the beginnings of you and me. That is a thought which may help to restore our self respect, because it makes us realize that it has taken millions upon millions of years to produce us. Our island universe began by condens-

ing itself into a number of more solid clots. These clots we call stars; our universe contains millions of them. One of them, the sun round which the earth now revolves, got in the way of another, with the result that a part split off from it and broke into fragments. One of these fragments is now the earth. In the book called *The Science of Life*, which H. G. Wells wrote with his son and Dr. Julian Huxley, our geographical status is thus summarized: "Man is an inhabitant of a thin rind on a negligible detached blob of matter belonging to one among millions of stars in one among millions of island universes."

Beginnings of Life

After the earth had discarded a piece of itself as the moon, it began to settle down as a fairly stable planet. The hot, moist, steamy blanket round it condensed, evaporated and re-condensed on the progressively cooling crust. Seas and oceans filled the hollow places. The blanket of cloud grew thinner and thinner until it was little more than a veil. Then the rays of sun broke through and the scene was set for the beginnings of life.

Most scientists now believe that all animals and plants are related, and that they are all the variously developed and modified descendants of some one primitive form of living organism, not unlike the simplest microscopic forms of life now existing on the earth.

Belief in such an evolutionary history has been characterized as an act of faith. Here evolution will be regarded as an established theory. The facts which will be narrated are, in any case, interesting and significant.

Material Manifestations

It seems clear that on this earth there was at first no life. When the waters settled on the cooling earth and dissolved the substances of the rocks, making a rather hot salty soup, and when the sun's rays played upon this mixture, something happened. Quite what, no one knows. Just how, no one knows. But the miracle of life had been achieved.

We must content ourselves with the mere chemistry and physics of the matter. These sciences cannot tell us what life is; they can only tell us of some of its usual manifestations. Chemistry tells us that the material embodiments of life are built up from elements, in units of matter once thought to be fundamental and indivisible, the atoms; and that among the important elements are carbon, hydrogen, oxygen, nitrogen, phosphorus and sulphur. Out of these were formed substances that are the groundwork of the living organism—protein, carbohydrate, fat. If it be possible to say that one of these is more important than another, we may say this of protein. Protein is the lean of meat, the stuff which forms our muscles. It seems to be of supreme importance to every living organism.

Viruses

The most elemental form of life with which we are acquainted is what we call an ultramicroscopic or filter passing virus. This is so small that it passes through the finest earthenware filters, and is invisible under the ordinary microscope. Viruses are responsible for many infectious diseases; they are the infecting agents in such conditions as the common cold, measles, infantile paralysis and influenza. They vary in size, but all are smaller than the smallest bacteria. Quite recently it has been discovered that some viruses exist in crystalline form, and the crystals have been found to consist mainly of protein. These crystals are able to grow and reproduce themselves, to turn out more crystals like themselves. They can be dissolved and re-crystallized; even so, they still continue to go on growing and reproducing.

Living Substance

Some scientists doubt whether the viruses ought rightfully to be included among living objects; others are strongly of the opinion that they should.

These minute forms are, they say, animated crystals of protein. The word animated introduces the difficulty. What do we mean by it? Is it not sufficient to say simply "crystals of protein"? The use of the additional qualification really begs the question. It takes something for granted which ought not to be taken for granted—that we really know what life is. As yet, we do not; or at least we cannot draw the line between living and non-living substance.

Similar to viruses are apparent forms of life that prey on bacteria and destroy them. These are known as bacteriophages, and the same doubt exists about their nature—whether they have life or are just chemical substances which take part in chemical reactions without altering their own structure. But the bacteria on which they prey are alive. Every one is agreed about that. They are certainly very much alive.

What does "being alive" mean? It is evident from the virus controversy that it is rather difficult to say exactly what it does mean. Spontaneous movement is one attribute of a living thing. Another—and this is important—is its ability to take in, to assimilate, matter and to change it

BACTERIA UNDER THE MICROSCOPE

Bacteria, which exist in millions in the human body, are one of the most primitive of life-forms.

chemically. Coincident with this building up process is a breaking down process. In the latter energy is liberated, appearing as movement or heat. This whole process—building up (or anabolism) and breaking down (or katabolism)—constitutes what is known as metabolism.

Metabolism

Metabolism is characteristic of life. In shuffling the chemical cards during the process of assimilation, the living organism builds them up into different regroupings. It arranges them in a different order; and, in so doing, grows and moves. In addition, the living organism has the ability to separate off a part of itself which will by similar chemical processes develop into a like living organism. The living organism initiates and controls chemical and physical processes, and it hands the secret on to its successors. This breaking down and building up of chemical substances in metabolism is carried out by ferments, or enzymes, as they are called; and in this activity oxygen is important. Oxygen is the essential element in the continuous combustion process which liberates energy.

Bacteria

Bacteria fulfil all these requirements of life. They move; they reproduce themselves; they break down chemical substances, build them up into their own structure, and break them down again. They take up oxygen from their surroundings for use in combustion, and they give out carbon dioxide. Most bacteria are exceedingly small; the average thickness of a bacterium is one twenty-five-thousandth of an inch. They reproduce by dividing into two; and they can do this at an enormous rate. Some kinds cause a lot of pain and suffering in the world, others do much good. Some kinds capture the nitrogen in the air and convert it into substances of great value for the soil and the plants that grow in it.

Others break up dead matter so that it can be used again by living matter. They are, in fact, the great scavengers of the world.

Some bacteria are spherical and are known as cocci; others are rod-shaped and known as bacilli (Fig. 2). Their activity is colossal, and the chemical changes they set in motion are of great complexity. These changes are carried out by means of the enzymes or ferments which the bacteria produce.

Animal and Vegetable

The name given to actual living substance is protoplasm. Its essential constituents are water and protein. We do not know whether to call these bacterial blobs of protoplasm animals or vegetables. On the whole, the balance is in favour of calling them vegetables; anyhow, they are units of life, near the beginning of things. From some such simple units of life as these science presumes that the animals branched off in one direction and the plants in another. The feature that is commonly said to distinguish plants from animals is the green pigment chlorophyll, which nearly all plants contain. Upon this depend fundamental differences in nutrition; the differences between animals and plants, in fact, come down to a difference in diet.

Chlorophyll is the substance that makes the grass green. With its aid the plant is able to manufacture foodstuff for itself out of the carbon dioxide in the air and the mineral ingredients taken in at its roots. The two processes are collectively called photosynthesis. In these chemical processes, the ultra-violet rays of the sun play an important part. With the help of sunlight, chlorophyll converts carbon dioxide and water into sugar, and, in doing this, plants give out oxygen. Animals, including man, take up oxygen and give out carbon dioxide; this interchange is of the essence of our breathing. Plants breathe in oxygen, but during daylight their oxygen absorption

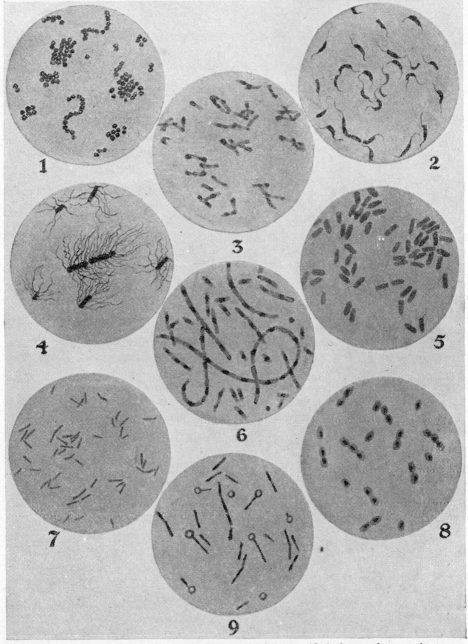

Fig. 2. *Bacteria associated with various diseases, highly magnified. Among the most elementary forms of existence which can definitely said to be alive are bacteria; they are able to move and to reproduce themselves, and to carry through metabolistic processes. Their average thickness is one twenty-five-thousandth of an inch. Their effect in the human system is to produce many of the most widespread diseases. 1, Streptococci and staphylococci; 2, cholera; 3, diphtheria; 4, typhoid; 5, bacillus coli; 6, anthrax; 7, tubercle; 8, pneumonia; 9, tetanus.*

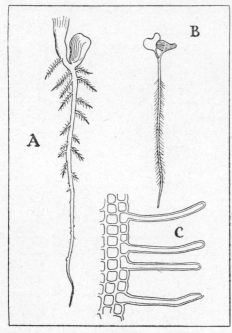

Fig. 3. *Seedlings of plants* (A) *Maize.* (B) *Mustard.* (C) *Magnified section showing root-hairs forming from surface cells. The roots suck up water and mineral salts.*

is concealed by the process of photosynthesis—the absorption of carbon dioxide and the retention of the carbon with other ingredients which are absorbed by the roots.

The roots of the plant (Fig. 3) suck up water and mineral salts from the earth. From the phosphorus, nitrogen and other elements drawn from the solution protein is formed. Characteristically, though there are exceptions, the plant takes simple substances from its surroundings—water, carbon dioxide, minerals—and builds them up into complex substances. Chlorophyll is a complex of carbon, hydrogen, oxygen, nitrogen and magnesium. The animal, on the other hand, takes in the ready-made complex substances supplied by the plant world, and breaks them down into the elements of which they are made up.

The green plant appeared quite early in the history of the earth. Its appearance before that of the animal kingdom was essential. It not only built up the materials of life, as we know them, from

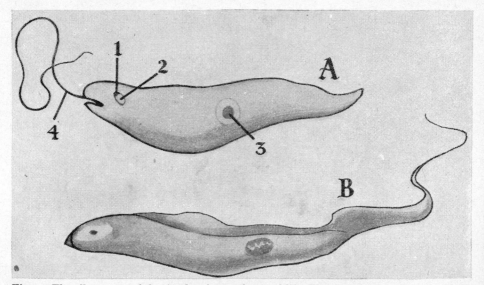

Fig. 4. *Flagellates, one of the simplest forms of animal life. The name is given because of their possession of "flagella" or whips, which they use to enable them to move.* (A) *Single-celled primitive animal "euglena viridis."* 1, *Pigment spot;* 2, *food receptacle (vacuole);* 3, *cell-nucleus;* 4, *flagellum.* (B) *Trypanosome, the organism which is responsible for sleeping-sickness.*

Fig. 5. *Types of foraminifera. These are single-celled organisms which form round themselves shells of calcium carbonate of a very great variety of shapes and complexity. Their shells form a considerable proportion of the covering of the ocean floor, and chalk rocks were formed in past geological epochs almost entirely of the shells of dead foraminifera.*

simple inorganic substances; it also replenished the air with oxygen, without which no living thing can maintain existence. The animal gets its energy and its heat from the combustion of protein, fat and carbohydrate; and this combustion is dependent upon oxygen. The plant also, once it has elaborated its protoplasm, breaks it down by oxidation. But it moves to a slower tempo and it gives out more oxygen than it takes in. The plant world acts as a direct storehouse of the energy of the sun.

Flagellates

Bacteria, as we have said, are commonly looked upon as belonging to the plant world, although they possess no chlorophyll. On the other hand certain minute, actively moving organisms, known as the flagellates (Fig. 4) which possess chlorophyll are classed as animals. They certainly have what may be described as mouths, by which they take in solid food (of course, in microscopic particles),

but they also, by means of their chlorophyll, take in carbon from the air. Both these groups are hard to classify. One can call them animal plants, or plant animals indifferently.

One of the simplest of unquestionable plant forms is found among the algæ, of which the fine green covering on the damp and shady side of trees and fences is one example, and the green slimy masses on ponds another. There is a great variety of these primitive plants to be found living in water or damp places; from the small one-celled plants up to the seaweeds, from which higher land plants have evolved. The algæ differ, among other respects, from the higher land plants in having no division into root, stem, leaf and flower; but they all contain chlorophyll.

Early animals and early plants, then, were single-celled organisms so much like each other in many ways as to be almost indistinguishable. Thus they are of great interest to all students of biology, for they were the beginnings of life. After hundreds of millions of years their direct descendants exist in hardly modified form; but also, by the long, tedious method of trial and error, all other forms of life have evolved from them.

The theory of evolution does not admit that man was specially created. Aeons ago a fermentation of water, sunlight and chemical substances brought life to the newly formed planet, earth, in the form of the living cell. To that original cell all subsequent cells, and all forms of life, including man, owe their being.

The one-celled organism is far from being so simple as one might imagine. It assumes a bewildering variety of shapes. There is, for example, the subdivision of one-celled organisms known as foraminifera (Fig. 5). These form round themselves shells of calcium carbonate beautiful in shape, variety and complexity. Most varieties inhabit the depths of the sea or the shore, but freshwater specimens are to be found in the layer of organic debris at the bottom of ditches and ponds. Some idea of their ubiquity and profusion is gained when it is realized that the chalk cliffs of Dover are composed of the shells of foraminifera which died ages ago. If you look at some chalk under the microscope you will see their shells. They illustrate one way in which Nature maintains a balance between living and non-living substances. The waters dissolve carbonate of lime from the surface of the earth. Foraminifera, in their development, take the carbonate of lime out of the solution, use it to create their shell homes, which, when they die, are returned again to the crust of the earth. So the wheel of life turns, taking up frcm the earth and giving back to it.

Some foraminifera float near the surface of the seas they live in. They do this in company with a vast number of minute animals and plants. The chlorophyll-containing algæ (Fig. 6) are there in

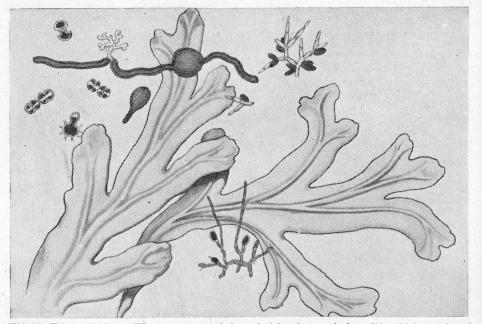

Fig. 6. *Types of algæ. These are some of the primitive forms of plant-life which are found floating near the surface of the seas in which they live, in company with a vast number of other minute plants and animals. They are also found on the bark of trees and on stones.*

abundance. This huge floating population of the seas is collectively known as plankton. Being relatively passive and helpless the little plant and animal forms which constitute it drift along the watery highways made by the great ocean currents, furnishing an ever-replenished source of nourishment for the fish that live in the sea. The action of sunlight on chlorophyll enables the plankton to build up complex organic material, which is passed on up the scale of life. The smaller fish which devour the plankton are themselves devoured by larger fish, which in turn fall a prey to still larger ones, or to man.

Fungi

While in general the possession of chlorophyll is a distinguishing feature of the plant, there are certain lowly organized living things which, perhaps irrationally, are looked upon as plants though they have no chlorophyll. These are the moulds, toadstools, and yeasts collectively known as fungi. They live on organic matter, alive or dead. Moulds exude a digestive juice on to their food and absorb the result. They prefer to feed on decaying organic matter, a method of existence known as saprophytism. (Living on live things is called parasitism.) A mould grows out in threads which branch. Yeasts (Fig. 7) are one-celled moulds. In the absence of oxygen a yeast cell will get its energy by turning sugar into alcohol and carbon dioxide, a process which is essential to the production of bread and beer.

For an understanding of evolution and of the basis of life we must have some knowledge of this world of one-celled animals and plants, which is visible to a large extent only under the microscope. One-celled animals, such as the foraminifera, belong to the protozoa or first animals. The simplest protozoon is, perhaps, the amœba (Fig. 8); from it much can be learnt about uni-cellular life.

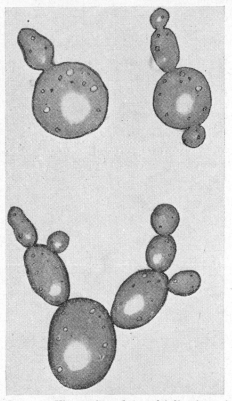

Fig. 7. *Illustrating the multiplication of yeast-cells. Yeasts are a group of plants without chlorophyll; they possess the quality of turning sugar into alcohol and carbon-dioxide. They are single-celled, and they reproduce by an infinite budding process.*

The amœba is found at the bottom of ponds and ditches. It is very minute, about one-hundredth of an inch long, and consists of a naked lump, jelly-like in consistence. It is called a one-celled animal, but the word cell is perhaps misleading in that it implies something set and unyielding. The cell of the higher plants, with its tough wall of cellulose, does correspond to this idea, but the animal cell must not be thought of as being anything like so rigid. The amœba is a minute blob of protoplasm presenting a surface to the world. But it is going too far to call this surface a wall, though under the microscope the amœba is seen to have a clear outer layer which is more solid than its inner granular layer.

This jelly-like unit of life, this drop of protoplasm, is on the move the whole time. It is always changing shape and going first in one direction and then in another. It moves, too, by changing shape. It can do this by virtue of the power of protoplasm to contract. It is this same power which makes it possible for us to move and have our being. The amœba thrusts out projections of its substance, called pseudopodia, or false legs, producing these only when it needs them. Then it moves in the direction of its pseudopodia by, so to speak, flowing into them. The white cells in our blood move in much the same sort of way.

On looking more closely, one can distinguish in the amœba a smaller, denser, rounded mass. This is the nucleus, the most important constituent of the cell, which controls the activities of the greyish, slimy, semi-liquid, semi-trans-

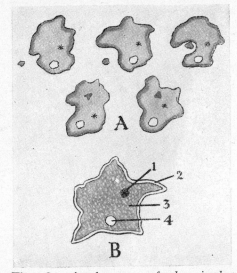

Fig. 8. *Amœba, one of the simplest protozoa.* (A) *Amœba absorbing food. It does this by projecting itself around the food and embracing it.* (B) *Construction of amœba: 1, Nucleus; 2, outer layer of clear protoplasm; 3, layer of granular protoplasm; 4, breathing and excretory orifice.*

parent protoplasm. It is formed of granules of chromatin, so called because they readily take up certain dyes, and when thus stained render the nucleus easily visible under the microscope. The nucleus is necessary for the life of the cell; for without it new protoplasm cannot be built up. It is the transmitter of heredity. Each of the white blood cells of the human body has a nucleus.

Metabolism of the Amœba

The amœba feeds in the simplest way by embracing its food and taking it into itself. It takes in and digests organic matter, for it is a genuine animal, and by breaking down the foodstuffs it has taken in, it creates the energy necessary to carry on its activities. To carry out this process (metabolism), and in its movements, the amœba needs oxygen for combustion purposes. This it obtains from the water in which it lives. It gives out carbon dioxide and also water; in fact, like ourselves, it is dependent for life on eating and breathing.

Enough has been said to show that life for this little lump of jelly is quite a complicated process. It does the same sort of things that we do, though on a much reduced scale. There is still one essential function that has not been mentioned, that of reproduction. How does this happen?

The amœba is, as we have seen, in very close contact with its environment. Whatever it does it does in a full-bodied fashion. It throws itself completely into every activity, whether it be moving over the bottom of a pond, closing in on a piece of organic matter, or just breathing. At the same time one might accuse it of living rather a superficial kind of life, for the surface it presents to the world is all-important. If the amœba becomes too bulky there will be something of a strain on this surface. The simplest thing to do in the circumstances would be to split into two, and this is precisely what the

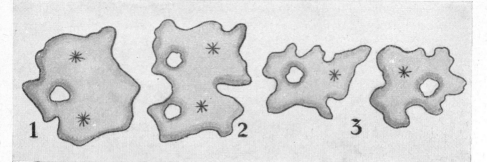

Fig. 9. *Stages in the reproductive process of the amœba. The nucleus divides into two halves. Equal amounts of protoplasm then close round the two halves of nuclei. Finally, the bridge between the two halves breaks and two separate individuals appear, each of which possesses exactly the same structure as the parent cell. This process is an infinite one.*

amœba does. The nucleus divides first, separating into two halves. A constriction then appears in the protoplasm, equal amounts of which close round the two halves of nuclei. The protoplasmic bridge between the two is finally broken, and the two halves part, to grow and lead independent existences (Fig. 9).

Reproduction by Splitting

The amœba does not delegate this business of reproduction to any one part of itself. It does not hand on a piece of itself to posterity and then die. It literally hands on itself. It becomes, so to speak, father and mother to itself. It just goes on and on, dividing and dividing. The amœba, short of catastrophic annihilation, is immortal. This method of reproduction by splitting or fission is called asexual.

In hard times the amœba can immobilize itself in a cyst, becoming smaller, rounder and harder. Meanwhile the nucleus divides and re-divides. The amœba may remain in such a state for a very long time, and then, in suitable conditions, take on a new lease of life. It can also unite with another amœba, and this it does in as whole-hearted a fashion as it does everything else. Two amœbæ come into contact with each other, and just flow into each other and become literally and truly one.

It is thought that this fusion of two beings into one is a way of avoiding senility, that the fusion is a process of rejuvenation. There is no apparent distinction between male and female, between active and passive. If we chose to call this union a manifestation of sex, it is clear that in the amœba sex and reproduction are two quite distinct things. In this act of union the number of cells is actually halved. It might even be looked on as part of the nutritional process.

Sex Differentiation

The earliest differentiation into male and female is to be observed in the elaborate world of the protozoa. In, for example, the one-celled little flagellate called bodo, reproduction takes place both by simple fission and as a result of conjugation. No difference in shape can be discerned between the male bodo and the female, but when the time comes for sexual union they behave differently. The male whips his way with his two flagella through the water to fuse with the female, which has remained immobile. The union is complete and absolute.

The result of union between two gametes, or sex cells, is called a zygote. The zygote formed as a result of conjugation between bodos differs in shape from the previously free-living individuals.

They have submerged their individuality in the interests of the future of the race. Inside the motionless sac which is the zygote a rapid cell division proceeds, and ultimately a large number of tiny spores escape and grow into adult bodos. This fruitful result shows clearly that the result of union is to speed up enormously the rate of reproduction. Sex in this case appears as an incitement or stimulus to the process of reproduction.

The next step in sex differentiation is also exemplified among protozoa. Not only is there a distinction in behaviour, but also one in form. In a protozoon called coccidium schubergi, male and female appear after a long period of asexual reproduction by fission. One coccidium grows into a large round cell, packed with food granules. It remains stationary. Another individual divides up into a number of smaller pointed cells, each provided with two flagella by which it swims actively about. The smaller active cell, which we may call a spermatozoon, is attracted by the stationary large female cell and finally bores its way into it. The large cell pushes out from its surface a cone of reception, and at this spot union takes place. The zygote thus formed divides and re-divides, and, as a result, new individuals eventually enter the protozoal world.

Sex in Evolution

So sex made its appearance right at the beginning of things in the microscopic one-celled animals which sometimes behave like plants and sometimes like animals. The sexual process—the union of two cells, and the union of two nuclei—has played a fundamental part in evolution. This process may be simply explained as a straightforward attempt at division of labour. The female cell grows large by storing the food necessary for the growth of future individuals. So as not to waste this valuable substance by dissipating it in energy she remains stationary and passive. The male concentrates on locomotion, this activity on his part ensuring that he will eventually meet his mate.

In a large protozoon by name paramœcium, or the slipper animalcule, which is a common inhabitant of decaying vegetable matter, conjugation takes place between like individuals, without, however, any sacrifice of individuality. Two animalcules come together and during their conjugation their nuclei divide and re-divide. Ultimately an interchange of nuclei takes place between the two, each animalcule receiving part of the nuclear material of the other. Fusion occurs between the part exchanged and the part remaining, and the two animalcules then separate. This shows that the essential point in conjugation is exchange and fusion of nuclear material or chromatin.

Multi-Cellular Organisms

Nature, having once demonstrated the advantages of division of labour, proceeded to experiment further. There were obvious limitations to what an isolated marauding one-celled unit of life could do. The units set about tackling their individual problems on a co-operative basis. There are, for example, certain protozoa which fasten themselves to objects by a stalk-like structure. When they reproduce by splitting, the daughter cells thus formed remain attached and a colony of cells is formed. In free-swimming varieties the products of fission remain grouped together, forming in some cases a sphere. In volvox (Fig. 10) the individual flagellate one-celled organisms stick together on the surface of a freely swimming sphere of jelly. The swimming is done by the united action of the individual flagellæ. This experiment in collectivity was highly successful, and must have started off the evolutionary process that ended in the many-celled animal.

One motive in sex differentiation was division of labour. The experiment started by volvox and other one-celled protozoa and protophyta (early one-celled plants) opened out further and obvious possibilities of specialized activity. The amœba could do only one thing at a time. Movement, reproduction, eating, breathing—all demanded the undivided attention of the animal. The amœba, of course, had great advantages. It carried no dead weight about with it in the form of a skeleton. It was wholly alive. But its opportunities for advancement were limited. Other protozoa became organized along more elaborate lines. Paramoecium, for example, has a definite mouth through which food can pass, and which is covered with fine hair-like structures known as cilia. (Our nasal and air passages are also lined with cilia.) These cilia, which are constantly vibrating, propel paramoecium through the water. This protozoon has also a more or less definite part of its structure where waste matter is thrown out, though there is no tube or alimentary canal connecting this with the mouth. It further ejects long threads from the surface of its body when irritated; it is presumed that these are stings or comparable weapons of offensive action.

Cell Specialization

But volvox showed another way. How much more efficient would it be for some cells to do nothing but reproduce, some cells to look after locomotion, others to concentrate on nutrition, and so on. In volvox, and other colonies formed by the union or, rather, non-separation of dividing cells, some colonies produce only female cells or ova, and others only male cells or spermatozoa. The conjugation of ovum and spermatozoon initiates the formation of a new colony. Other colonies are asexual and produce daughter colonies by simple fission.

In the volvox colonies each cell is united to adjacent cells by fine threads of protoplasm, and all the cells are embedded in a jelly formed by their own secretion. In this case the interests of the cell are completely submerged in those of the colony; the cell cannot exist apart from the community. Where the community goes, there the cell has to go with it. The fine threads of protoplasm forming the network that keeps the individual cells in touch with each other probably serve as a communicating system of a physico-chemical nature.

How far is the volvox colony an individual and how far is each cell in it an

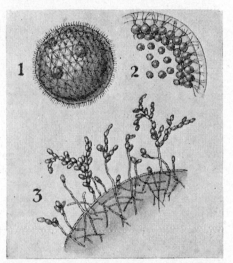

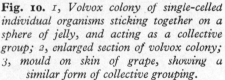

Fig. 10. *1, Volvox colony of single-celled individual organisms sticking together on a sphere of jelly, and acting as a collective group; 2, enlarged section of volvox colony; 3, mould on skin of grape, showing a similar form of collective grouping.*

individual? Volvox may consist of anything between 10,000 and 20,000 cells. One thing is clear: the increase in size was a great advantage. The animal was much less at the mercy of its environment, not such an easy prey to other animals, and more able to secure food for itself. And it did not have to interrupt the ordinary day-to-day business of living when it wanted to reproduce. Certain cells—or rather, individuals—carried out this task. All the same, volvox could not be called a multicellular animal. It was a colony of one-celled animals, which, for the sake of unity, co-operation and additional protection gave up their right to a free and unfettered existence.

Sponges and Coelenterates

Although we do not know just what the intermediate steps were, from the protozoa life branched off into two main forms —the sponges and the coelenterates. From an evolutionary point of view the sponges were a failure. No progress was found possible along those lines. The coelenterates represent a more successful venture on the part of Nature; the line of development they started was to end eventually in the human being.

Sponges are sessile, that is, stationary, masses of cells through which water is continually streaming. Flagella lash water through hundreds of tiny holes and out through a single large opening. They extract minute food particles from circulating water. Sponges have no mouths; each of the cells constituting a sponge feeds on its own account. They have no common digestive cavity, no sense organs, no nerves. The whole constitutes a rather passive and lazy aggregation of cells, each self-absorbed in its own existence.

Methods of Classification

Before going on to the coelenterates and the animals beyond these, something must be said about classification. Classification means the arrangement of animals, plants or forms of inorganic matter according to common characteristics in an orderly and comprehensive manner.

Philosophers have employed the method since the days of the Greeks, but it is only comparatively recently that it has invaded the domain of science. Not until the eighteenth century did the great Swedish naturalist Linnæus put the classification of animals and plants on a sound basis.

To begin with, we can divide the world of life into two kingdoms—the animal and the vegetable. The animal kingdom is further divided into phyla, or groups, and then into classes, orders, families, genera (plural of genus), species and varieties. There is nothing mystical or magical about these words. They simply are used to represent different sizes of groupings.

The first division in the animal world consists of a grouping together of all those animals made along fundamentally similar lines. For example, human beings have many things in common with the fish. We both have backbones made up of blocks of bone called vertebræ. We have eyes and a brain at the head end. Where we have arms and legs, the fish has fins which serve roughly the same purpose, that of locomotion. We both have a nervous spinal cord enclosed in the arches of the vertebra, and a digestive system on the belly side of the backbone. These and a whole number of other similarities of structure are common also to birds, monkeys, frogs, lizards and snakes —in fact, to all animals grouped in the great phylum known as the vertebrates.

Divisions of Vertebrates

Whatever differences they exhibit, all the vertebrates have backbones; hence the name. But among the vertebrates certain obvious differences in structure make further division into classes at once necessary. Mammals are clearly different from birds, fish, reptiles or amphibia. In the mammalian class marked differences still appear, for the class includes the very primitive monotremes, which lay eggs; the marsupials, which carry their young in a pouch; and the placentals, which carry them to a high state of development in the womb. The placentals include a number of great mammalian families, among which are the primates. The primates include lemurs, monkeys and apes, and human beings. To the group human beings is given the generic name of *homo* and the identifying species name of *sapiens*. So *Homo sapiens*—that is, man as he exists today—is a primate (family), a placental (order), a mammal (class), a vertebrate (phylum) and an animal. As we shall see later, from these classifications we can infer quite a lot about ourselves.

Progressive Specialization

To return now to the phylum coelenterates. This phylum represents the first many-celled animals, the first representatives of that second large division of the animal kingdom, the metazoa or animals that came after (*meta*) the protozoa, or first animals. It includes sea firs, jelly fish, sea anemones and corals. In the coelenterates, the single cell to all intents and purposes gave up its right to independent existence. It did this so completely that the individual unit, the complete animal, comprised the entire collection of cells. In the course of evolution, there was a progressive specialization of various groups of cells for various animal activities: of muscle cells for movement, digestive cells for purposes of nutrition, blood cells for carrying oxygen to the tissues, and so forth. But even in man there are still cells exactly similar to the most primitive free-living forms. The white blood cells move like amœba and engulf organic matter—for example, bacteria. The cells of the windpipe possess vibrating cilia. The spermatozoon is an actively moving single cell.

One of the earliest specializations was into body, or somatic, cells and germ, or reproductive, cells. The germ cells are of two kinds: the large, passive eggs or ova, and the small, energetic spermatozoa, which swim about with the aid of flagella. We find this division into two sorts of cells—the body cells and the germ cells—in the freshwater polyp known as hydra (Fig. 11), a coelenterate.

Hydra is like a thin thread about one-third of an inch long and is found attached to water plants in ponds. Essentially it is a tube lined with cells (the endoderm) and covered with a second layer (the ectoderm). Between the two layers is a thin sheet of jelly-like material. At the free end of the tube is an opening or mouth surrounded by tentacles, which catch the food and shove it into the mouth. Between the cells on the outside

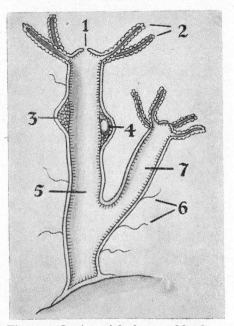

Fig. 11. *Section of hydra: 1, Mouth; 2, tentacles; 3, testis; 4, ovary; 5, digestive cavity; 6, stinging hairs; 7, new bud. Hydra reproduces both sexually, through fertilization of the ovum by spermatozoon from another hydra, and asexually, by budding. It is hermaphrodite, but not self-fertilizing.*

of the tentacles are concealed cells which contain stinging capsules. These are tiny bodies with a spiral thread coiled inside. When the trigger hair which is on the surface of the cell is stimulated the spiral thread is uncoiled and shot out, poisoning whatever it comes into contact with. In this way the hydra possesses itself of such morsels as the larvæ of water insects. Other and larger cells on the outside of hydra send out at their bases protrusions on to the sheet of jelly separating them from the inner layer. These protrusions or elongations have the power of contraction, so that hydra can move and close its tentacles on its prey. They are in fact muscle cells. The cells lining the tube are digestive cells.

Hydra can reproduce sexually or asexually. In the latter way, little buds and cells grow out from the main body and develop into full-grown hydras. For a time colonies are formed. Later the fully developed daughter hydra breaks away. In the sexual way, eggs and spermatozoa are formed. A few cells of the ectoderm multiply and form a lump. In one lump eventually a large ovum or egg-cell appears. In another lump, cells multiply and give rise to a number of spermatozoa, for all the world resembling flagellate protozoa. The lump producing the ovum may be termed the ovary, and that producing the spermatozoa the testis. The general

Fig. 12. *A group of jelly fish (medusæ). These possess a primitive nervous system, and also eye-spots and balancing organs. They bulk their frame with jelly, and some varieties may weigh as much as half a ton.*

name for sex glands (that is, testes and ovaries) is gonad. The testis is a gonad; so is the ovary. Hydra grows both and is therefore hermaphrodite. Hermaphroditism is quite common among the lower animals, but usually development of the gonads is so timed and arranged that self-fertilization is discouraged. The eggs of one animal are fertilized by the sperms of another, not by its own.

Growth of Hydra

After fertilization of a hydra egg by a hydra spermatozoon the resulting zygote (the result mainly, it will be remembered, of the fusion of the male and female nuclei) divides and forms a ring of cells round a hollow sphere which is rather like a volvox colony. (At one stage of its development the human embryo does the same sort of thing.) Later the cells multiply and a solid sphere of cells is produced. A shell is secreted round this solid embryo. Then the solid mass develops into the two-layered adult, with mouth and tentacles and digestive tube.

A close relation of hydra is the coelenterate obelia, which occurs as a furlike growth on seaweeds and breakwaters, and is essentially a colony and polypus. Like hydra, obelia is a two-layered animal. The ectoderm is surrounded by a hornlike shell, which extends at the extremities of the branches into a cup. Within the cup is the polyp, with its mouth and tentacles. The tubular digestive cavity is common to the whole colony. This colonization is an asexual, budding affair. Occasionally some of the buds develop in a different way and produce little umbrella-shaped creatures, called medusæ, which swim away. They are built on the same plan as the jelly fish; the truncated handle of the umbrella is the mouth and gut, and this radiates out to the edge of the umbrella, which is a two-layered cell mechanism with the sheet of jelly in between greatly enlarged. These little jelly fish swim about and eat and finally produce eggs and spermatozoa. When the time is ripe, eggs and spermatozoa are shot into the sea and unite, to produce new obelia.

In obelia there is an alternation of generations produced by asexual and sexual methods. The asexual phase gives rise to a stationary colony of polyps, which leads rather a vegetable form of existence. The sexual phase produces an active, freely swimming organism. In hydra, this free swimming phase seems to have been suppressed; the eggs and sperms grow from the polyp itself.

Primitive Nervous Systems

We have already observed differentiation of cells into digestive cells, muscle cells and stinging cells. There is also in the coelenterates a primitive nervous system which consists of a network of fine fibres of protoplasm with occasional nerve cells in their course. In the medusæ (Fig. 12) there can also be observed eye spots and balancing organs. The reserve network ensures that any stimulus transmits its message simultaneously to the whole jelly fish, which then, by contracting its entire bell-like body, moves in the required direction. Every part is immediately put in touch with every other part. This has obvious disadvantages and a more selective arrangement appears in higher animals.

Sea Anemones and Corals

The other two main classes of the coelenterates (hydra and obelia belong to a single class) include the jelly fish, sea anemones and corals. In all, the ground plan is the same: two layers of cells with a sheet of jelly in between. The inner layer is simply a digestive tube. The outer one is differentiated into muscle cells, nerve cells, stinging cells and eye cells; and it can secrete a protective tube of hornlike substance. Sea anemones are polyps grown big by putting on jelly, corals "colonial" polyps which have made a

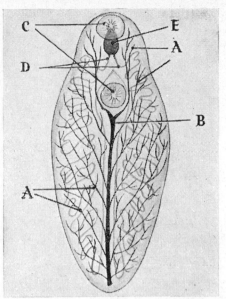

Fig. 13. *Digestive and excretory system of the flatworm (planaria).* (A) *Digestive canal.* (B) *Excretory duct.* (C) *Suckers.* (D) *Excretory system.* (E) *Throat (pharynx). As there are no blood vessels, the digestive system reaches every part of the body.*

skeleton of lime. The Great Barrier Reef of Australia, more than a thousand miles long, has been entirely built up by coral polyps. Jelly fish, as the name suggests, bulk their frame largely with jelly. Varieties are known which may weigh as much as half a ton.

The coelenterates constitute a rich and varied world, but the place they occupy in the scheme of things has been well summed up by Professors Haldane and Huxley in their book *Animal Biology*: "If one desires to visualize evolutionary progress, one may do worse than to remember that in its nervous and muscular organization a jelly fish, for all its beauty, is pretty much on the level of the human gut." That is to say, the comparison is between the entire jelly fish and the human intestine, which, continuously and all uncontrolled by our conscious mind, carries out a succession of peristaltic waves capable of little modification.

The coelenterates, however, could not go much further in the evolutionary experiment. They are radially symmetrical. The higher groups of animals quite early on showed bilateral symmetry and developed three layers of cells. In place of the sheet of jelly between ectoderm and endoderm, there appeared a middle layer of cells, the mesoderm.

The Flatworm

A particularly interesting example of an early three-cell-layered animal is planaria (Fig. 13), the flatworm, a white, flat creature about three quarters of an inch in length which lives at the bottom of ponds. Planaria has a head and a concentration of nerve cells at the head end called the brain. It also has eyes. It has no blood vessels, and its mouth serves also as an anus, in this resembling obelia. Planaria is without a body cavity or cœlom—that is, a space between the digestive tube of endoderm and the outer layer of ectoderm. Owing to the absence of blood vessels, the digestive and excretory tubes have to branch into every recess of planaria's body, so as to convey food there and remove waste. And the flatworm has to be flat so that the interchange of oxygen and carbon dioxide can take place between it and the water it lives in. Blood vessels would have made this unnecessary. The great advance shown by the flatworm is the possession of a brain.

Segmented Worms

The annelida, or segmented worms, of which the earthworm (Fig. 14) is a familiar example, are the most primitive forms to possess a body cavity or cœlom. All the animal kingdom above these lowly but useful creatures is known as cœlomates. Annelida have a cœlom between the gut and the outer layer, a blood system and an anus at the lower end of the digestive tube.

The presence of a cavity or gap between the gut and the body wall makes it possible for either to contract independently of the other. The cavity is also a barrier between the gut and the muscular body wall, a barrier which can trap bacteria. As animals grow in bulk, the absorptive surface for food must increase; a body cavity makes it possible for the gut to be coiled without having to kink the body wall. Blood vessels, too, allow the body to increase in thickness, for they take oxygen and foodstuff to every recess and carry away waste products. In the absence of blood vessels to carry out this function, every cell of the body has to be near either the inner or the outer surface.

Results of Segmentation

The earthworm and other members of the phylum annelida, such as the graceful marine worms, are all segmented. Each segment, except the terminal ones, is like the one behind and the one in front of it. Through segmentation the animal grows in size. The first segment, which comes into direct contact with what is immediately in front of the animal, becomes specialized in certain ways. It develops sense organs: eyes to see and ears to hear with. The nerve cells controlling these organs also collect at the head end, and go to form the brain. Mouth parts develop in the head end to cope with the food the animal meets in its path. The segments behind, monotonously repeated, offer opportunities for subsequent specialization, including reproduction (Fig. 15). Each segment has a pair of excretory tubes or kidneys and a collection of nerve cells. A central nervous system runs along the belly and an artery along the back. The sandworm, nereis, has sticking out from the side of each segment projections supplied with bristles and hairs. These can be looked upon as very primitive limbs, as they are used for getting about. Earthworms are hermaphrodite, but do not practice self-fertilization.

The segmented annelids are of special interest in that from them there probably

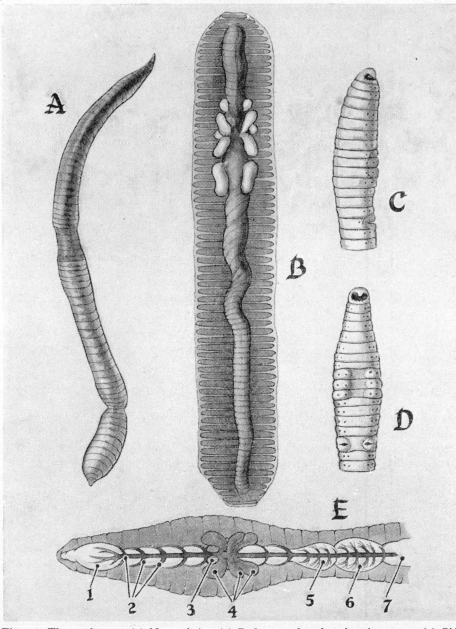

Fig. 14. *The earthworm.* (A) *Natural size.* (B) *Body opened to show interior organs.* (C) *Side view of front end.* (D) *Under view of front end.* (E) *Diagrammatic section: 1, Throat (pharynx); 2, heart; 3, glands producing calcium; 4, seminal vessels; 5, crop, where food is prepared for digestion; 6, gizzard; 7, intestines. The earthworm is one of the segmented worms; the various segments become specialized for the performance of different functions, such as digestion, excretion, respiration, reproduction, and so on. The segmented worms are the most primitive forms of life which possess a body cavity, or cœlom.*

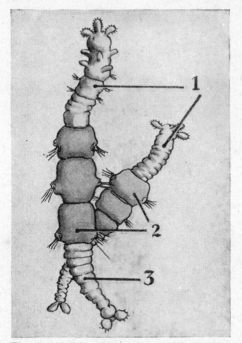

Fig. 15. *Reproduction by segmentation.* *The segmented worms (of which the worm* *procerastea, illustrated here, is one), repro-* *duce by growing new segments. 1 and 3, new* *growths; 2, segments of original worm.*

developed the tremendously important phylum of the arthropods. This large group of the animal kingdom includes all the insects, crabs, lobsters, shrimps, scorpions, spiders, mites and centipedes. The arthropods have conquered air, sea and land. There is a simple little creature called peripatus which hides under stones and is found in Australia, South Africa and South America. It looks like a cross between a worm and a centipede.

Links in Evolution

In many ways it is like a worm and in many like an arthropod. It is, in fact, looked upon as a very primitive arthropod, and is a living link between the phylum of segmented worms and the phylum of arthropods.

It is interesting to observe that the description of animals of increasing com-

plexity is made simpler by taking evolution for granted. To proceed from the one-celled, freely living organism to the colony stage (for example, volvox), from the colony stage to the two-layered animal (for example, hydra), from this to the three-layered, and so on to the three-layered cœlomate, is to proceed in a fairly orderly and understandable way. We are, indeed, collecting as we go evidence of the fact of evolution. Peripatus provides us with an intriguing example of a living clue. There are other similar examples of the same thing.

Arthropods

We have now traced the development of life up to a highly complicated stage. Before leaving the invertebrates, or animals without backbones, let us consider the arthropods in rather more detail.

As with the annelids, segmentation is characteristic of the whole of the arthropod kingdom, which has developed a large number of varieties of segments. To get

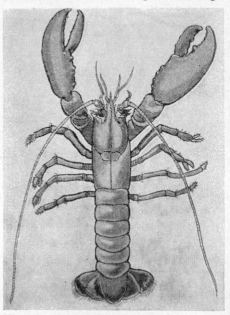

Fig. 16. *The common lobster. The shell of* *the lobster is both a protection for its soft* *organs, and also an external skeleton.*

Fig. 17. *The spiders are members of the arachnid class of the arthropods. They possess a nervous system running along the belly and a heart along the back; their skeleton is external; and the body cavity is filled with pale blue blood. The illustration shows three different types of this widespread group. 1, Garden spider; 2, common British spider; 3, Barbary spider.*

some idea of what the arthropod phylum has done with segments let us have a look at the anatomy of the lobster (Fig. 16).

The most obvious thing about the lobster is its suit of armour, or shell. This is made of a horny stuff called chitin, which is reinforced with lime salts. The protection offered by this structure is evident. Less evident is the fact that the shell is a skeleton to which the muscles are attached and which houses the soft organs. The lobster lives inside its skeleton.

External Skeleton

The external skeleton has, as against the internal, at least one grave disadvantage, which has probably proved a severe handicap to what is on the whole an extremely successful phylum. When the lobster wants to grow it has to get rid of its skeleton and grow a new one. It has to moult. This process renders the lobster for the time being very vulnerable, a state the dangers of which it attempts to minimise by retiring to a safe crack in a rock until the moulting is over and the new armour fitted. Its so-called liver is stored with lime for the purpose of providing new shells. In its stomach is a chewing mincing machine made of chitin and called the gastric mill. This and the lining of the stomach have also to be moulted in the process of growth.

On the other hand the lobster has carried out some very successful experiments with the little bristly projections found sticking out of the segments of nereis. Look at the hard jointed limbs and the variety of purposes to which they have been put. The feelers, the huge claws, the busy little limbs round the mouth which tear up the food, the appendages that bear gills for breathing purposes, and those which in the male are shaped for transferring the sperms to the female—all this very highly specialized development has taken shape on a most simple ground plan. But note that the specialization has been carried too far for much adaptability.

Liver of the Lobster

The lobster has fused the first thirteen segments to form a box for enclosing and protecting its stomach, heart, liver, gonads and other soft organs. This box is packed in with pale blue blood, the colour of which is due to the copper-containing pigment. Human blood pigment contains iron, and is accordingly red. The so-called liver of the lobster in no way corresponds to the human organ of that name. In addition to storing lime for shell repairs, it secretes the digestive ferments which in us are secreted by the salivary and intestinal glands and the pancreas. The segments of the hinder part of the lobster have remained flexible and form a strong tail, the vigorous contraction of which propels it backwards through the water. In short, the ground

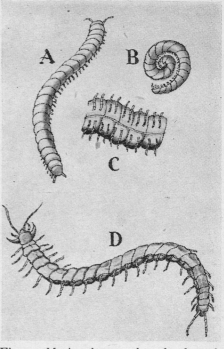

Fig. 19. *Myriopoda are a class of arthropods possessing a head and a trunk bearing many jointed limbs. (A and B) Millipedes. (C) Section of millipedes showing pairs of legs. (D) Centipede, showing segmentation of body.*

plan of the lobster differs radically from that of the vertebrate.

All the other members of the arthropod phylum are the result of variant themes Nature has played on the simple segmented tube. The general plan remains the same; the nervous system runs along the belly and the heart along the back; the skeleton is outside the animal; the body cavity is filled with pale blue blood, and the segmental limbs are fitted out for every variety of activity.

Classes into which the arthropods are divided are the crustacea (crabs, lobsters, water fleas, shrimps), arachnida (spiders, ticks and scorpions, Figs. 17 and 18), myriapoda (centipedes and millipedes, Fig. 19), insecta (butterflies, Fig. 20; moths, flies, fleas, bugs, lice, cockroaches, locusts, Fig. 21), and finally

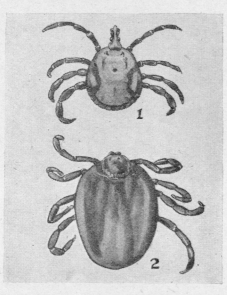

Fig. 18. *Ticks are another variant on the arthropod theme. They are parasites, and possess a toothed probe by which they adhere to the host whose blood they suck.*

Fig. 20. *Butterflies, some well-known varieties of which are illustrated here, are members of the insect class of arthropods. They are found in an astonishing number of varieties and colorations but all possess the fundamental arthropod characteristics, such as bodily segmentation and blue blood. 1, Trojan; 2, Camberwell Beauty; 3, Trojan; 4, Purple Emperor.*

onychophora, represented by the single genius peripatus.

One point about the arthropods is that they are, from our point of view, a rather unpleasant crowd. Some of the species are indeed very dangerous to human life. Mosquitoes, for example, deal out ill-health and death to millions yearly in the form of malaria and yellow fever. Fleas carry plague, lice typhus, flies typhoid. Locusts consume the plant life that sustains us. Cockroaches raid our larders. Gnats, ticks and mites bite us and suck our blood. There is, in fact, a continual and gigantic warfare going on between us and the arthropod phylum. And in this ceaseless struggle the arthropod occasionally gets the upper hand.

Arthropods live in the sea, on the ground and in the air. They have, in fact, explored every medium of living, from life in solitary state to highly organized communities. Numerous and amazing variations have been made of the common arthropod stock. There is in all this variety an astonishingly close adaptation to circumstances: the gills of the lobster for breathing; the fine little air tubes permeating the body of the insect, an air radiator that brings oxygen into intimate contact with every part of it; the development of the segmental appendages for hopping, eating, fighting, breeding, biting or sucking; the formation of wings from the skeleton for flying—all these variations adapt the arthropods to a rich and varied environment.

Mimicry is another adaptation employed by the arthropods. It is an adaptation to danger which brings security from prying enemies. Wasps are rather unpleasant creatures and to be avoided. They have a vicious sting. If a harmless sort of insect wanted to elude its enemies it could not do better than try to look like a wasp. Accordingly a large number of

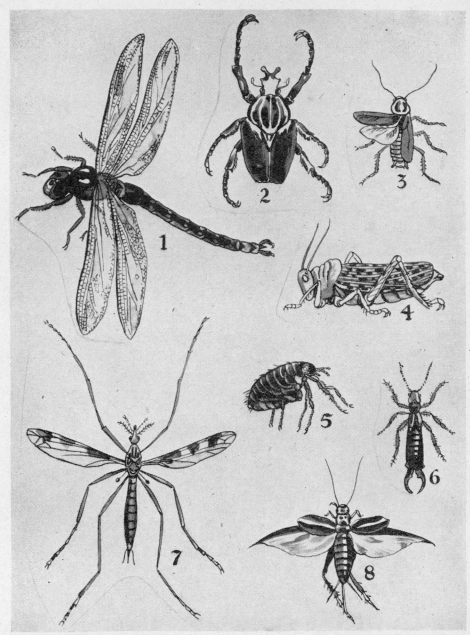

Fig. 21. *Insects, which are all arthropods. Notice in each case the hard external skeleton which houses the soft organs, and the segmentation which allows for the development of specialized organs. 1, Dragon fly; 2, burrowing beetle; 3, cockroach; 4, locust; 5, human flea; 6, earwig; 7, daddy long legs; 8, house cricket. The arthropods as a group, and particularly the insect class, are generally rather unpleasant animals from the human point of view. They are among the most active spreaders of disease and infection among both humans and other animals, and they are also responsible for a great deal of destruction of crops and food.*

harmless insects deck themselves out in black and yellow just like a wasp. Not that there has been any conscious attempt at imitation; the process must be envisaged somewhat as follows. One day an insect of a particular species was born that happened to look something like a wasp. The resemblance lengthened its life, because traditional enemies did not immediately recognize it. Consequently it propagated a larger number of descendants. Among these, those which looked most like wasps tended to survive longest. So by selection the species became more and more wasp-like in appearance in the process of time.

Ants and Termites

Ants also are rather fierce little arthropods. The East African grasshopper ensures its survival by resembling an ant when it is in the larval state and the leaf of the plant it lives on when fully adult. Some crustaceans resemble seaweeds. Plenty of other examples could be given.

One of the most fascinating developments in the insect world is the appearance of highly organized social communities. In ant societies, for example, there are slaves, fighters who have forgotten how to feed themselves, ants that turn themselves into reservoirs of honey for the community, sterile workers. The social development of the ant, bee (Fig. 22) and termite (Fig. 23) communities is, however, automatically regulated and appears to be entirely at the mercy of instinct. In effect it increases the size of the unit, and this increase makes for security and enlarges the possibilities of existence. But in the cause of the society the individual has to make an enormous sacrifice of its own freedom and individuality.

The hard external skeleton has put a limit to the size an arthropod can reach. After moulting, the arthropod has to make another skeleton, and if its body were too large the process would take a long time. The danger, to which so long a period

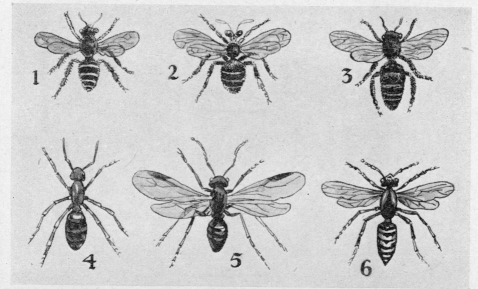

Fig. 22. *Bees and ants have developed an extraordinary system of living in communities whose individual members each have a highly specialized function, imposed on them by the automatic workings of instinct, and resulting in increased security for the whole group. 1, Working bee; 2, drone; 3, queen bee; 4, wood ant worker; 5, wood ant male; 6, wasp.*

of vulnerability would expose it, would appreciably lessen its chances of survival.

There are instances of arthropods which have gone back in development. Sacculina is a good illustration of degeneration. In its adult form it is little more than a reproductive sac which sucks the life out of its victim. This unpleasant parasite

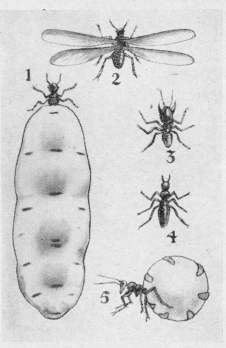

Fig. 23. *The termites also live in highly-organized and specialized social communities. 1, Queen termite; 2, male; 3, soldier; 4, worker; 5, honey-ant.*

would hardly be recognizable as an arthropod if it were not that the larva which hatches out of the egg resembles a perfectly good crustacean, having a skeleton and jointed limbs like any other crustacean. The larval form repeats the traditional story. It resembles the ancestral stock infinitely more closely than does the adult. Among the higher animals, development of the embryo often gives us a valuable clue to the course of their evolutionary history.

We have now come a long way from

paramœcium, hydra, planaria. Throughout this sequence we have seen an increase in complexity and in organization; a great experimentation in form and activity. It would seem as though we are quite justified in describing this as progress. There are, it is true, instances of retrogression, such as sacculina, but these are rare, and only serve to throw up more clearly the main line of development, which steadily proceeds from the simple to the more complex.

Molluscs and Echinoderms

There are two other invertebrate families to which reference may be made —namely, the molluscs and the echinoderms. The molluscs include oysters, whelks, mussels, scallops (Fig. 24), cuttle-fish and octopuses (Fig. 25). They have shells and their blood is pale blue, but they are not segmented. The scallop, for example, looks rather as if its organs had been laid out on a plate. It is one of the bivalve molluscs which keep the two halves of their shell closed by a very powerful muscle. Snails and slugs move about on a muscular foot. The foot of the cuttle-fish and the octopus has been modified into a number of flexible and strong arms, or tentacles. In order to put its enemies off the scent the cuttle-fish can change colour rapidly as it swims away. If this fails, it goes dead white and at the same time ejects a dark fluid, sepia, in order further to mislead its pursuer. Some varieties of octopus reach a formidable size—as much as thirty feet or more across the outstretched arms.

Another of Nature's experiments is the echinoderms, typified by the starfish. They are radially symmetrical (Fig. 25), but the form of the larva shows definitely that they once came from a bilateral stock, thus affording yet another example of how the origin of a species may be traced in its biological development. The individual in its growth to adulthood repeats the main characteristics of its

Fig. 24. *Scallops are members of the mollusc family, another group of animals without backbones. Like the arthropods, they have shells and their blood is pale blue, but their bodies are not segmented. The scallop keeps the two halves of its shell closed by a powerful muscle.*

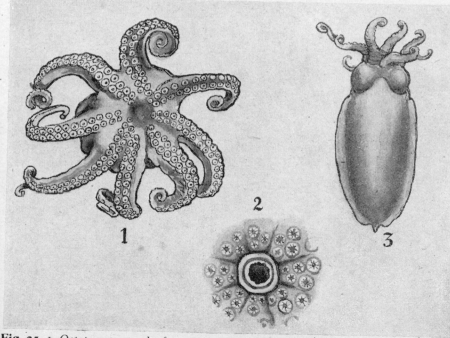

Fig. 25. *1, Octopus; 2, mouth of octopus; 3, cuttle-fish. Although these creatures, which are of the family of the molluscs, are radially symmetrical, the form of the larva shows that they once came from a bilateral stock. They are among the most highly developed of non-vertebrate creatures. Some varieties of octopus reach a formidable size—as much as thirty feet across*

ancestry. Sea urchins, sea stars and brittle stars are further examples of echinoderms (Figs. 26 and 27).

Molluscs, echinoderms and arthropods represent experiments along different lines with the cœlomate structure. One cannot say that any one of these phyla is higher than another, though the arthropods are the most successful in numbers and in enterprise.

Beginning of Vertebrates

At some point in this exuberant production of animal forms a very primitive and simple, bilaterally symmetrical and segmented creature started off an experiment that has ended in the species *Homo sapiens*. The earliest vertebrate probably resembled the tiny shore-living animal known as amphioxus (Fig. 28), or the lancelet. Amphioxus has a number of vertebrate features. It possesses a tail,

that is, a muscular extension of its body beyond the anus. All invertebrates come to an end at the anus or exit of the digestive tract. The development of a muscular tail was an important evolutionary move.

Amphioxus has also a spinal cord of nerve tissue down its back, and, most important of all, a stiff rod running the whole length of the body between the spinal cord of nerve tissue and the digestive tract. This rod, called the notochord, is the forerunner of our backbone. A rod like the notochord of amphioxus develops in the embryos of all vertebrate animals: fish, reptiles, birds, mammals. On either side of this solid axis, muscles are attached, and, compared with a worm, amphioxus has a very well-developed muscular apparatus.

Bilateral symmetry, which will give a right and a left, a back and a front, is

Fig. 26. *Echinoderms. 1, Sea urchin; 2, starfish; 3, brittle star. Echinoderms resemble arthropods and vertebrates in the possession of a body cavity. They have also a quite highly-developed nervous system. The name echinoderm means "prickle-skinned," denoting one of their principal characteristics, which is especially pronounced in the make-up of the sea urchins.*

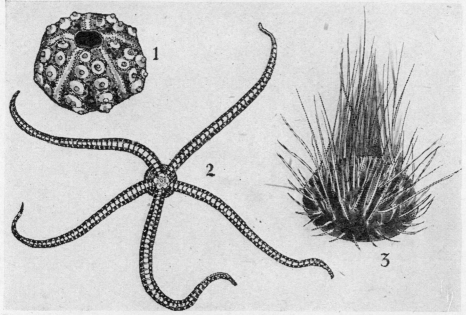

Fig. 27. *1 and 3, Sea urchins; 2, starfish. The echinoderms are not a very familiar form of life, but they play a large part in the economy of Nature. They have built up huge masses of rock; and they fill a valuable role as scavengers of the ocean.*

apparently necessary for active and quick movement. It is unnecessary to stress the advantages in both fight and flight which speed and power give their possessors in a world largely made up of adversaries. Another structure which amphioxus possesses is a perforated pharynx or throat. Water is whisked into the pharynx by cilia on its surface, passes out through the holes in the pharynx into the space round it and then goes through a further exit into the surrounding water. This is a mechanism for use in trapping food particles, foreshadowing the gills of the fish.

Amphioxus has no recognizable head, no heart—though it has a contracting blood vessel—and a mere pouch of gut to act as a liver: in fact, it can be regarded as no more than a first rough sketch which gave Nature ideas for some of her grandest designs. As Professors Haldane and Huxley say: "It (amphioxus) serves to remind us of a time long before that of

the earliest fossils preserved to us now, when none of the chordate (that is, animals possessing a notochord) stock had reached a higher organization than this; and all the highest types of life—bird, horse, lion, dog and man himself—were no more than a potentiality slumbering in the germ cells of little amphioxus-like creatures in the sea."

Other Primitive Vertebrates

There are other primitive chordates of a more curious nature. The sea-squirt (Fig. 29), which is a shore-living beast, is a tubular jelly-like mass which at a glance looks as little like a vertebrate as a sea anemone. But the larva of the sea-squirt is a free swimming chordate, built on the amphioxus plan. Some of the near relations of the sea-squirts reproduce by budding and in this way they contrive to build up a colonial system.

Another primitive chordate, balano-glossus, resembles in its larval form the

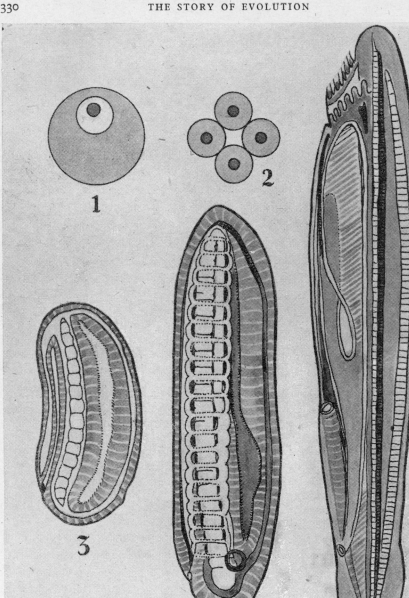

Fig. 28. *Amphioxus or lancelet. This tiny shore-living animal is the type of the earliest vertebrates. It possesses a spinal cord of nerve tissue down its back, and also a stiff rod, called the notochord, running the whole length of the body. This is the forerunner of our backbone. A similar rod develops in the embryo of all vertebrates. To this notochord, a well-developed muscular system is attached. The illustration shows the stages in amphioxus' growth. 1, Stem-cell; 2, ovum in segmentation; 3, young larva; 4, older larva; 5, adult amphioxus.*

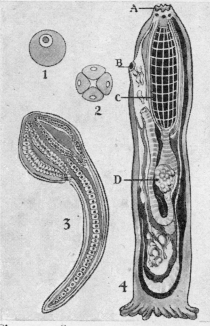

Fig. 29. *Sea-squirt, another primitive vertebrate. 1, Cell; 2, cell in segmentation; 3, larva; 4, adult. (A) Mouth. (B) Anus. (C) Gills. (D) Ova. Notice the developed notochord, or primitive backbone, in the larval stage of the sea-squirt's development.*

echinoderms. This suggests that both echinoderms and vertebrates branched off from a common stock, and supplies a link between vertebrates and invertebrates. A very curious experiment was once done with developing eggs of the echinoderm sea urchin (Figs. 26 and 27). The eggs were brought up in sea water from which all calcium had been removed. The effect of this was that when each egg began dividing into two, and then into four, eight, sixteen, thirty-two cells and so on—just as we all begin life—the cells, instead of sticking together, separated and swam about freely just as if they were flagellate protozoa. They reverted to type, that is to say, they regressed to a form of existence which their stock had put behind them for millions of years before these individuals existed.

The next stage in vertebrate com-

plexity is shown by the lamprey (Fig. 30), which shows an advance on amphioxus in that it has a brain, a sort of skull, a heart and a liver. It has no teeth and no limbs, and though a long way ahead of amphioxus, is still a long way behind the fish. A very interesting point about the lamprey is that in it the thyroid gland makes its first appearance. In the larva of the lamprey there is a groove in the floor of the throat: in the adult the cells in this floor become, so to speak, rolled up and shut off from the throat. These cells form the thyroid gland.

In man the thyroid gland is normally located on either side of the windpipe in the neck, but occasionally it appears at the back of the tongue, where it began at the lamprey stage of vertebrate development.

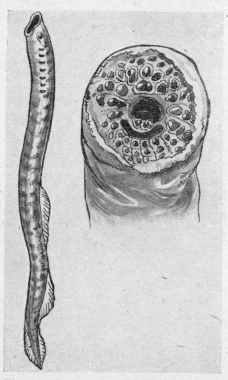

Fig. 30. *Lamprey and mouth of lamprey. This animal is a further stage in vertebrate development, showing an advance on amphioxus by possessing brain, heart and liver.*

Fig. 31. *Dogfish; inset* A, *egg-case with embryo. This represents the more primitive group of fish, those without any bone in their skeleton (elasmobranchs). The dogfish is modelled on the same lines as the mammal, possessing head, eyes and nostrils, and two sets of paired fins.*

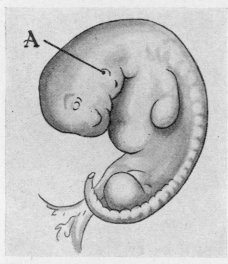

Fig. 32. *Human embryo at fifth week of growth.* (A) *Gill slits. These develop in the human embryo exactly as in the fish; the first slit separates from the others during the period of foetal growth and becomes the passage connecting the ear with outside.*

We pass on to fish. This great phylum is divided into two main groups, the lower group of the elasmobranchs, or those without any bone in their skeleton, and the teleosts, or bony fish.

The first and more primitive group is represented by the dogfish (Fig. 31). This has a head, eyes, nostrils and gill slits at the side of the throat. The first gill slit differs from the others. It opens just behind the eye, passes close to the inner ear and ends up in the mouth. In mammals the outer ear leads by a short tube to the middle ear, being separated from it by the ear drum. On the other side of the drum the middle ear leads via the Eustachian tube to the back of the throat. This ear passage from outside to inside developed from the first gill slit. That this is so is shown by the fact that during individual development of the embryo mammal, gill slits are formed (Fig. 32), the first of which separates off from the others and gives rise to the ear passage. The tubular ear passage of the mammal is thus comparable with the first gill slit of the fish. Both are formed from a common anatomical ground plan.

The dogfish has two sets of paired fins, the first pair being just below the last gill slit and the second on either side of the anus. These correspond to our arms and legs. It breathes by taking water through the mouth and passing it over the gills, which extract oxygen from it. The notochord of amphioxus (Fig. 28) has given place to a jointed backbone, which houses the nervous spinal cord, and this is continuous with a brain lodged inside the skull. Even down to minute details, the dogfish is modelled on the same lines as the mammal. As H. G. Wells says in his *Science of Life* ". . . if we had a model dogfish made of plasticine we could twist and stretch and bend it bit by bit, increasing the quantity at this point perhaps and diminishing it at that,

but adding nothing essentially new, until we had a very passable model mammal. . . ."

The skin of a dogfish is very rough. If it is examined closely it is found to have little spines or denticles modelled exactly like teeth, with enamel on the outside, then dentine, and a pulp cavity through which enter blood vessels and nerves. The dogfish is in fact covered with miniature teeth. The true teeth of the mammal have developed from the rough skin covering the jaws of the dogfish.

The bony fish made an advance on the non-bony or gristly fish when they developed a gas bladder or swim bladder (Fig. 33). This enabled them to deal with the problem of gravity and devote themselves to streamlining and developing powerful muscles. Their heavy bulk tended to carry them to the bottom of the sea unless they continually expended an enormous amount of energy in fighting the attraction of gravity. The development of what may be called internal

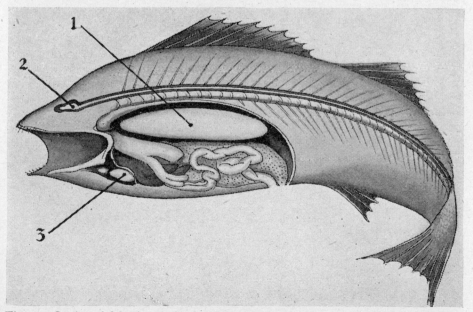

Fig. 33. *Section of fish of more developed type, possessing bones in their skeleton (teleosts). 1, Swim bladder; 2, brain; 3, heart. Notice how the brain, as in mammals (including man) is a continuation of the spinal cord. The swim bladder, a sort of internal balloon, is another development in this group which played an important part in the evolution of land animals.*

balloons was a most ingenious device on the part of Nature. It not only gave buoyancy, but enabled the fish, by altering the pressure, to move at a desired level in the sea, or to rise to the surface as it pleased (Fig. 34).

But the over-riding importance of the gas bladder lay in the fact that it made it possible for the vertebrate phylum to experiment with living on the land. There are found today in Australia, Africa and South America what are called lung fish (Fig. 35). During conditions of drought these fish find themselves stranded on dry land, but unlike other fish they do not die, because they are capable of taking air into their gas bladders and of extracting oxygen from it. In other words, whenever faced by this emergency, they breathe. It is possible that in the first place the gas bladder appeared in the fish world as an adaptation to drought conditions in freshwater surroundings, that it was subsequently exploited as a balancing and depth organ, and later used again as an aid to the creatures permanent survival on land.

The larva of a lung fish looks for all the world like a tadpole, and the tadpole is itself, in appearance and habits, a living reminder of the fact that land vertebrates evolved from water vertebrates.

Leaving the Water

The possibility of leaving the water for the dry land was provided for by the development of the gas bladder in bony fish. Some of these lung fish went on being lung fish, normally living in the sea but capable of existing on land. Others went back to the sea again and used their lungs as internal floats—an adventure which proved highly successful. Others became permanent inhabitants of the land. We have no record of just how this was done. Having mastered the breathing of air, these early land fish would have to learn how to pull themselves along, to crawl, with the aid of their fins. Something of how this became possible is

Fig. 34. *Deep water fish coming to the surface. This illustrates the use of the swim bladder. The heavy bulk of the bony fish tended to carry them to the bottom of the sea. The development of the swim bladder, however, gave them buoyancy, and also enabled the fish, by altering the gas pressure of the bladder, to move at a desired level in the sea, or rise to the surface.*

Fig. 35. *Lung-fish. This animal, which is found today in Australia, Africa and South America, represents the earliest type of animal which was able to live on land. This is possible for it because when stranded on dry land by drought, it is capable of taking air into its swim bladder and extracting oxygen from it. In other words, it can breathe.*

shown by the living fish called the mud hopper, which crawls about on the mud by means of its very muscular fins.

We have already shown that the embryo which leads an independent existence (the larva) often betrays the origin of the adult. The frog is an excellent illustration of this. It sheds its eggs into the water, and these hatch out into free swimming larvæ known as tadpoles (Fig. 36). The tadpole is much more a fish than a frog. It breathes by means of gills and gill slits, it swims with its tail, and its internal organs are laid down on fish-like lines. In developing into a frog, it scraps its fish-like organs and grows its frog-like land-living organs. Gills and tail disappear, various internal organs are reconstructed, lungs grow, arms and legs appear.

The interesting discovery has been made that this change of tadpole into frog is regulated by the secretion of the thyroid gland. If, for example, you give a young tadpole an extract of thyroid gland, you can accelerate the change at a great rate and produce very miniature frogs. On the other hand, if the thyroid gland of the tadpole is removed—and this has been done—the metamorphosis into a frog never takes place; the tadpole goes on being a tadpole and grows to a size never attained by normal tadpoles. It remains an overgrown baby. It will be remembered that essentially the same arrest of growth is effected in the human being by absence of or deficiency in the thyroid gland.

Frogs and Men

The adult frog is only partially adapted to a dry life. Its skin is fine and moist and must be kept moist, or the animal will die. In its fundamental structure

(Figs. 37 and 38) the frog has everything we have. Like ourselves, it is built on the vertebrate plan. We both have brains and a spinal cord, housed respectively in the skull and the spinal column and forming the central nervous system. Its vertebræ, like ours, are jointed. We both have a liver, two kidneys and a spleen. We both have fore-limbs and hind-limbs, eyes, ears and nostrils, and they all appear in similar positions. The frog, like us, has one bone in the upper arm corresponding with the humerus, and two in the lower arm, corresponding with the radius and the ulna. It has wrist bones and five fingers and toes. There are, of course, differences of shape, degree and function; otherwise frogs would be men, and men frogs. For example, the frog breathes through its skin as well as through its lungs.

The axolotl (Fig. 39) is a very odd amphibian which lives perpetually in a larval form. Inhabiting the dry Mexican plateau, it finds life in the water infinitely preferable to life on land. So it keeps its gills and reproduces itself as a gilled water-living beast. But if some thyroid extract is given to the axolotl it will turn into a perfectly mature adult salamander. This perpetual immaturity is an astonishing example of adaptation to difficult conditions. If the axolotl, ages back, had not discovered the device of holding up its secretion of thyroid, it would probably have become extinct.

The Reptiles

The reptiles advanced beyond the amphibians by learning how to breathe entirely through the lungs. Thus they did away with a restrictive dependence on water and moist conditions, though the fondness for water of most reptiles reveals their close relationship with the amphibian. Some, such as the crocodile, have

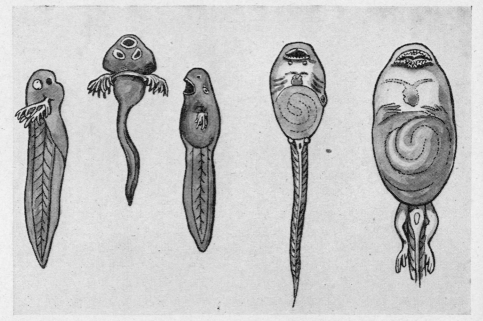

Fig. 36. *Tadpoles and more advanced frogs' larvæ. The tadpole, or immature frog, is in many ways more of a fish than a frog, and thus is an illustration of the fact that land vertebrates evolved from water vertebrates. It breathes by means of gills and gill slits, it swims with its tail, and its internal organs are laid down on fish-like lines.*

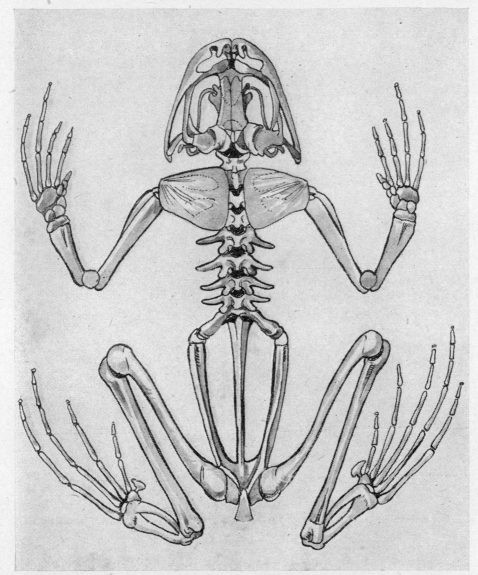

Fig. 37. *Skeleton of frog. As the tadpole develops into a frog, it gets rid of its fish-like organs, and becomes a land-living animal. The gills and tail which were necessary to it as a water animal disappear, and it develops lungs, arms and legs. In its fundamental structure, the frog has exactly the same sort of body as man.   Notice the jointed vertebræ, the spinal column, which houses the spinal cord and is connected with the skull, the arm with one large bone in its upper part and two in its lower part, the wrist bones and the five fingers and toes on each hand and foot. It also has a liver, two kidneys and a spleen, in similar positions to those which these organs occupy in man. It is of interest that the change from tadpole to frog is regulated by the secretion of the thyroid gland, which plays a similar part in human development. If a young tadpole is given a thyroid extract it rapidly changes into a miniature frog. If the tadpole's thyroid gland is removed it never becomes a frog at all.*

taken almost completely to the water again. But so has the whale, which is a mammal. Every advance made by Nature can show such regressions. A further advance was made when they shifted their limbs so that they became supports for their body. The reptiles were the first genuine land creatures, and once upon a time they dominated the world as completely as we dominate it now. Today there only exist the four orders represented by the crocodile, the tortoise, the snake, and the sphenodon. Twenty other orders have become extinct.

Yet another device which helped to make the reptile independent of the water was the development of the amnion, a water cushion within the egg which allows the embryo to develop in fluid, and to be protected from pressure. The amphibian frog sheds its eggs naked into the water.

The reptile found a solution to the problem of the fluid environment required by the embryo by forming the water inside an egg protected by a shell. The human mother, though in common with other mammals she has discarded the egg method, has inherited the same water forming device.

The Tuatara

The fourth class of reptile to which we referred above was sphenodon or the New Zealand tuatara (Fig. 40). This astonishing animal is looked upon as the oldest surviving type of land vertebrate. It is found only in New Zealand, and it dates back to the end of the Palæozoic period, in the Permian epoch. (Oldest surviving types of animals are common in New Zealand and Australia. On the theory that animals have evolved from ancestral types,

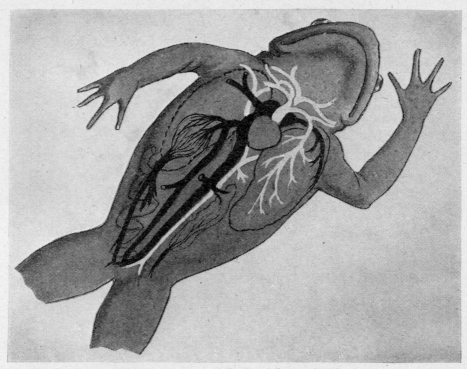

Fig. 38. *Circulatory system of the frog. Like its skeleton, the blood system of the frog is fundamentally similar to that of man; the same system of arteries and veins appears in approximately the same positions and functions in precisely the same way.*

Fig. 39. *Axolotl. This animal is an amphibian, found in Mexico, which normally never emerges from its larval form. Life is easier for it in water than it would be on land, so it retains its water-living features and reproduces itself as a gilled, water-living beast. If, however, it is given thyroid extract, it becomes a perfectly mature adult salamander.*

this is not surprising, as these countries were separated from the main land masses millions of years ago). One of tuatara's features is that it has a quite well-developed third eye behind and between the usual two. This is known as the pineal eye, and is represented in us by the pineal gland, a small stalked structure lying on the roof of the brain.

Development of Birds

Both birds and mammals are believed to have developed from reptiles. There is some interesting evidence in support of this belief. Birds resemble reptiles in many ways. For example, they lay large yolked eggs covered with a shell, inside which embryos have the comforting support of the amnion. But they differ in many ways. The scales of the reptile have given way to feathers. Birds, unlike both reptiles and amphibians, are warm blooded and take more care of their young. Their forelimbs have been modified into wings, and only one finger or digit projects freely

from the front border of the wing (Fig. 41). The tail has been shortened and modified to form a bone which supports the tail feathers. Teeth have been replaced by a beak. The lungs of birds communicate with air sacs which burrow into different parts of the bird's body, into the bones, along the neck, among the viscera. These air sacs extend to the surface for breathing and they also lighten the body and help to streamline it.

Fortunately the remains of the earliest known bird have been preserved in the rocks. These indicate clearly a reptilian ancestry. Archæopteryx, as this bird is called, was found in the Upper Jurassic rocks of Bavaria. The fine lithographic stone composing this stratum is well suited to preserve the detail even of feathers. Archæopteryx was about the size of a rook. It had feathers and bird-like wings. But instead of only one projecting digit on the front edge of the wing, it had three. Its tail was like that of a lizard and consisted of twenty separate vertebræ each carrying

Fig. 40. *Tuatara. This reptile (found only in New Zealand, where many primitive animals survive, as a result of its separation from the main land masses millions of years ago) is thought to be the oldest surviving type of land vertebrate. Among other unusual features, tuatara possesses a third eye between the usual pair. This survives in humans, in atrophied form, as the pineal gland, a small stalked structure which lies on the roof of the brain.*

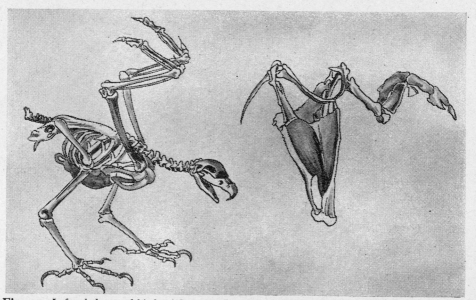

Fig. 41. *Left, skeleton of bird; right, scapula of bird. Birds are believed to have developed from reptiles, but have changed in many ways. The skeleton shows the same fundamental structure, but limbs have been modified into wings, teeth replaced by a beak and scales by feathers. However, the fossil remains of the earliest known bird, archæopteryx, have many reptilian features. This creature possessed a long jointed tail like a lizard's, and a good set of teeth.*

a pair of feathers. And it had a perfectly good set of teeth. Archæopteryx was mostly bird but partly reptile. The long jointed tail, the teeth, and the clawed fingers show reptilian affinities.

Mammals are so called because they have mammæ, or breasts, with which they suckle their young. The monotremes—of which there are two living examples, the spiny ant-eater and duck-billed platypus (*see* CHAPTER XIII)—are links between reptiles and mammals. They, like mammals, suckle their young and are covered with hair. But, like reptiles, they lay eggs. Their brains are rather reptiles' brains, as are parts of their skeleton. They have one bone in their skeleton which is typically found in reptiles and is present in no other mammal. They find it difficult to maintain their blood at a constant temperature.

The monotremes exist only in Australia, where also are found the animals which nourish their young in a pouch formed in the belly wall—the marsupials, of which the kangaroo (Fig. 42) is a familiar example. The young kangaroo is born blind and, so to speak, prematurely. So it has to be protected in the mother kangaroo's pouch. The marsupials are primitive mammals which differ in many other ways, apart from the possession of a pouch, from the higher animals.

Placental Mammals

The third division of mammals, the placental mammals, are more advanced than the marsupials in brain development, but also and chiefly in the development of the placenta. When the embryo of the placental mammal grows in the uterus or womb, it remains attached by the umbilical cord to the wall of the vesicle in which it grows. This vesicle, called the chorion, expands into the cavity of the uterus. But at one point, opposite the attachment of the umbilical cord, it fuses with the wall of the uterus, dovetailing into it. Here the blood vessels of the embryo are separated from the blood vessels of the mother only

by a thin partition, through which the embryo is nourished. This union of embryo and maternal uterus is called the placenta. When the embryo is born, the placenta is separated from it and is later discharged from the womb. The important thing about the placenta is that it enables the embryo to stay a longer time inside the mother and thus to reach a fairly high stage of maturity before it is born. This longer protection affords a greatly increased security to the young and thus avoids the

Fig. 42. *Kangaroo. Like New Zealand, Australia has many primitive animal types. One of these is the marsupials, a primitive mammal which carries its young in a pouch.*

necessity for the wasteful proliferation of, say, the herring, which spawns in millions.

The placental mammals may be divided into four great categories: the hoofed mammals or ungulates (e.g., horses, pigs, deer, goats, sheep, elephants); unguiculates or clawed mammals (rabbits, rats, moles, cats, dogs, seals, walruses); cetaceans, or wholly aquatic mammals (dolphins, porpoises, whales); and lastly the primates, which includes lemurs, monkeys, apes, and man. The primates are distinguished by the great development of the brain and the astonishing use made of the hand, which curiously enough is in them a very primitive, almost reptilian structure. It is vastly more primitive than the hoof of a horse, which has become specialized for one kind of activity.

In tracing this continuous story of the increasing complexity of living things we have indicated an important part of the evidence for evolution. Here and there have appeared clear links between one group of animals and another more highly specialized group. The development of the embryo gives valuable clues to the history of the adult form. Life, we see, has become marvellously adapted to all manners of living in sea, on land and in the air. It has radiated out in all directions. There has been progressive mastery by living forms of the problems set by the physical and chemical structure of the world, a mastery which has reached impressive proportions in the primate man.

Evidence of Fossils

But the reader will want more evidence of evolution than has yet been given him. The various manifestations of life have been roughly sketched out. It has been shown how living things can be conveniently classed together on the basis of similarities and how they can be separated on the basis of dissimilarities. It has been shown, too, how many old life features survive in the most highly organized mammal. Occasionally, human beings, for example, are born with tails (every human embryo at one stage has one), with a persistent gill slit, with muscles that are normally only found in monkeys, and so forth. All vertebrates have on the roof of the brain a pineal body, which is the vestige of a second pair of eyes the very earliest vertebrate stock is thought to have possessed. Sphenodon gives us the hint here.

We have also indicated in the note on archæopteryx how valuable is the evidence provided by the fossil. It is to this evidence, as it is told in the story of the rocks, we shall now turn. Archbishop Ussher, it will be remembered, was rash enough some

300 years ago to date the creation of the world as 4004 B.C. But it became increasingly clear to scientists during the eighteenth and nineteenth centuries that this was a fantastic underestimate. If evolution really had taken place by the gradual development of simple forms of life into more complicated forms, the time required for this must have been truly colossal. Many estimates were made on various hypotheses, and finally a reasonably secure basis for calculation was secured when Madame Curie discovered radium in 1898.

Radio-Activity

Radio-active substances are substances of great atomic weight which are continually breaking down by radiating out particles known as alpha particles and beta particles. The former consist of the nuclei of the helium atom and the latter are electrons. At the same time a gamma ray is also given out which is the same as the X-ray. In this process of radiation there is a transformation of one atom into another. The heaviest of all atoms and the parent atom of all natural radio-active substances is uranium. After losing so many particles uranium changes into radium which, carrying on the radio-active process, eventually becomes lead. Lead undergoes no further change; its atoms are stable. But lead resulting from the disintegration of a radio-active substance has a different atomic weight from that of ordinary lead.

Geological Clocks

The life of these radio-active substances varies from less than one eleven-hundredth of a second to thousands of millions of years, uranium having the longest life of all. Their disintegration proceeds in a perfectly regular way. Their length of life is fixed and definite. They are therefore excellent geological clocks. If, for example, we take a stratum of radio-active rock we can by calculating the proportion of helium and lead to the uranium in it gauge accurately its age. The physicists have thus

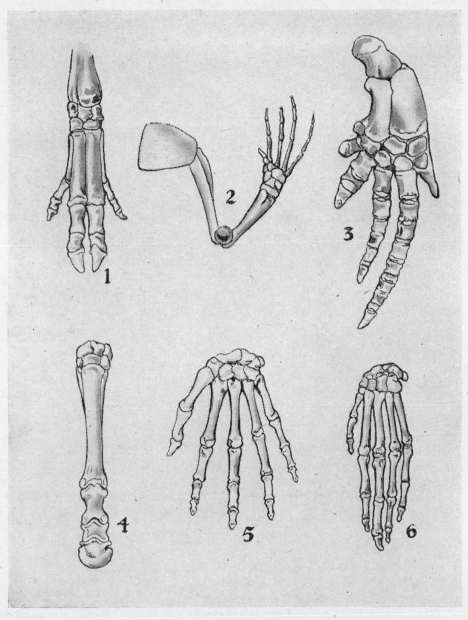

Fig. 43. *The study of comparative anatomy is often a useful guide to the development of features in individual species. The illustration shows the extremities of various mammals, indicating that they are nearly all built on the same plan, and suggesting that in the case of the horse, the modern one-toed foot must have developed from a limb which originally had five toes, the other four toes having gradually retrogressed. 1, Foot of pig; 2, leg of frog; 3, right fore-limb of whale; 4, foot of horse; 5, hand of man; 6, hand of chimpanzee. All the animals shown are mammals, but the same ground plan is also characteristic of amphibians and reptiles. Theories suggested by comparative anatomy are supported by the fossil evidence.*

been able to confirm the theory that the earth is quite old enough for there to have been plenty of time in which life could evolve through the gradual process from the simple to the complex.

There are ways of checking the radio-active calculations, such as by estimating the rate of land erosion and of deposition of sediment. We have already mentioned that the chalk cliffs of Dover are to a large extent formed by the shells of the little flagellate foraminifera. The strata of which the cliffs are composed were laid down under the sea. The skeletons of tiny animals and plants are perpetually dropping in a fine shower to the floor of the ocean. For millions of years this deposition of sediment has been going on. In the course of time, it results in what we know as the sedimentary or stratified rocks.

Rock Strata

In these rocks, as is well known, fossils of all kinds can be found. The gradual and gentle method of their deposition is emi-nently favourable to the preservation of at least the imprint of indissoluble substances. Two main points emerge from an exami-nation of such rocks: the higher animals are never found in the oldest strata, and the remains of certain types of life are con-fined to certain localities and layers. Further, the unfolding of the story of the rocks show that a gradual increase of com-plexity in their fossil contents occurs as the rock formations became more and more recent. At this point it will be oppor-tune to show diagrammatically what the various strata of rocks are and then to refer to the fossils found in them.

It is perhaps obvious that the oldest strata will as a rule be found beneath the younger, and that these strata have been built up by the continuous deposit of sedi-ment over millions of years. These sedi-mentary rocks are deposited on top of igneous rocks which were formed by the cooling of the molten matter of which the earth was originally composed. Shrinkage

of the earth's surface, volcanic upheavals and ice ages have all helped to make things difficult for the geologist by tilting and turning upside down and grinding down and cracking nice orderly layers. But with great patience and skill the story has been in part at least pieced together. The chief divisions of geological time are called eras, and each era is divided into epochs or periods. Most of the coal in the world, for example, was deposited towards the end of the Palæozoic era in the Carboniferous epoch. The duration of each epoch is estimated by the thickness of the stratum which represents it. The relative thick-nesses of each era and epoch are approxi-mately as shown in the diagram opposite.

Below the stratified rocks there is a mass of rock which appears to have been origin-ally sedimentary but which has probably been considerably altered as the result of pressure and heat. These pre-Cambrian rocks represent an immense age. If we date, as in the diagram, the beginning of the Cambrian epoch as 500 million years ago, the beginning of the Proterozoic era has been given as 1,100 millions of years ago. Life dawned before this, in the Archæozoic era.

Evolution of Horse

Before we discuss the various inhabit-ants of the different epochs and eras, we may perhaps trace the evolution of the horse, as shown by the fossil record, since this provides a useful picture of an orderly progression from one form to another. The horse has a complete fossil pedigree behind it, extending over some forty million years.

The comparative study of anatomy, which shows us that the limb of amphibian, reptile, and mammal, is built on the same plan (Fig. 43), suggests that the modern one-toed horse must have developed from an original five-toed animal, and that through millions of years the other four toes have slowly retrogressed (Fig. 44). The story of the rocks supports this assumption very neatly, and in its own

Era	Period/Epoch	M.Y.	Age of	Palaeozoic	Event	Event
CAENOZOIC	Pliocene	10				Pithecanthropus erectus
	Miocene	17½	AGE OF MAMMALS			
	Oligocene	30				
	Eocene	50				Separation of N. America from the old world
					Appearance of primates	
MESOZOIC	Cretaceous		AGE OF REPTILES			Australia and S. America separated from main land mass
					True flowers appear	
	Jurassic				Archæopteryx, the oldest bird	
	Triassic	175			Mammal-like reptiles in this and in the previous epoch	
PALAEOZOIC	Permian		AGE OF AMPHIBIANS	LATE PALAEOZOIC	Oldest reptiles in this epoch and later part of the Carboniferous	
					Diversity of amphibians	
	Carboniferous					Formation of coal-measures
	Devonian		AGE OF FISHES	MID-PALAEOZOIC	Footprint of ? amphibian	By this time green plants with roots and stems were abundant. Spore-producing plants without roots
					Earliest fossil fish	First land plants evolved from seaweeds
	Silurian				Arthropods take to land	
	Ordovician		AGE OF INVERTEBRATES	EARLY PALAEOZOIC	Earliest fossil chordate	
	Cambrian	500				

individual development the horse tells the same ancestral tale. The embryo horse has three distinct toes. As the embryo develops, the middle toe grows rapidly at the expense of the other two. In the adult horse these two toes that are left behind in the race appear as two small splint bones attached to the cannon bone.

Horse Fossils

The earliest fossil of a horse was found in the strata of the Eocene period (Fig. 45). This animal was much smaller than the modern horse (Fig. 46). It had a shorter neck. Its teeth had not such efficient grinding surfaces, necessary for grass eating. And it had four toes. The fifth toe or "thumb" was represented by a splint bone. This retrogression of the fifth toe was more complete in the hind feet. In both fore feet and hind feet, the middle or third toe was already much larger than the others. Throughout the Eocene period fossil remains show a gradual diminution in the importance of toes. The last of the Eocene horses had four toes in the fore feet and three in the hind feet; and the side toes had become much smaller.

In the Oligocene epoch the four toes of the fore feet were reduced to three; in the Miocene epoch, when the horse tribe flourished and grew in size, the three toes remained, but those on either side of the middle one became very much smaller. By the Pliocene epoch, though the three-toed horse was still to be found, the modern one-toed horse had made its appearance and the two lateral toes had been reduced to splint bones.

These fossil discoveries present a clear and unequivocal picture of evolution actually in process. The purpose of the

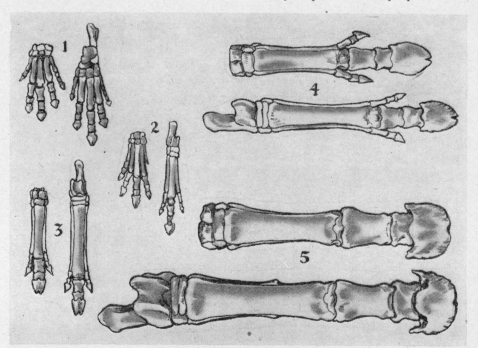

Fig. 44. *The suggestion derived from comparative anatomy that the horse is descended from an animal which originally possessed five toes is borne out by the evidence of fossils. The illustration shows a series of the feet of fossil horses in order of age, and indicates how this change has gradually been brought about. 1, Phenacodus (found in rocks of the Eocene epoch); 2, Protohippus (Eocene); 3, Mesohippus (Miocene); 4, Hipparion (Pliocene); 5, Horse.*

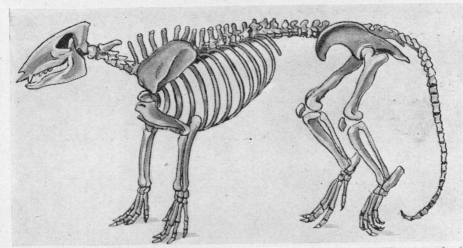

Fig. 45. *The earliest fossil of a horse. This fossil was found in rocks of the Eocene epoch, the first epoch in which mammals became the dominant form of life. This animal was much smaller than the modern horse. It had a shorter neck, and its teeth were not such efficient grinding weapons, which are necessary for grass surfaces. Note that it had four toes. Throughout the Eocene period, fossil remains show a gradual diminution in the importance of toes. The last of the Eocene horses had four toes in the fore feet and three in the hind feet.*

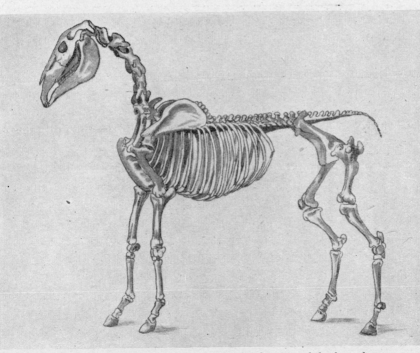

Fig. 46. *Skeleton of a modern horse. Notice the development of the foot, the purpose of which was to ensure speed in running over grassy plains. The first one-toed horse made its appearance in the Pliocene epoch, the most recent period of the three great geological eras.*

FOSSILS OF SEA-LILIES

These two large sea-lilies, found in Swabia, are about seven feet long, and pre-date mammals.

FOSSIL OF FISH

This is the fossil of a prehistoric fish with black metallic scales, found in the Swabian Jura.

development of the feet was to ensure speed in running over grassy plains, a necessity if enemies were to be evaded. Many similar serial records of the gradual evolution of animal form could be instanced.

Pre-Cambrian Fossils

C. D. Walcott discovered, ten thousand feet below the earliest sedimentary (Cambrian) rocks, fossil evidence of the existence of calcareous algæ. Above these were found worn trails and remains of crustacean-like creatures. Also in these pre-Cambrian rocks, Walcott found a bacterium. It seems clear that in the Proterozoic era, between 500 and 1,100 million years ago, life had evolved as far as most of the invertebrate phyla we recognize today. According to this evidence the evolution of unicellular life took place over eleven hundred million years ago.

On the geological diagram (page 345) the early Palæozoic era is marked as the Age of the Invertebrates. In the Cambrian epoch there were no vertebrates at all, the earliest possible forerunners of vertebrates being found in the latter part of the Ordovician epoch. In the Cambrian epoch not only were there no vertebrate animals;

there were not even land animals. None of the higher arthropods or molluscs had yet appeared. There were no spiders and no cuttle-fish. And the land was barren, for there were on it no plants with roots, seeds or flowers. The dominant living creatures in the Cambrian epoch were the trilobites (Fig. 47), primitive segmented arthropods. The trilobites radiated out into numerous species: they crawled, burrowed, swam, and made use of all sorts of devices for dealing with varying environmental problems. Predominant then, the trilobites have long since been extinct.

Sea-Scorpions

The trilobites declined towards the end of the Ordovician period, being outclassed by their contemporaries the sea-scorpions or eurypterids (Fig. 48). Traces of these have been found in pre-Cambrian rocks. But the hey-day of the eurypterids was in the Silurian epoch, and they attained a length of eight feet in the Devonian epoch. By the time of the Permian epoch the eurypterids had become extinct. They appear to have lived largely in fresh water.

The true scorpions (Fig. 51), which appeared towards the end of the Silurian epoch, are the first beasts known to have tried to live on land. The arthropods — a phylum which is still coping with life with conspicuous success— were not only the first to take to the land, but they have vigorously contested ever since every animal that has followed suit. We will not follow here the development of the echinoderms or the molluscs in detail, but merely note that the snail put the final twist into its spiral shell at the end of the Ordovician epoch,

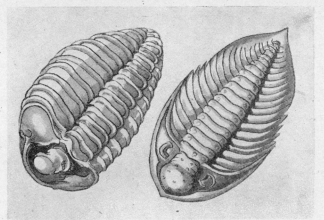

Fig. 47. *The dominant living creatures during the Cambrian epoch were the trilobites, which were primitive segmented arthropods; they have long been extinct. There were during this epoch no vertebrates and no land animals.*

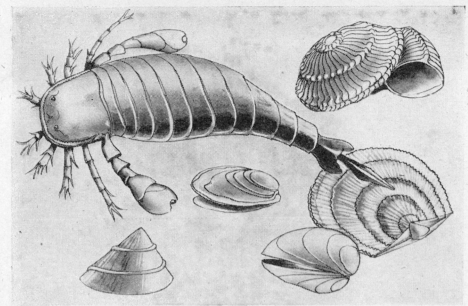

Fig. 48. *Molluscs and sea-scorpions, or eurypterids, of the Silurian epoch, the period during which the first land plants evolved from seaweed. Fossil traces of eurypterids have been found in earlier rocks but the Silurian epoch was their hey-day. They lived in fresh water, and at their largest attained a length of eight feet. They have long been extinct.*

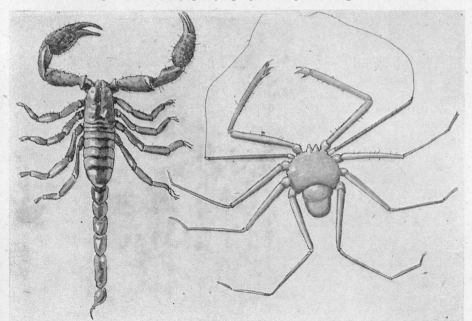

Fig. 49. *The true scorpions (left, scorpion; right, African whip scorpion) are the first beasts which are known to have attempted to live on land. They appeared, according to the fossil evidence, towards the end of the Silurian epoch. Scorpions in various forms are still extant.*

and that those highly advanced molluscs, the modern cuttle-fish and octopuses, did not work out their destiny until the Mesozoic era.

The advance on to the land had to wait upon a prior conquest of the soil by the plant world. Without the mysterious co-operation of chlorophyll a successful life cannot be led. The first land plants appeared near the end of the Silurian epoch, and by the middle of the Devonian epoch green plants with root and stem were abundant (Fig. 50), and the earliest forests were in being. The Carboniferous period was rich in the vegetation which, fossilized, became coal (Fig. 51). The true flowering plants did not come into existence until the early Cretaceous epoch.

Flowers and Insects

Hand in hand with the growth and development of the true flowers there went an enormous development of the insects. The two, so to speak, went into partnership. In exchange for a little sweetened water, the insects assisted the reproductive life of the flowers by transporting pollen from one to the other. Flowers have gone to all lengths to attract insects. One orchid has adopted the strange device of smelling like a female ichneumon fly. The male ichneumon fly, eternally deceived, attempts to mate with the orchid and in the process of making this attempt, he deposits orchid pollen on the orchid stigma.

The Reptile Age

The story of the rocks is too long to tell at length here, but something must be said about that fantastic era, the Mesozoic, between 50 and 175 millions of years ago, when the reptiles dominated all life and reached out into a wide variety of activity. The reptiles which survive today give no idea of the magnificence and pride of the great reptilian orders that vanished in a geological night. Fossil remains in Mesozoic strata tell a dramatic and at times slightly macabre story of the insolent

abundance and adventures of the reptilian giants which lorded the earth for some hundred million years.

The reptile evolved from the amphibian and cut itself loose from the latter's dependence upon a watery environment. Its tough skin, preventing loss of water, its shelled egg and the amnion, made its survival certain in the circumstances attending the opening of the Mesozoic era, when

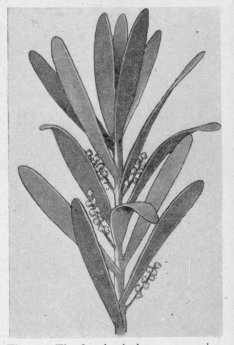

Fig. 50. *The first land plants appeared towards the end of the Silurian epoch. The illustration shows a green plant called cordaites, of the Devonian epoch.*

the swamps and damp forests were being shrivelled by colder and drier conditions. The dinosaurs formed the principal land group. They walked mainly on their hind feet. Some of them hopped like kangaroos; others ran, employing their long tails as counter-balancing structures to their long necks. Others used their tails as a support, just as the sportsman uses a shooting stick. Some of the dinosaurs became vegetarians; some became carnivores and attacked their

Fig. 51. *Animal life on land was not possible until there was a comparatively abundant plant life on land, since the respiratory systems of animal and plant are complementary to each other. The illustration shows plants of the Carboniferous period; it was this vegetation which fossilized became coal. There were, however, no true flowering plants until very much later.*

M.H.B.—M

vegetarian brethren. The vegetarians protected themselves by growing larger and developing hides resembling armour. The carnivores also grew larger, and grew even more vicious teeth. They evolved increasingly formidable modes of attack. The giant tyrannosaur held its head twenty feet above ground; another dinosaur had a tail forty feet long, while its body and neck extended for another forty feet in the opposite direction!

Flying Reptiles

Dolphin-shaped ichthyosaurs (Fig. 52) adapted themselves to live in the water, turning what once had been a hand into a fin. Ichthyosaurus swam about like a fish. Another aquatic reptile, plesiosaurus, turned its limbs into paddles. Other Mesozoic reptiles took to the air. The huge pteranodon had a wing-span of twenty-five feet. The pterodactyl extended its wing — or stretched skin — between an elongated little finger and its hind legs. Other bird reptiles kept their hind limbs free from this entanglement and so could run as well as fly. But one disadvantage was common to all the Mesozoic reptiles: they had very small brains.

On the whole the climate of the Mesozoic period—or certainly of the Jurassic epoch which formed part of it—was equable and warm. This was of great advantage to the reptiles, for they were cold blooded, that is to say their blood varied in temperature with their surroundings. They were obviously ill-equipped to withstand a harsh and cold climate. They were restricted to the warm belt, which in Mesozoic times was extensive and allowed the reptiles scope for their extraordinary development. Unfortunately for their possibilities of survival, towards the end of the Mesozoic period the climate became increasingly colder and drier.

The Cænozoic era was heralded by a cold spell for which the reptiles were physiologically quite unprepared, and the bulk of them perished. In their place small creatures which had developed the

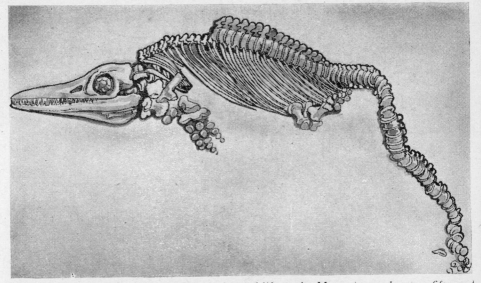

Fig. 52. *The reptiles were the dominant form of life in the Mesozoic era, between fifty and one hundred and seventy-five millions of years ago. They developed an abundant and astonishing variety of forms. Some of them grew to gigantic sizes; others developed armour-like hides; yet others grew wings and took to the air. In the main, they were land animals. Some, however, took to the water; the illustration shows one of these, the ichthyosaurus.*

A REPTILE MONSTER OF THE MESOZOIC ERA

The dinosaurs, one type of which is illustrated here, were the principal group of the land-living reptiles of the Mesozoic era. This one is in the collection of skeletons in the Museum of Brussels, and is part of a group of fossilized remains found in Belgium in 1877. The dinosaurs walked mainly on their hind feet; some used their huge tails as a support on which they balanced. They attained a fantastic size; one type had a tail forty feet long, while its body and neck were also forty feet in length, and another held its head twenty feet high.

Fig. 53. *The kiwi, a bird though it has no wings, is one of the strange creatures which are found in the Australian continent.*

capacity of keeping the temperature of their bodies at a constant level, whatever the conditions, began to become predominant in the struggle for supremacy. A rigorous environment stimulated the development of the mammal.

Rise of the Mammal

Towards the end of the Cretaceous epoch marsupials were dominant among mammals. In their travels they spread to the Australian continent, which at the end of this epoch became separated off from the main land mass. This separation explains why Australia is today the unique home of the marsupial. Throughout the rest of the world the marsupial was open to fierce competition of the placental mammal, which had not to any extent penetrated into Australia. As a result the marsupial, with the exception of the opossum, became extinct on the land masses of the other continents, but flourished exceedingly in

the great southern island. Australia is also the home of the most primitive of all living mammal species, the reptile-like monotremes, and there, too, one of the lung fish survives. In New Zealand we find the wingless kiwi bird (Fig. 53) and that most ancient reptile, the tuatara (Fig. 40). A relatively early geographical isolation, which took place some fifty million years ago, seems to have turned these lands into living fossil preserves.

Man is a very recent arrival on the scene of life. During these hundreds of millions of years when invertebrates, fish, amphibians, and reptiles were working out the problems of living in the water, the air, and on land, man was still so much lifeless and formless chemistry.

One of the major problems facing the first land animals was locomotion. The earliest amphibian (Fig. 54) developed

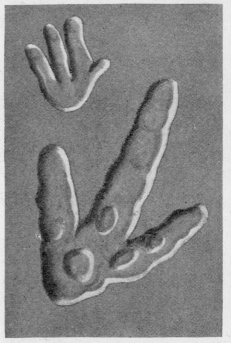

Fig. 54. *Footprints of amphibians. Moving about was one of the major problems of the first land animals; they gradually developed rudimentary arms and legs.*

AN ARMOUR-PLATED REPTILE

The Stegosaurus was another of the great Mesozoic reptiles: it lived in England about one hundred million years ago. It was a vegetarian, and to protect itself from its carnivorous neighbours it developed great plates on its back and spikes on its tail. It was twenty-five feet long and twelve feet high; but like the other Mesozoic reptiles, it had a small brain, the whole brain case being only as big as a clenched fist, in spite of the animal's huge bulk.

rudimentary arms and legs, but these were good for hopping only, and when stationary he had to support himself partly with his belly. The reptile tucked his legs under him (Fig. 55) and so got his belly clear of the ground. Throughout the ages an intricate specialization of limbs to various forms of progression then went on. The primitive five-fingered or five-toed limb underwent strange changes, becoming according to its possessor a wing, flipper, one-toed hoof, muscular clawed limb, or other type of appendage.

Hand and Brain

The monkey and man wisely kept their limbs from becoming entirely specialized for locomotion. In particular they began using the fore-limbs for other purposes. The development of man is the story of the simultaneous development of hand and brain. The hand increases the range of the senses. It brings objects close to the eyes, to the ears, to the nose. It picks out things to eat. With increase of power and precision it enables its possessor to make things. The prehensile hand (Figs. 56 and 57)—only possible because of its primitive structure; it is more like a frog's than a whale's—brought so many things to its possessor's attention that a brain had to develop to cope with these new experiences.

Professor Dendy has written: "So close is the anatomical agreement between the genus Homo and the higher apes that there is little room for connecting links between them, the difficulty being rather to find any definite characters by which they can be separated than to discover reasons for bringing them together." Man, in fact, resembles the anthropoid apes—gorilla, chimpanzee, orang-outang—in a remarkably close way. Man has not a single anatomical feature that the anthropoid has not got. The apes have no tail. We both have nails and not claws, and the thumb can be opposed to the rest of the fingers. The teeth are closely similar and differ from the teeth of all other animals. The skeletons (Fig. 59) correspond bone for bone. The skulls (Fig. 58) may differ in shape, but the brains are exactly similar in design, the only difference—an important one—being that man's brain is larger (Fig. 60). The chief differences, apart from the size of the brain, can be attributed to the fact that man walks upright.

As the anthropoid apes and man are very recent arrivals on the scene we cannot expect much help from the rocks. But what may justifiably be described as a link was found in the upper Pliocene strata in the island of Java. *Pithecanthropus erectus*, as this ancestor was called, was half ape,

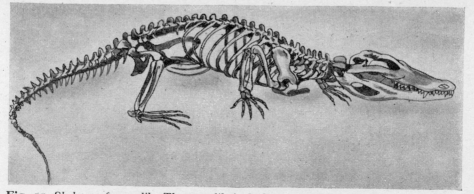

Fig. 55. *Skeleton of crocodile. The crocodile is the largest living reptile; the largest species is believed to attain a length of thirty-three feet, but there are species which do not grow to more than four feet. The illustration shows how reptiles contributed to the problem of locomotion by developing legs tucked under the body, and so raising the belly off the ground.*

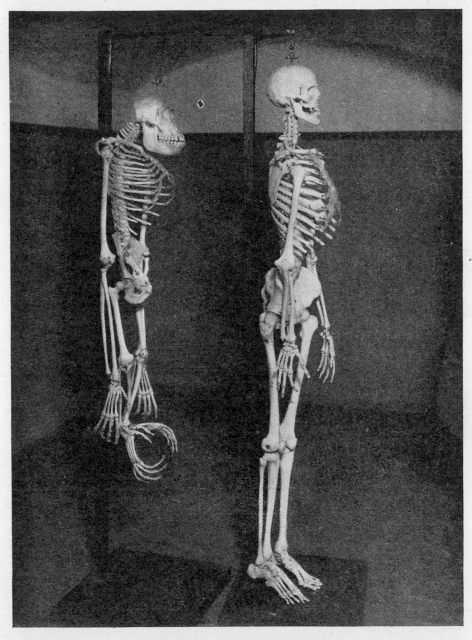

SKELETON OF APE AND OF MAN

Man does not possess a single anatomical feature which is not also possessed by the anthropoid ape. There are, it is true, some differences in detail. The human skeleton lacks the excessive development of the jaw which is characteristic of the ape. The pelvic basin of the ape is somewhat longer than that of man. But bone for bone, the skeletons of man and of the anthropoid ape correspond. Just as sprat and shark are both fish, so man and ape are both primates.

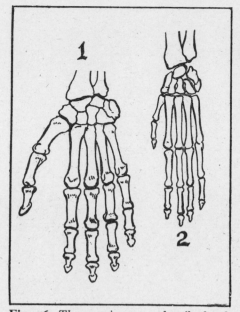

Fig. 56. *The grasping, or prehensile, hand. 1, Bones of man's hand; 2, bones of orangoutang's hand. It was largely due to the power of grasping things by hand that it became necessary to develop a brain.*

the great Ice Age. There were two main ice periods when vast sheets of ice lay thick upon all Ireland and Scotland and England as far south as the Thames. The first Ice Age began somewhere between five hundred thousand and five hundred and fifty thousand years ago and was separated from the second by about two hundred and fifty thousand years. The ice sheet of this second age began to retract about twenty-two thousand years ago, the climate became gradually warmer, reaching its present stage about 5000 B.C. By this time we have emerged into the age of history. Civilization was already in its infancy.

When it is said loosely that man has evolved from monkey it is not meant that once upon a time man was just like the modern ape, or that in the dim future the modern ape will develop into man. What is meant is that man and the ape have sprung from a common stock. Zoologists believe that both species are descended

half man. His brain was much larger than the brain of any living apes, and he walked upright like a man. A few remains of other extinct species of man, or of man-ape, have been found—at Piltdown in Sussex, in China, in Heidelberg, in Rhodesia.

Forerunners

In Neanderthal man we have a more recent example of an extinct species. Neanderthal man had no chin and very heavy brows, but he walked on the outer side of his feet as does *Homo sapiens*. He used tools and buried his dead. He held his own for tens of thousands of years, but between twenty-five and forty thousand years ago he was displaced by true modern man.

The fossil remains of *Pithecanthropus erectus* belong to the Pliocene or the beginning of the Pleistocene era. This can be dated approximately six hundred thousand years ago. The Pleistocene was the era of

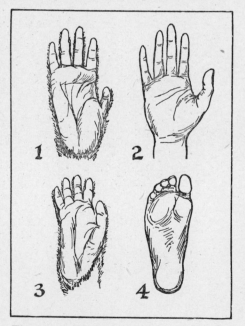

Fig. 57. *1, Hand of chimpanzee; 2, hand of man; 3, foot of chimpanzee; 4, foot of man. The limbs of man and ape are more primitive than in some other creatures.*

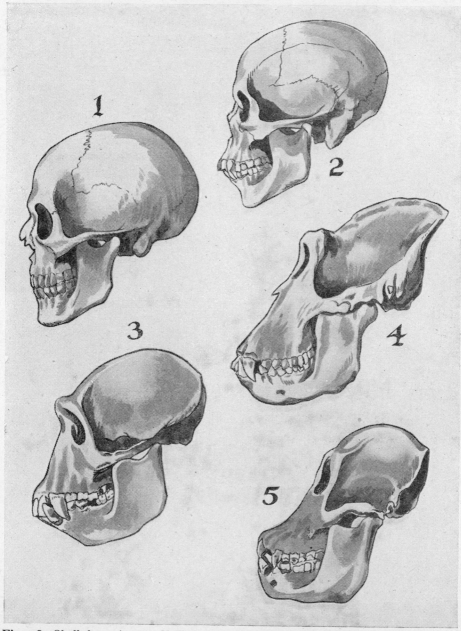

Fig. 58. *Skull formation. 1, Skull of modern man; 2, skull of negro, showing projecting (prognathous) jaw; 3, skull of male chimpanzee; 4, skull of male gorilla; 5, skull of orang- outang. Although the shapes of the skulls vary considerably, the fundamental features are substantially the same. The bones correspond exactly. Most important of all, the brains of man and of the apes are exactly similar in design, although man's brain is much larger. Little evidence on the evolution of man and anthropoid ape can be obtained from fossils, since they are such recent arrivals on the scene; but some links in the chain have been discovered.*

M.H.B.—M*

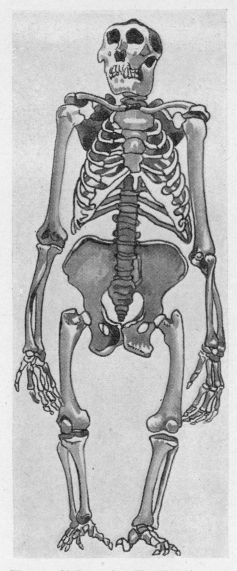

Fig. 59. *Skeleton of gorilla. Notice the degree of correspondence between this skeleton and that of man, shown on page 4. If one compares these two drawings one can see how close is the parallel between them. Breastbone and ribs, the spinal column, shoulder blade and collar bone, the single bone of upper arms and legs and the two bones of forearm and lower leg, the structure of the pelvis and of the skull, are essentially the same, although there are differences in detail, notably the relative proportions of the limbs.*

from a timid little insect-eating, tree-living animal, of which the creature called tarsius is a living example.

So we complete, in very rough outline, the story of the rocks. Here we have direct and, to the scientist, incontrovertible evidence of evolution. Other evidence has been referred to. We have seen, for example, how often the embryo gives away the secret of its origin and reveals in its own development the evolutionary history of its species.

In addition to the evidence of embryology, there is the important evidence of comparative anatomy. If we compare the skeleton of a man with that of an ape, we find they tally, bone for bone. If we see a shark and a sprat side by side we have no hesitation in calling them both fish, although they resemble each other much less than do man and a chimpanzee. They are different kinds of fish. Man and ape are different kinds of primates. Vestigial organs provide another piece of evidence. These are surviving remains of structures and organs which were fully used in the early days of the development of a species, but which have now outlived their usefulness and exist only in attenuated or truncated form. Hair on the surface of the human body is one good example, the hind limbs of a whale another.

Causes of Evolution

How and why evolution takes place has already been referred to. We suggested that the majority of the reptiles became extinct at the end of the Mesozoic era because they were not equipped to meet the climatic changes that then took place. Changes of climate, scarcity of food, geological upheavals, multiplication of foes, and finally the increasing ascendancy of man—all these factors have helped to extinguish or diminish some species and to cause others to increase and multiply. Darwin, in his *Origin of Species*, published in 1859, advanced the theory of natural selection. Young animals, he pointed out, tend to

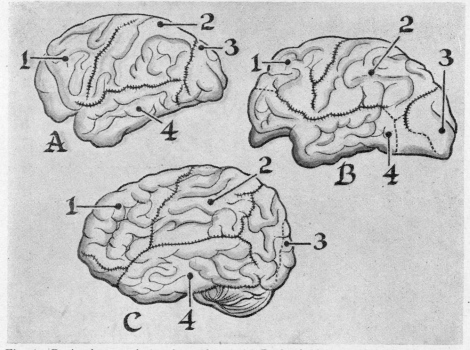

Fig. 60. *Brain of man and of anthropoid apes.* (A) *Brain of chimpanzee.* (B) *Brain of orang-outang.* (C) *Brain of man. 1, Frontal region; 2, parietal region; 3, occipital region; 4, temporal region. The structure and design of the brains of these animals are exactly similar. But there is one important difference—man's brain is larger than those of the others. It is in this respect that man has outstripped his fellow-primates.*

vary in detail from their parents. This law of variation is universal, and by means of it Nature is enabled gradually to select those individuals most fitted to survive, and to stamp their successful characteristics upon their descendants. In the constant struggle between animal and animal, animal and circumstance, the less successful tends to go under more readily, the more successful to go from strength to strength. In the process of time, this continuous sharpening of life on Nature's whetstone leads to continual change and to biological progress; that is, to more complicated and more successful attempts at adaptation to all kinds of circumstances.

So the process of continual development goes on. It represents a constant series of adjustments and adaptations to a constantly changing set of environ-mental factors. By the interplay of forces, and the ceaseless experimentation which Nature undertakes, there emerge from time to time variants on the theme of life which are strikingly successful, and which are even sometimes able to stamp their own desires on the structure of their environment, or, at any rate, part of it. So far, in the history of the universe, man has succeeded more fully than any other creature in this respect. He has been able, thanks to the development of his sensory and emotional machinery, and above all, of his brain, to a degree of efficiency unequalled in the animal kingdom, to overcome obstacles and to modify the world in which he lives in such a way as to justify his claim to be, so far, the supreme achievement of the evolutionary process.

GLOSSARY

A

ABDUCENT NERVE. The nerve which supplies the muscles which move the eyeballs.

ABDUCTION. Withdrawal of limb from natural position.

ACCOMMODATION. Adjustment of the eye for different distances.

ACETABULUM. The cup in which the top of the thigh bone rests.

ACROMEGALY. Disease characterized by an overgrowth of the hands, feet and the face.

ACROMION. The triangular-shaped prominence at the summit of the shoulder blade.

ADDUCTION. Any movement whereby a part is brought towards another or towards the middle line of the body.

ADENOID GROWTHS. Overgrowth of the glandular tissue on the back of the upper part of the throat, into which the nose opens.

ADRENAL GLANDS. The glands over the kidneys, which secrete adrenalin.

ADRENOTROPIC HORMONE. Hormone produced by the pituitary gland.

AGGLUTINATION. Clumping in the blood.

ALÆ NASI. Wings of the nose.

ALGÆ. Forms of primitive plant life, including the green slimy masses on ponds.

ALLELOMORPHIC. Alternative forms of the same characteristic.

ALVEOLI. The small air sacs of the lung.

AMINO-ACIDS. The simplest breakdown products of proteins.

AMNION. The innermost membrane enclosing the fœtus before birth; a water cushion within the fertilized egg which allows the embryo to develop in fluid and to be protected from pressure.

AMNIOTIC. Relating to the amnion.

AMŒBA. A colourless, single-celled, jelly-like, protoplasmic organism found in sea and fresh water.

AMPHIBIANS. Animals which live on land or in water.

AMPULLA. Dilated end of vessel, canal, duct.

AMPULLA OF VATER. Eminence in the wall of the descending portion of the first part of the small intestine.

ANABOLISM. The process by which living things take in matter, assimilate it and change it chemically.

ANÆMIA. Deficiency of blood as a whole, or deficiency of the number of red corpuscles.

ANAL SPHINCTER. Muscular ring which closes the anus.

ANNELIDS. The class of worms with segmented bodies, e.g., earthworms.

ANNULAR LIGAMENT. Flexible compact tissue surrounding the wrist and the ankle.

ANTIBODIES. Bodies in the blood which neutralize hostile germs.

ANTRUM. A cavity or hollow space, especially in a bone.

ANTRUM OF HIGHMORE. A cavity in the bone of the upper jaw.

ANVIL BONE. One of the bones in the middle ear.

AORTA. The main blood vessel of the body, arising from the heart.

APEX CORDIS. The apex of the heart.

AQUEDUCT OF SYLVIUS. Narrow channel between third and fourth ventricles of the brain.

AQUEOUS HUMOUR. Watery substance in the front chamber of the eye.

ARACHNIDS. The class of animals which includes spiders and ticks.

ARACHNOID MEMBRANE. Delicate membrane enclosing brain and spinal cord.

AREOLA. Ring surrounding the nipple of the breast.

ARTERIES. Vessels which convey the blood from the heart.

ARTERIOLES. Small arteries.

ARTHROPODS. A sub-division of the animal kingdom containing animals with segmented bodies to which hollow appendages (antennæ, wings, legs) are attached; it includes insects and crustaceans.

ARTICULATE (JOINTS). The manner in which two bones join.

ASTHMA. A disease of respiration, characterized by difficult breathing and cough.

ASTIGMATISM. An error of the eye-lens, causing distorted vision.

ASTRAGALUS. The ankle bone, upon which the shinbone rests.

ATLAS VERTEBRA. The first vertebra of the neck.

ATROPHY. Diminution in the size of a tissue, organ or part, the result of degeneration of the cells or a decrease in the size of cells.

AUDITORY NERVE. Nerve of hearing.

AURICLES. The thin-walled upper cavities of the heart, which receive blood from the veins and lungs.

AXILLA. The armpit.

AXILLARY ARTERY. Artery which runs across the armpit.

AXIS VERTEBRA. The second vertebra of the neck.

AXON. Long process of a nerve cell.

B

BACILLI. Rod-shaped bacteria.

BACTERIA. Microscopic organisms which are the cause of many diseases.

BACTERIOPHAGE. A primitive microscopic organism which consumes bacteria.

BASAL GANGLIA. Part of the brain.

BASILAR MEMBRANE. A part of the inner ear.

BICEPS BRACHII. Muscle used in bending and turning of the forearm.

BICEPS FEMORIS. A muscle at the back of the thigh, used in bending and turning the leg.

BICUSPIDS. Teeth with two cusps, used for chewing.

BILE. The substance secreted by the liver.

BIOCHEMISTRY. The chemistry of the living tissues.

BIPOLAR NERVE CELLS. Nerve cells which have two prolongations of the cell matter.

BLASTOCYST. The hollow structure of the embryo.

BLASTODERM. Germinal membrane round yolk in impregnated ovum, which is the superficial layer of the embryo in its earliest state.

BRACHIAL. Relating to the arm.

BRACHIAL ARTERY. Main artery of arm.

BRACHIAL PLEXUS. A network formed in the neck by the union of nerve branches.

BRACHIORADIALIS. Muscle used in bending the arm and turning the forearm, more commonly called the supinator longus.

BROAD LIGAMENT. A fold of membrane extending from the womb to the pelvic wall.

BROCA'S AREA. Part of the brain governing the activities of speech and writing.

BRONCHI. Main air tubes of the lung.

BRONCHIAL ARTERIES. Arteries supplying the tissues of the lungs with blood.

BRONCHIOLES. Small air tubes.

BUCCINATOR. A muscle of the neck.

C

CÆCUM. A blind sac, at the beginning of the large intestine.

CÆNOZOIC. Relating to the third of the great geological periods, during which the animals of the mammal class became the dominant form of life.

CALCAREOUS. Composed of, or containing, lime or limestone.

CALCIS, OS. The heel bone.

CALORIE. A unit of heat, that is, the amount which raises the temperature of 1 c.c. of water 1 degree centigrade.

CAMBRIAN. The first epoch of the Palæozoic era.

CANINE TOOTH. Eye-tooth; one of the four strong pointed teeth between incisors and molars.

CANINUS. A muscle of the face, which in action produces a snarl.

CAPILLARIES. Smallest blood vessels.

CAPSULAR LIGAMENT. The sac or membraneous bag which surrounds every movable joint or articulation.

CARBONIFEROUS. The sixth epoch of the Palæozoic era, during which flourished plants which became fossilized into coal.

CARBOXY-HÆMOGLOBIN. Hæmoglobin combined with carbon monoxide.

CARDIA. 1, The heart; 2, the orifice of the stomach near the gullet.

CARDIAC. Relating to the heart; 2, relating to the cardia of the stomach.

CARDIAC IMPULSE. The impulse of the heart felt on the chest wall.

CARDIAC PLEXUS. A network of nerves connected with the heart.

CAROTID ARTERIES. Arteries of the neck.

CARPUS. The eight wrist bones.

CARTILAGE. Firm elastic tissue; gristle.

CATALYST. A substance which greatly increases the rate of a chemical reaction.

CAUDA EQUINA. The roots of the nerves in the base of the spine.

CEREBELLUM. Part of the hindbrain.

CEREBRAL CORTEX. Outer layer of brain.

CEREBRAL PEDUNCLES. Narrow part connecting the main portion of the brain with the pons, a white eminence at the base of the brain.

CEREBROSPINAL. Relating to the brain and spinal cord.

CEREBROSPINAL AXIS. The central nervous system.

CEREBROSPINAL FEVER. An acute infectious disease with inflammation of the membranes enclosing the brain.

CEREBROSPINAL FLUID. The fluid between the arachnoid membrane and the pia mater, two membranes which envelop brain and spinal cord.

CEREBRUM. The main part of the brain.

CERVICAL. Relating to the neck.

CERVICAL PLEXUS. A network formed in the neck by branches of the upper four cervical nerves.

CERVIX. The neck.

CETACEANS. Aquatic mammals: dolphins, porpoises, whales.

CHIASMA. A crossing.

CHITIN. Horny material of which the shell of the lobster and other arthropods is composed.

CHLOROPHYLL. The pigment responsible for the green colour of plants.

CHOLESTEROL. A fatty substance, a constituent of bile, gall-stones, nervous tissue, egg yolk and blood.

CHORDATE. Possessing a notochord, or primitive form of backbone.

CHORION. The outermost membrane enveloping the fœtus before birth.

CHOROID COAT. Layer of the eyeball outside the retina.

CHROMATIN. Granular material of which the nuclei of cells are composed.

CHROMOSOMES. Strands of chromatin formed when a cell divides.

CILIA. Hair-like processes from cells.

CILIARY MUSCLE. Muscle of accommodation in the eye.

CIRCUMDUCTION. Circular movement of a limb.

CIRCUMVALLATE. Surrounded by a wall or prominence.

CIRCUMVALLATE PAPILLÆ. Protuberances at the base of the tongue.

CISTERNA CHYLI. Elongated swelling in the abdomen at juncture of several large lymphatic vessels, forming the beginning of the thoracic duct.

CLAVICLE. The collar bone.

CLITORIS. Rudimentary part of female genitals analogous to penis.

COCCI. Spherical bacteria.

COCCYGEAL. Relating to the coccyx.

COCCYGEAL PLEXUS. A network of nerves on the back surface of the coccyx and tail end of the sacrum.

COCCYX. The last bone of the spine, the vestigial remains of a tail.

COCHLEA. A spiral-shaped cavity of the inner ear.

CŒLENTERATES. The most primitive many-celled animals.

CŒLOM. A body cavity between the inner and outer layer of cells.

CŒLOMATES. Those animals possessing a cœlom.

COLON. Part of the large intestine.

COMMISURAL FIBRES. Fibres connecting the two hemispheres of the brain with each other.

COMPLEXUS MUSCLE. Muscle used in drawing in and turning the head.

CONCHÆ. The coiled bones of the nostril.

CONDYLE. Rounded process at the end of a bone, forming part of joint with another bone.

CONJUNCTIVA. Membrane lining the lids and front of the eyeball.

CONNECTIVE TISSUE. Fibrous tissue connecting and supporting the organs.

CONVOLUTION. A fold, twist, or coil of any organ, especially any one of the prominent parts of the brain.

CORACOBRACHIALIS. The muscle used in drawing the arm forwards and inwards.

CORACOID PROCESS. Beak-shaped process of the shoulder blade.

CORIUM. The deep layer of the skin.

CORNEA. The transparent front part of the eyeball.

CORONA GLANDIS. The ridge at the head of the penis.

CORONARY ARTERIES. Arteries of the heart muscle.

CORPORA CAVERNOSA. Bodies of erectile tissue forming chief part of penis.

CORPORA QUADRIGEMINA. The optic lobes of the brain, four rounded eminences situated under the corpus callosum.

CORPUS CALLOSUM. The broad band of white matter uniting the hemispheres of the cerebrum.

CORPUS LUTEUM. Yellow body formed in the ovary; it produces the hormone progestin.

CORPUS SPONGIOSUM. The spongy part of the penis encircling the canal connecting the bladder with the outside of the body.

CORPUS STRIATUM. A mass of grey matter extending into the cavities of the brain.

CORPUSCLES. Cells; blood cells.

CORPUSCLES OF HASSALL. Cells found in the thymus gland.

CORRUGATOR SUPERCILLII. Face muscle used in drawing the eyebrow down.

CORTEX. Outer layer.

CORTEX CEREBRI. The external grey layer of the brain.

COTYLOID. Cup-shaped.

COTYLOID LIGAMENT. A ligament surrounding the acetabulum or cup of the thigh bone.

COWPER, GLANDS OF. Small glands situated in front of the prostate gland.

CRANIAL FOSSÆ. Three depressions in the base of the skull for the reception of the lobes of the brain.

CRANIAL NERVES. Nerves arising directly from the brain and leaving through a hole in the skull.

CRANIUM. The skull.

CRETACEOUS. The third and latest epoch of the Mesozoic era, during which the first true flowers appeared.

CRETIN. Deformed imbecile.

CRIBRIFORM. Perforated like a sieve.

CRIBRIFORM PLATE. The upper perforated plate of the ethmoid bone in the skull, through which passes the nerve of smell.

CRICOID. Ring-shaped.

CRICOID CARTILAGE. The ring-shaped cartilage of the larynx.

CRUCIATE LIGAMENTS. Ligaments between thigh bone and shin bone.

CRUSTACEA. The class of animals which includes crabs, lobsters, shrimps.

CRYSTALLINE LENS. The lens of the eye.

CUBOID BONE. A bone of the foot.

CUNEIFORM BONES. A wedge-shaped bone of the wrist, and three wedge-shaped bones of the instep.

CUTICLE. The outer layer of skin covering the body.

D

DECUSSATION. A chiasma or X-shaped crossing, especially of symmetrical parts, such as nerve fibres, nerve tracts, or nerve filaments.

DEFECATION. The emptying of the bowels.

DELTOID MUSCLES. Muscles covering the shoulder, used in lifting the arm.

DENDRITES. Short processes of a nerve cell.

DEPRESSOR MUSCLES. Muscles of the face.

DEVONIAN. The fifth epoch of the Palæozoic era.

DIAPHRAGM. The muscular wall between the chest and the abdomen; the chief muscle used in breathing.

DIASTOLE. Interval between heart-beats.

DIGESTIVE TRACT. The whole alimentary canal from the mouth to the anus.

DIGIT. A finger or toe.

DOMINANT CHARACTERISTICS. Inheritable characteristics which always appear in the offspring if transmitted by either of the parents.

DORSAL. Relating to the back or to the back part of an organ.

DUCT. A tube or channel, especially one for conveying the secretions of a gland.

DUODENUM. First part of small intestine.

DURA MATER. The fibrous membrane forming the outermost covering of the brain and spinal cord.

E

ECHINODERMS. The group of animals that includes starfish and sea urchins.

ECTODERM. The external or upper layer of cells in primitive animals and in the embryo.

EJACULATION. The ejection of semen.

EJACULATORY DUCT. The duct which carries the semen into the urethra.

ELASMOBRANCHS. Fish which have no bones in their skeletons.

EMBRYO. The developing fœtus.

END-BULB. The terminal bulb of a nerve in the skin.

END-ORGAN. The terminal part of a sensory nerve fibre.

ENDOCARDIUM. Membrane lining the interior of the heart.

ENDOCRINE GLANDS. Glands of internal secretion which pour their juices, called hormones, directly into the blood stream.

ENDODERM. Inner layer of cells in primitive animals and in the embryo.

ENDOTHELIUM. Layer of cells lining blood vessels.

ENTODERM. The outer of the two primitive cell layers of the embryo.

ENZYME. A substance made in the body by living tissues, which speeds up the chemical actions which take place.

EOCENE. The first epoch of the Caenozoic era, during which primates appeared.

EPIBLAST. The external or upper layer of the cells forming the embryo in the early stages of its development.

EPIDERMIS. The outer layer of skin.

EPIDIDYMIS. Small body lying above the testicles.

EPIGLOTTIS. Leaf-like structure at top of the voice-box or larynx.

EPITHELIUM. Cells which form the epidermis or outer layer of the skin, which line all canals having communication with the external air, and which are specialized for secretion in certain glands, such as the liver, kidneys, etc.

EPOCH. A sub-division of one of the great geological periods called eras.

ERA. One of the three great periods of formation of sedimentary rocks—the Palæozoic, Mesozoic and Cænozoic eras.

ETHMOID BONE. The sieve-like bone at the base of the skull, perforated for the transmission of the nerve of smell.

ETHMOIDAL. Relating to the ethmoid bone.

EUSTACHIAN TUBE. Tube from ear to throat.

EXTENSOR MUSCLES. Muscles used in stretching or extending.

F

FACIAL NERVE. The nerve which supplies the muscles of expression.

FÆCES. Excretion from the bowel.

FALLOPIAN TUBE. Tube running from ovary to uterus.

FASCIA. Thin sheath of fibrous tissue.

FAUCES. The upper part of the throat.

FEMORAL. Relating to the thigh.

FEMUR. The thigh bone.

FERMENT. Any substance which, in contact with another substance, is capable of producing changes in the latter without itself undergoing much change.

FIBRIL. Small fibre; subdivision of a fibre; ultimate subdivision of root.

FIBROCARTILAGE. Cartilage with an intermixture of fibrous elements.

FIBULA. The slender bone at the outer part of the leg, joined above with the shin bone and below with the ankle bone and the shin bone.

FIMBRIA. A fringe.

FLEXOR MUSCLES. Muscles used in bending or flexing a limb or a part.

FŒTUS. The growing embryo in the womb.

FOLLICLE. A small lymphatic gland, the tissue of which is arranged in the form of a little sac; also a small secretory cavity or sac.

FOLLICLES, HAIR. The depression containing the root of the hair.

FONTANELLES. Gaps between the bones of the infant's skull.

FORAMEN. A perforation or opening, especially in a bone.

FORAMEN MAGNUM. A large oval opening in the bone of the back of the skull through which pass the spinal cord and its membranes, the spinal accessory nerves, and the vertebral arteries.

FORAMEN OVALE (OF THE HEART). A fœtal opening between the two auricles of the heart.

FOSSA. A depression or pit.

FRÆNUM. A fold of skin or mucous membrane which checks or limits the movement of any organ.

FRONTAL BONES. Bones of the forehead.

FRONTAL LOBE. Part of the brain near the forehead.

FRONTAL SINUSES. The hollow air spaces in the forehead above the eye sockets.

FUNDUS. The base of an organ.

FUSIFORM. Spindle-shaped.

G

GAMETE. A sex cell.

GANGLION. A collection of nerve cells.

GASTROCNEMIUS. Muscle of calf of leg.

GENE. A heritable factor which is carried by a chromosome, and is responsible for the transmission of heritable characteristics.

GERMINAL. Relating to a germ or to the development of a tissue or organ.

GESTATION. Pregnancy.

GLANS PENIS. The conical body forming the head of the penis.

GLENOID. Having or resembling a shallow cavity or socket.

GLENOID CAVITY. Depression in the shoulder blade for the reception of the bone of the arm.

GLENOID FOSSA. Depression in the temporal bone.

GLOBULE. A small spherical particle, such as a blood corpuscle.

GLOMERULE. Capillary blood vessels found in the kidney.

GLOSSOPHARYNGEAL NERVE. The nerve which supplies the muscles of the throat and some of the muscles of the tongue; it also carries taste fibres.

GLOTTIS. Upper end of voice-box.

GLUTEUS. One of the large muscles of the buttock.

GLYCOGEN. The form in which the body stores glucose.

GOBLET CELLS. Cells found in mucous membranes.

GONADOTROPIC HORMONE. Hormone produced by the pituitary gland and affecting the sex glands.

GONADS. Sexual glands; the testicles or ovaries.

GRAAFIAN FOLLICLES. Small bodies found in the ovaries.

GUSTATORY. Relating to the sense of taste and its organs.

H

HÆMATIN. Iron-containing pigment.

HÆMOGLOBIN. Combination of hæmatin and globin in the blood.

HAMMER BONE. A bone of the middle ear.

HEPATIC ARTERY. Artery of the liver.

HERMAPHRODITES. Creatures possessing the reproductive organs of both sexes.

HILUM. A pit or opening in an organ, usually for the entrance and exit of vessels or ducts.

HORMONES. Chemical substances produced in certain organs, which on absorption into the blood influence the action of tissues and organs other than those in which they are produced.

HUMERUS. The bone of the upper arm.

HYDROID. Living in water.

HYOID BONE. A bone between the root of the tongue and the larynx, supporting the tongue and giving attachment to its muscles.

HYPOGLOSSAL. Situated under the tongue.

HYPOGLOSSAL NERVE. The nerve which supplies the muscles under the tongue and also sends branches to the muscular tissue of the tongue itself.

HYPOGLOTTIS. The under part of the tongue.

I

ILEOCÆCAL. Relating to the region of junction between the small and large intestines in the right lower corner of the abdomen.

ILEOCÆCAL VALVE. A structure which allows the contents of the intestine to pass onwards from the small to the large intestine, and mostly prevents their passage in the opposite direction.

ILEUM. The lower part of the small intestine.

ILIAC ARTERIES. Arteries running from the aorta to the thigh.

ILIACUS. Muscle used in turning the thigh outwards.

ILIUM. The uppermost of the three bones forming each side of the pelvis.

INCISORS. The four front teeth of each jaw.

INFRASPINATUS. Muscle attached to the shoulder blade, used in turning the arm outwards.

INFUNDIBULUM. The stalk of the pituitary gland.

INGUINAL. Relating to the groin.

INNOMINATE BONE. The irregular bones forming the sides and front wall of the pelvis, and composed of the ilium, ischium and pubis.

INSTINCT. A fundamental drive or urge which finds release in action.

INSULIN. The internal secretion of the pancreas.

INTERCOSTAL. Between the ribs.

INTEROSSEI MUSCLES. Small muscles of the hand and the foot.

INTERSTITIAL. Situated between important parts; occupying the interspaces of a part.

INTESTINE. The part of the digestive tube extending from the end of the stomach to the anus. It consists of the small and the large intestine.

INVERTEBRATES. Animals without a spinal column.

IRIS. The curtain which surrounds the pupil of the eye.

ISCHIUM. Bone which forms the lower and hinder part of the pelvis and upon which the body rests in sitting.

ISLETS OF LANGERHANS. Groups of cells found in the substance of the pancreas; they produce insulin.

J

JEJUNUM. Middle part of the small intestine.

JUGULAR VEIN, EXTERNAL. Vein which carries the blood from the exterior part of the skull and parts of the face.

JUGULAR VEIN, INTERNAL. Vein which collects the blood from the brain, part of the face and the neck.

JUGULUM. The collar bone; also the throat.

JURASSIC. The second epoch of the Mesozoic era, during which the first birds appeared.

K

KATABOLISM. The process by which living things break down assimilated matter and liberate energy.

KERATIN. The basis of horny tissues, hair, nails, etc.

L

LACHRYMAL BONE. Bone of eye socket.

LACHRYMAL GLAND. The tear gland.

LACTATION. Suckling period of supplying human milk.

LACTIFEROUS. Conveying or secreting milk.

LARYNX. Upper part of windpipe, holding vocal cords.

LATERAL VENTRICLES. Cavities in the brain.

LATISSIMUS DORSI. Muscle used in drawing the arm backwards and downwards and turning it inwards.

LEUCOCYTES. The colourless or white corpuscles of the blood.

LEVATOR ANI. Muscle which forms the floor of the pelvic basin.

LEVATOR MUSCLES. Muscles used in raising or elevating parts.

LIGAMENTS. Strong bands of fibrous tissue which serve to bind together the bones entering into a joint.

LOBE. A rounded part or projection of an organ.

LOBULES. Small lobes.

LONGISSIMUS DORSI. Muscle used in erecting the spine and bending the trunk backwards.

LUMBAR. Relating to the loins.

LUMBAR PLEXUS. Network formed by divisions of the lumbar spinal nerves.

LUMBRICAL MUSCLES. Muscles used in bending fingers and toes.

LUMBUS. The loin.

LYMPH. The fluid round the tissue cells.

LYMPHATICS. The vessels which convey lymph.

LYMPHOCYTES. White blood cells produced in the lymphoid tissues and lymphatic glands of the body. They form about twenty-five per cent of the white corpuscles of the blood.

M

MACULA LUTEA. The yellow spot of the retina; it is the point of clearest vision.

MALAR BONES. The two cheekbones.

MALLEOLUS. A part or process of bone having a hammer-edged shape.

MALLEUS. A bone of the middle ear.

MALPIGHIAN CORPUSCLES. Small whitish bodies found in the substance of the spleen.

MAMMALS. Animals which suckle their young.

MAMMARY GLANDS. The breasts.

MANUBRIUM STERNI. Part of the sternum or breast bone.

MARSUPIALS. Animals of the mammal class which have a pouch for carrying their young, including kangaroo and wallaby.

MASSETER. Muscle which closes the jaw.

MASTICATION. The act of chewing.

MASTOID PROCESS. The protruding part of the bone of the temple which can be felt immediately behind the ear.

MATRIX. (1) A mould, the cavity in which anything is formed.

(2) That part of tissue into which any organ or process is set, like the matrix of a tooth or of a nail.

(3) The intercellular substance of a tissue.

(4) The womb.

MAXILLA. The bone of the upper or lower jaw.

MAXILLARY ARTERY, INTERNAL. Artery which supplies the nose, the throat and the dental sockets with blood.

MAXILLARY SINUS. Cavity in the upper jaw.

MEATUS. An opening or passage.

MEATUS OF NOSE. One of the three passages (the superior, the middle and the inferior meatus) into which the turbinal bones divide the nasal cavity.

MEDIAN NERVE. Spinal nerve supplying muscles of the arm and hand.

MEDULLA. The marrow. Also the innermost parts of certain organs.

MEDULLA OBLONGATA. The hindermost part of the brain at the top end of the spinal cord. In it are situated several of the most important nerve centres.

MEIBOMIAN GLANDS. Little sebaceous glands embedded in the eyelids.

MEMBRANE. A thin layer of tissue surrounding a part or separating adjacent cavities.

MENINGES. Membranes of the brain and spinal cord.

MENINGITIS. Inflammation of the membranes enclosing the brain.

MENTALIS. Muscle of the face, used in raising the lower lip.

MESODERM. The middle layer of cells in animals possessing three layers and in the developing embryo.

MESOZOIC. The second of the great geological periods, about 50 to 175 millions of years ago, during which the great reptile monsters flourished.

METABOLISM. The total chemical changes which take place within the body.

METACARPAL BONES. Bones of the hand.

METACARPUS. Part of the hand between wrist and fingers, consisting of five bones.

METATARSAL BONES. Bones of the foot between the instep and the toe joints.

METATARSUS. Part of the foot.

METAZOA. Animals that came after the protozoa, or first animals.

MICTURITION. The act of passing urine.

MIOCENE. The third epoch of the Cænozoic era.

MITRAL VALVE. Heart valve between left auricle and ventricle.

MODIOLUS. A bone of the inner ear.

MOLAR TEETH. The last three teeth on each side of the jaw.

MOLLUSCS. The class of animals that includes oysters, whelks, mussels and scallops.

MORULA. The solid mass of cells formed by complete segmentation of the yolk of an ovum.

MOTOR. Concerned in or relating to motion, e.g., motor cells, motor centre, motor nerves.

MOTOR END PLATE. The point at which a motor fibre comes into contact with a muscle fibre.

MOTOR NERVES. Nerves containing only or chiefly motor fibres, and designed to excite muscular activity.

MUCOUS MEMBRANE. Membrane lining cavities and canals communicating with the air.

MUCUS. Slimy substance secreted by mucous membrane.

MUSCULOCUTANEOUS. Relating to or supplying the muscles and skin.

MUTATION. Change in a gene which gives rise to a heritable variation.

MYELIN SHEATH. The sheath of a nerve.

MYLOHYOID MUSCLE. Muscle which runs from the hyoid bone to the lower jaw.

N

NARES. The nostrils.

NEANDERTHAL MAN. A primitive type of man, who used tools and was closely akin to true man, but became extinct between 25,000 and 40,000 years ago.

NEURAL. Relating to nerves or nervous tissue.

NEURILEMMA. The sheath encasing a nerve fibre.

NEUROGLIA. Tissue forming the basis of the supporting framework of nervous tissue.

NEURONE. Nerve cell.

NISSL BODIES. Fine granular bodies which exist in nerve cells.

NODE. A knob or swelling.

NODULAR. Composed of or covered by nodules, or resembling nodules.

NODULE. A small node.

NOTOCHORD. Cartilaginous band forming the basis of the spinal column; a primitive form of backbone possessed by some early vertebrates.

NUCLEUS. Vital, central part of a cell, made up of a granular material called chromatin.

O

OBLIQUE MUSCLES. Muscles of abdomen.

OCCIPUT. The back part of the head.

OCULOMOTOR (NERVE). The third cranial nerve, supplying the muscles which move the eyeball.

ODONTOID. Toothlike.

ODONTOID PROCESS. Part of the neck bone.

OESOPHAGUS. The gullet.

OESTRIN. Hormone produced by the ovaries.

OLECRANON PROCESS. Part of the bone of the forearm.

OLFACTORY. Relating to the sense of smell.

OLFACTORY BULB. The bulbous end of the olfactory nerve.

OLFACTORY CENTRE. The centre in the brain concerned with the sense of smell.

OLIGOCENE. The second epoch of the Cænozoic era.

OPSONIN. Substance which enables white blood cells to destroy bacteria.

OPTIC CHIASMA. The union and crossing of the two optic nerves.

ORBICULAR. Circular.

ORBICULARIS OCULI. Muscle surrounding the eyes, used in closing the eyelids.

ORBICULARIS ORIS. Circular muscle used in closing the mouth.

ORBIT. The eye socket.

ORDOVICIAN. The second epoch of the Palæozoic era.

ORIFICE. An opening.

OSSICLE. A small bone.

OSSICLES, AUDITORY. A chain of three small bones in the middle ear.

OSSIFICATION. Bone formation.

OVARY. Female sex organ.

OVIDUCTS. Small tube from the ovary to the womb.

OVUM. A female reproductive cell; an egg cell in the ovary.

OXYHÆMOGLOBIN. Oxidized hæmoglobin, found in arterial blood.

OXYNTIC CELLS. Cells of the glands of the stomach.

P

PACINIAN BODIES OR CORPUSCLES. Tiny bulbs at the end of nerves in the skin and subcutaneous tissue; they are the end organs for sensation.

PALÆOZOIC. The first of the great geological periods, about 175 to 500 millions of years ago, during which invertebrates and subsequently fishes and amphibians were the dominant forms of life.

PANCREAS. Gland situated at the back of the abdomen, which secretes digestive juice and insulin.

PAPILLA. Small nipple-like protruberance in a part or organ.

PARASYMPATHETIC NERVES. Nerves of the autonomic nervous system, which supply involuntary muscle fibres, glands and the small arteries.

PARATHYROID GLANDS. Glands lying in the neck behind the thyroid.

PARATHYROTROPIC HORMONE. Hormone produced by the pituitary gland, affecting the parathyroid glands.

PARIETAL BONES. Bones of the skull cap.

PARIETAL LOBE. Part of the brain near the skull cap.

PAROTID GLAND. Salivary gland in the cheek.

PATELLA. Knee-cap.

PATELLAR. Relating to the knee-cap.

PECTORAL MUSCLES. The muscles of the chest.

PEDUNCLE. A narrow part acting as a support.

PELVIS. Basin-shaped cavity connecting the lower limbs with the spine.

PELVIS OF THE KIDNEY. The cavity of the kidney, lined by mucous membrane.

PENIS. Male sex organ.

PEPSIN. Digestive ferment of the stomach.

PEPSIS. Digestion.

PEPTIC CELLS. Granular cells producing pepsin.

PEPTONES. Protein substance formed by the action of pepsin during digestion.

PERICARDIUM. Fibrous sheath round the heart.

PERINEUM. Region between the anus and the genital organs.

PERIOSTEUM. Fibrous sheath round bones, which carries blood vessels and nerves for the nutrition and development of the bones.

PERISTALSIS. Movement of the gut.

PERISTALTIC. Relating to peristalsis.

PERITONEUM. Lining membrane of the abdominal cavity.

PERMIAN. The sixth and latest epoch of the Palæozoic era, during which the reptiles began their development.

PERONEAL. Relating to the fibula, or splint bone of the leg.

PETROUS. Stony or hard.

PHAGOCYTES. White blood cells which devour bacteria.

PHALANGES. Small bones of the fingers and toes.

PHARYNX. The back of the throat.

PHOTOSYNTHESIS. The process by which plants manufacture food for themselves from the carbon dioxide in the air and the minerals taken in at their roots.

PHRENIC NERVE. Nerve supplying the diaphragm.

PHYLUM. A term used in classification to denote a great subdivision of the animal or vegetable kingdoms, e.g., the vertebrate or arthropod phylum.

PIA MATER. Membrane attached to the surface of the brain and spinal cord.

PINEAL BODY. Small stalked structure lying on the roof of the brain, the vestigial remains of a third eye.

PINNA. The outer ear.

PITUITARY GLAND. Gland at the base of the brain ; the most important of the endocrine glands.

PLACENTA. The spongy organ within the womb to which the fœtus is attached and by means of which it is nourished, and which is subsequently expelled as the afterbirth.

PLACENTALS. Mammals which carry their young to a high state of development inside the womb.

PLANTA. The sole of the foot.

PLANTAR LIGAMENT. A band of tissue in the sole of the foot.

PLASMA. The fluid part of the blood, composed of serum and fibrinogen, the material which produces clotting.

PLATELETS. Smallest bodies in the blood —essential to the process of clotting.

PLATYSMA MUSCLE. Muscle of the face, which wrinkles the skin.

PLEURA. Lining of chest wall and lungs.

PLEXUS. A network of vessels or nerves.

PLIOCENE. The fourth and latest epoch of the Cænozoic era.

POLYPS. Various types of primitive and lowly-developed animals.

PONS. A process or bridge of tissue connecting two parts of an organ.

PONS CEREBELLI. A broad bridge of nerve fibres connecting the two hemispheres of the cerebellum.

POPLITEAL ARTERY. Artery behind knee.

POPLITEAL SPACE. Hollow space at the back of the knee and thigh.

POPLITEUS. The ham or hinder part of the knee joint.

PORTAL VEIN. Large vein leading into the liver.

PREMOLARS. Chewing teeth.

PREPUCE. The foreskin of the penis.

PRESYSTOLE. The period of the heart's pause preceding its contraction.

PRIMATES. The highest and most developed class of mammals, including lemurs, monkeys and man.

PROCESS. A prominence or outgrowth, usually used of a bone.

PROGESTIN. Hormone produced by the ovaries.

PROLACTIN. Hormone produced by the pituitary gland, which stimulates the mammary glands to secrete milk.

PRONATION (of the hand). Turning the palm downwards.

PRONATOR QUADRATUS. Muscle of the arm, used in turning palm downwards.

PRONATOR RADII TERES. Another muscle of the arm, used in turning the hand.

PROSECRETIN. Substance found in the cells of the first part of the small intestine, which plays an important part in digestion.

PROSTATE GLAND. Male sex gland, lying at the neck of the bladder.

PROTEINS. Complex chemical substances containing mainly nitrogen, carbon, hydrogen and oxygen.

PROTEROZOIC. The period before the beginning of the first great geological era.

PROTOPLASM. The material constituting the essential substance of living cells, upon which all the vital functions of nutrition, secretion, growth, reproduction and mobility depend.

PROTOPHYTA. The simplest forms of plant life : the first plants.

PROTOZOA. The simplest forms of animal life : the first animals.

PSOAS. Muscle running from the region of the loin through the pelvis to the upper end of the thigh bone.

PTYALIN. A substance found in saliva, which converts starch into sugar.

PUBIS. Bone which forms the front part of the pelvis.

PULMONARY. Belonging to or affecting the lungs.

PUS. Thick, white, yellow, or greenish fluid formed in abscesses, on ulcers, and on inflamed and discharging surfaces.

PYLORUS. The lower or right opening of the stomach, through which the softened and partially digested food passes into the small intestine.

PYRAMIDAL TRACT. Tract of nerve cells from brain to spinal cord, along which the impulses governing movement travel.

PYRAMIDS, RENAL. Little conical prominences of kidney tissue, which make up the inner part of the kidney.

R

RADIAL ARTERY. Artery of the wrist.

RADIAL NERVE. Nerve supplying the muscles of the back of arm and forearm, and the skin of the back of the hand.

RADIUS. Bone of the forearm.

RAMUS. A branch, especially of a vein, artery or nerve.

RAMUS COMMUNICANS. A branch of a spinal nerve.

RECESSIVE CHARACTERISTICS. Inheritable characteristics which will appear in the offspring only if transmitted by both parents, and will otherwise remain latent.

RECTUM. Last part of the large intestine.

RECTUS ABDOMINIS. A muscle of the abdomen.

REFLEX ARC. The nerve mechanism responsible for reflex action.

REGURGITATION. A back-flow of blood through a defective heart valve.

RENAL. Relating to the kidney.

RENNIN. The milk-curdling enzyme of the gastric juice.

RETINA. The innermost and light-sensitive coat of the eyeball.

RHOMBOID MUSCLES. Muscles attached to the shoulder blade.

RISORIUS. Laughing muscle.

S

SACCULE. Small chamber in the central part of the inner ear.

SACRAL. Relating to the sacrum.

SACRO-ILIAC JOINT. Joint of the pelvis.

SACRO-ISCHIAL JOINT. Joint of the pelvis.

SACRO-SPINAL. Relating to the sacrum and the spine.

SACRUM. Lower part of the backbone between the bones of the loin and the coccyx.

SALIVARY GLANDS. The six glands, situated three on each side of the mouth, which secrete saliva. They include the parotid, the submaxillary and the sublingual glands.

SALIVATION. The production of saliva by the salivary glands, excited by the taste, smell or thought of food.

SAPHENOUS NERVE. Nerve supplying the skin of the leg and foot.

SAPHENOUS VEINS. Veins of the leg and foot.

SARTORIUS. The "tailor's muscle" used in bending and crossing the legs.

SCALENE MUSCLES. Muscles used in bending the neck.

SCAPHOID BONE. Boat-shaped bone of the foot and of the hand.

SCAPULA. The shoulder blade.

SCIATIC NERVE. Nerve of the hip, which supplies the muscles of the thigh, leg and foot.

SCLEROTIC COAT. The firm, fibrous outer membrane of the eyeball.

SCROTUM. Bag holding the testicles.

SEBACEOUS GLANDS. Glands which secrete oily matter.

SEBUM. The oily secretion of the sebaceous glands.

SECRETIN. Internal secretion of the first part of the small intestine which stimulates the action of the pancreas.

SEDIMENTARY ROCKS. Rocks formed in layers, or strata, by the deposition of sediment.

SEGMENT. Any of the parts into which a body naturally separates or is divided.

SEGMENTATION. The process of cleavage or division.

SEMICIRCULAR CANALS. Part of the inner ear concerned with balance.

SEMI-LUNAR CARTILAGES. Two cartilages of the knee.

SEMI-MEMBRANOSUS. Muscle used in bending the leg and turning it inwards.

SEMINAL. Relating to the semen.

SEMINAL VESICLES. The little sacs at the base of the bladder which hold the semen.

SEMINIFEROUS. Producing or carrying semen.

SEMI-TENDINOSUS. Muscle used in bending the leg on the thigh.

SENSORY. Relating to or conveying sensation.

SENSORY DECUSSATION. The crossing of sensory fibres in the brain.

SEPTUM. A partition ; a division wall.

SEPTUM OF THE NOSE. The partition between the two nasal cavities.

SEROUS. Relating to or producing serum.

SERRATI. Muscles which are attached to the ribs and assist respiration.

SERUM. The fluid which separates from blood, lymph, and other fluids of the body when clotting takes place in them.

SESSILE. Stationary.

SHEATH. Coverings of arteries, muscles, nerves, etc.

SIGMOID FLEXURE. The part of the large intestine immediately above the rectum which is freely movable and hangs down into the pelvis.

SILURIAN. The third epoch of the Palæozoic era, during which the first land animals appeared.

SINUS. Cavity of bone or tissue.

SINUSITIS. Inflammation of a sinus.

SOLAR PLEXUS. A network of sympathetic nerves and ganglia, situated behind the stomach.

SOLEUS. A flat muscle of the calf, used in extending the foot.

SOMATIC. To do with the body.

SPASM. A sudden, involuntary contraction of a muscle or of a hollow organ with a muscular wall.

SPERMATIC CORD. The cord of the arteries, veins, lymphatics, nerves, and the excretory duct of the testicles, passing from the testicles to the abdominal cavity.

SPERMATOZOA. Male reproductive cells.

SPHENOID BONE. Bone at the base of the skull.

SPHENOIDAL SINUS. The air-space in the sphenoid bone, communicating with the nasal cavity.

SPHINCTER. A circular muscle which surrounds the opening of an organ, and by maintaining constantly a state of moderate contraction prevents the escape of the contents of the organ, e.g., the anal and pyloric sphincters.

SPHYGMOGRAPH. An instrument for recording graphically the features of the pulse and variations in blood pressure.

SPHYGMOMANOMETER. An instrument for measuring blood pressure.

SPINAL ACCESSORY NERVE. The motor nerve to some of the neck muscles.

SPINAL NERVES. The thirty-one pairs of nerves arising from the spinal cord.

SPINALIS DORSI. Muscle used in erecting the spinal column.

SPLANCHNIC. Anything belonging to the internal organs of the body as distinct from its framework.

SPLEEN. Ductless gland situated on the left side of the abdomen.

STENOSIS. Constriction or narrowing, especially of a channel or an opening.

STERNOMASTOID MUSCLES. Muscles each side of the neck.

STERNUM. The breast bone.

STIRRUP BONE. A bone of the middle ear.

STRIATED MUSCLES. Muscles consisting of striped, or voluntary, muscular tissue.

SUBARACHNOID. Beneath the arachnoid membrane, one of the membranes enclosing the brain and spinal cord.

SUBARACHNOID SPACE. The space between the arachnoid membrane and the pia mater, which is attached to the brain and spinal cord. It contains the cerebrospinal fluid.

SUBCLAVIAN ARTERY. Artery running from the main artery of the body to the artery of the arm pit.

SUBCUTANEOUS. Beneath the skin.

SUBLINGUAL GLAND. Salivary gland beneath the tongue.

SUBMAXILLARY GLAND. Salivary gland beneath the lower jar.

SUBMUCOUS. Situated beneath a mucous membrane.

SUPINATION (of the hand). The turning of the palm upwards.

SUPINATOR BREVIS. Muscle of arm, used in turning the palm of the hand upwards.

SUPPURATION. The formation of pus.

SUPRAORBITAL. Above the eye sockets.

SUPRARENAL GLANDS. Glands on top of the kidney which secrete adrenalin ; also known as suprarenal capsules, or adrenal glands.

SUSTENTACULUM. Part of the heel bone.

SYMPATHETIC NERVOUS SYSTEM. A system of nerves forming a chain from the skull to the end of the spinal column supplying the interior organs and blood vessels.

SYMPHYSIS. The line of junction of two bones.

SYNAPSE. The junction between the nerve cells by means of which nerve impulses pass from one to another.

SYNOVIAL MEMBRANE. Layer of fibrous tissue lining a joint.

SYSTOLE. Contraction of the heart and arteries ; the systole alternates with the resting phase, called the diastole.

T

TARSUS. The instep, consisting of the calcaneous, astragalus, cuboid, scaphoid and cuneiform bones.

TARSUS OF THE EYE. The cartilage of the eyelid.

TASTE-BUDS. Cells, shaped like buds, in the tongue.

TELEOSTS. Fish which possess a bony skeleton.

TEMPORAL ARTERY. An artery of the head.

TEMPORAL BONES. Bones forming the "temple" of the skull.

TEMPORAL LOBE. Part of the brain.

TEMPORAL MUSCLE. Muscle used in bringing the front teeth together.

TENDON. A band of dense, fibrous tissue forming the termination of a muscle and attaching it to a bone.

TERES LIGAMENT. A round, fibrous cord attached to the head of the thigh bone.

TERES MAJOR. Muscle used in drawing the arm down and back.

TERES MINOR. Muscle used in turning the upper arm.

TESTES OR TESTICLES. Male sex glands.

TESTOSTERONE. Internal secretion of the testes.

THALAMUS. A mass of grey matter at the base of the brain.

THORACIC. Relating to, or situated in, the chest.

THORACIC DUCT. Large lymph vessel which collects the contents of the lymphatics proceeding from the lower limbs, the abdomen, the left arm, and left side of the chest, neck and head.

THORACIC NERVES. Nerves running round the chest wall in grooves beneath the ribs and supplying the muscles between the ribs.

THORAX. The chest.

THYMUS. A gland in the neck below the thyroid gland.

THYROID CARTILAGE. The largest of the cartilages near the larynx.

THYROID GLAND. A gland in the neck concerned with normal growth.

THYROTROPIC HORMONE. Hormone produced by the pituitary gland and affecting the thyroid.

THYROXINE. The hormone produced by the thyroid gland.

TIBIA. The shin bone.

TIBIAL, ANTERIOR (MUSCLE). Muscle of the leg, which flexes the ankle.

TIBIAL, POSTERIOR (MUSCLE). Muscle of the leg, which extends the ankle.

TRACHEA. The windpipe.

TRAPEZIUS. A muscle of the neck and back, used in drawing the head backwards.

TRIASSIC. The first epoch of the Mesozoic era.

TRICEPS BRACHIALIS. Muscle used in extending the forearm.

TRICUSPID VALVE. Valve of the heart, guarding the passage from right auricle to ventricle.

TRIGEMINAL NERVE. The fifth cranial nerve; it supplies the skin and structures of face, tongue and teeth.

TROCHANTER. Process of bone at the upper end of the thigh bone.

TROCHLEAR NERVE. The fourth cranial nerve; it supplies the muscles used in moving the eyeballs.

TROPHOBLAST. Layer of cells in the fertilized ovum, concerned in the nourishment of the embryo.

TRYPSIN. Digestive ferment of the pancreas, which acts on proteins.

TUBEROSITY. A protuberance on a bone.

TUBEROSITY, ISCHIAL. The thick downward projection of bone on which the body rests in sitting.

TUBULES. Minute, tube-shaped structures.

TURBINATE BONES. Coiled bones in the nose.

TURKISH SADDLE. Part of the skull, enclosing the pituitary gland.

TYMPANIC MEMBRANE. The ear drum.

TYMPANUM. The middle ear.

U

ULNA. The bone on the inner side of the forearm.

ULNAR ARTERY. Artery of the forearm.

ULNAR NERVE. Nerve supplying muscles of the shoulder joint and wrist joint, and the skin of the little finger.

UMBILICAL CORD. Cord connecting fœtus and placenta.

UMBILICUS. The navel.

UNGUICULATES. Clawed mammals including rabbits, rats, cats, dogs, seals, walruses.

UNGULATES. Hoofed mammals, including horses, pigs, deer, elephants.

UNSTRIATED MUSCLE TISSUE. The un-striped, or involuntary, muscular tis-sue, composed of spindle-shaped muscle fibres.

URÆMIA. Condition of poisoning from kidney failure.

UREA. Waste product formed from un-used amino-acids by the liver.

URETER. Tube conveying the urine from the kidney to the bladder.

URETHRA. Canal from bladder to the outside of the body, through which urine is discharged.

URIC ACID. Substance found in urine.

URINIFEROUS TUBULES. Tubules of the kidney.

UTERI, OS. Mouth of the womb.

UTERUS. Womb.

UTRICLE. Small chamber in the central part of the inner ear.

UVULA. The conical appendix hanging from the soft palate in the mouth.

V

VAGINA. Canal leading from the womb to the surface of the body.

VAGUS NERVE. The tenth cranial nerve supplying most of the internal organs.

VALLATE PAPILLÆ. Small protuberances on the tongue.

VARIATION. A change in the form of an individual or group which may or may not be heritable by the offspring.

VAS DEFERENS. Duct carrying sperm from testicles to urethra.

VASCULAR. Consisting of, relating to, or provided with vessels.

VASO-CONSTRICTOR. A nerve which causes constriction of blood vessels.

VASO-DILATOR. A nerve which causes dilatation of blood vessels.

VASO-MOTOR CENTRE. Nervous centres in the spinal cord and the part of the brain adjoining it.

VENA CAVA, INFERIOR. Main vein of lower part of the body.

VENA CAVA, SUPERIOR. Main vein of the upper part of the body.

VENTRICLE. A small cavity or pouch.

VENTRICLES OF THE BRAIN. Cavities in the interior of the brain, comprising the two lateral ventricles, the third, fourth and fifth ventricles.

VENTRICLES OF HEART. Two of the four compartments into which the heart is divided, by means of which the blood is circulated through the body.

VERTEBRÆ. Bones forming the spinal column, or backbone.

VERTEBRATES. Backboned animals.

VESICLE. A small bladder ; a small sac containing fluid.

VIBRISSÆ. Hairs of the nostrils.

VILLUS. One of the minute club-shaped projections from the mucous mem-brane of the intestine.

VIRUS. A substance produced in the body as the result of some disease.

VISCERA. Any of the organs enclosed within the skull, the chest, the abdomen or the pelvis.

VITREOUS HUMOUR. Transparent, jelly-like substance in the posterior chamber of the eye.

VOMER. A bone of the nose.

VULVA. External opening of vagina.

X

XEROPHTHALMIA. Inflammation of the eyes, which in severe cases may result in blindness.

Z

ZYGOMATIC PROCESS. Bone protuberance, forming prominence of the cheek.

ZYGOMATICUS. Muscle of the face leading from zygomatic process to lip.

ZYGOTE. The result of the union of two sex cells.